D1306071

THE INTRAPSYCHIC SELF

ALSO BY SILVANO ARIETI

Interpretation of Schizophrenia
American Handbook of Psychiatry, 3 volumes (editor)

Silvano Arieti

THE INTRAPSYCHIC SELF

Feeling, Cognition, and Creativity

in Health and Mental Illness

BASIC BOOKS, INC., *Publishers*
NEW YORK ⊙ LONDON

© 1967 by Basic Books, Inc.
Library of Congress Catalog Card Number: 67–13345
Manufactured in the United States of America
by H. Wolff, New York

To Marianne, David, and Jimmy

PREFACE

What is the psyche of man—this never finished, forever un-folding entity, which in its complexity has no equal in the world known to science? What is man—this lonely spectator of all times and of all existences, who in his biologico-his-torical finitude is "touched inside" by all times and all exist-ences?

There are many approaches to these timeless questions. The biologist, the anthropologist, the philosopher, the psy-chologist, the psychiatrist—and many others—define and illuminate the nature of man from their special points of view. But the central factor—which develops out of man's biologi-cal origins and ultimately reaches the highest expressions of feeling, cognition, and creativity—is what I call the "intra-psychic self," this inner world of man. This is the core from which whatever is human expands and irradiates. This is the area which we shall explore, in search again of an under-standing of what we are.

Although, at the present stages of our knowledge, no all-embracing synthesis of man is yet in sight, I have long wished for a study of the intrapsychic which would integrate many points of view. After the publication of my book *Interpretation of Schizophrenia*, I decided to undertake such a study of the intrapsychic realm. The work ahead soon revealed itself to be much vaster than I had expected, for connections and implications appeared on all sides. Not just two, three, or four years passed by, as I had anticipated, but ten, eleven, twelve. In Part I of this book I have tried to describe the evolving of the intrapsychic self from the level of rudimentary sensorimotor behavior to that of a willed entity. In Part II I have illustrated the basic intrapsychic mechanisms, as they appear in the major psychiatric disorders; and in Part III, as they evolve in the process of creativity.

In exploring the evolution and psychodynamics of the self in Part I, it seemed to me that one of the important topics to investigate was the various roles of cognition. Many authors have studied cognition; in particular, Jean Piaget and Heinz Werner follow a methodology which inspired me in many ways. However, I believe that cognition as treated by these two great authors and by many lesser ones has not been integrated into a psychodynamic study of man. Piaget's cognition, important as it is, is more an illustration of a maturing process of adapting to environmental reality than a representation of the intrapsychic life. Although Werner's cognition is more pertinent to psychiatric studies than Piaget's, it makes no significant use of the concepts of the unconscious, the primary process, motivation, and the conflict of forces.

Another important topic developed in Part I is emotional life—not merely in its elementary forms, but also in complex affective states. Contrary to usual practice, I have tried to show how great a part of complicated emotions is related to cognition: for instance, how cognitive processes change an instantaneous fear into a prolonged symbolic anxiety, a sudden rage into premeditated and calculated hate, a state of deprivation into one of depression, a simple appetite of the body into mature love.

These findings of Part I are applied in Parts II and III. The reader will recognize that in Part II I have focused on the areas of psychopathology in which I have done intense personal work, and particularly on schizophrenia. In Part III, I have tried to interpret the processes by which the primitive unites with the highest levels of the psyche to produce the process of creativity. In Parts II and III the reader will recognize the basic importance which I attribute to the relationships between normality, psychopathology, and creativity.

In correlating such a large amount of material, I found it necessary to make short tangential excursions into neighboring fields and to present well-known and familiar notions together with others which are less known and, at times, difficult to assimilate. The reader trained in a particular specialty may therefore encounter some unevenness. I trust that this unevenness will appear as a secondary characteristic and that the underlying unitary principles will stand out when the book is read in its entirety. The reader, however, who is particularly interested in special topics, such as the psychopathic personality, schizophrenia, the aesthetic process, or the origin of language, may wish to start with the chapter covering that subject. Each chapter retains a partial autonomy and can be adequately understood on its own. Abundant cross references to material in other chapters make it possible to follow up a given topic and move on to related ones.

I wish to thank the many people who have helped me, particularly Dr. John Meth, Rev. Jack Bemporad, Mrs. Sonya Bemporad, Dr. Jules Bemporad, and Dr. Carlos Paes de Barros, who read parts of the manuscript and offered valuable criticism. Miss Mary Barnett's contribution as a careful editor is deeply appreciated. My thanks go also to my many devoted patients whose cooperation has enabled me to accumulate the data I have reported and the ideas I have suggested.

A portion of Chapter 20 originally appeared, in somewhat different form, in *Psychiatry*, Vol. XIII (1950), under the title "New Views on the Psychology and Psychopathology of Wit and of the Comic."

SILVANO ARIETI

New York
August 1967

CONTENTS

PART II

The Psychopathological Transformation

PART I ⊙

The Evolving of the Self

1 ⊛ *THE CORE OF MAN*

An overview of concepts

The feelings, the ideas, the choices, the actions of man attain their highest development in the state of social mutuality, but begin and end in the intimacy of the sentient self. If the clearest forms of mental health and mental illness are to be found in the great dialogue of the interpersonal world, it is within the individual that the long journey leading to the dialogue is initiated. It is in the inner self that the dialogue is reflected as a mental representation.

As Allport wrote (1955), there are two ways of studying man psychologically: one approach follows the Leibnizian tradition, the other the Lockean. The psychological, psychiatric, and psychoanalytic schools which follow the Leibnizian tradition see man predominantly as Leibniz did: a psychological entity already equipped with full human status at birth. Some functions, like judgment, skilled actions, and sexual behavior, may mature later, but they exist at least in a state of potentiality at birth, waiting for the proper time to unfold. According to this viewpoint man is endowed with biological equipment by which he makes contact with the world, trying to satisfy his needs and to understand his environment. In this approach the focus is on the intrapsychic, and the interpersonal receives secondary consideration.

The psychological, psychiatric, and psychoanalytic schools which follow the Lockean tradition see man's psyche basically as Locke did: a *tabula rasa* at birth, an entity which is molded gradually by the experiences of life passing through his senses. Related to this approach is the conception that society and culture, rather than being made by man, are among the makers of man. Without that which he receives from society and culture, man would not be much different from infrahuman animals. In this tradition the focus is on the interpersonal, and the intrapsychic receives secondary consideration.

Three fundamental positions taken by this author are that (1) man must be studied through both approaches, (2) some of the richest forms of human development are in the realm of the interpersonal, and (3) the interpersonal presupposes an intrapsychic core. In this work I shall deal with the core of man—the intrapsychic realm, seen in normal conditions as well as in psychopathology and creativity. This book is meant to be a prerequisite to the study of the interpersonal and forerunner of attempts to integrate the intrapsychic with the interpersonal.

Although theoretically the intrapsychic should be studied independently of the experiences to which man is subject in life, intrapsychic and interpersonal factors are intermingled in most psychological aspects of man. Moreover, interpersonal influences are necessary to trigger many basic intrapsychic functions. This book will therefore take some interpersonal factors into consideration, especially in reference to particular functions and conditions such as the function of language and the conditions of psychopathic personality and schizophrenia. Moreover, in any study of the intrapsychic, the interpersonal does appear as inner reality which reflects the richness of the external world and adds to it the imprint of the individual.

Since the intrapsychic is rarely obvious in the daily occurrences of human life, an analysis which focuses on it has a somewhat artificial quality. This artifact, however, is scientifically justified if it deepens our knowledge of some psychological events—if it uncovers common trends in the plurality of psychological phenomena and helps us move closer to a unifying concept of man.

Our inquiry will concern psychological forms and developments. By *forms* I mean psychological structures that belong to various levels of organization, from the simplest to the most complex. They include psychological entities such as feelings in general, emotions, images, language, thought, action, etc. We shall study them as separate structures but as interrelated functions, which constitute different selves and self-images according to the stage of development.

By *development* we mean the unfolding in time either of the individual as a whole or of particular psychological forms or functions. Three types of development can be distinguished, two of which are well known. The first is the phylogenetic, or unfolding of a psychological mechanism through the evolution of the species. The second is the ontogenetic, or unfolding of a mechanism through the maturation of the individual. The third type of development is the microgenetic. As this type is not well known, some explanation is required.

Microgeny, as described by Werner (1956), is the immediate unfolding of a phenomenon, that is, the sequence of the necessary steps inherent in the occurrence of a psychological process.[1] For instance, to the question, "Who is the author of Hamlet?" a person answers "Shakespeare." He is aware only of the question (stimulus) and of his answer (conscious response), not of the numerous steps that in a remarkably short time led him to give the correct answer. Why did he not reply Sophocles or George Bernard Shaw? How did he reach the correct answer? There are numerous proofs that the answer was not necessarily an established and purely physical or neuronal association between Hamlet and Shakespeare, but that an actual unconscious search went on. In fact, if the same question is asked of a mental patient (either

---

[1] For a comprehensive and accurate review of the topic of microgeny see the article by Flavell and Draguns (1957). See also my article (Arieti, 1962a).

affected by cerebral arteriosclerosis or by schizophrenia in a stage of advanced regression), or put to a person who is very sleepy or drunk or paying little attention, he may reply "Sophocles" or "George Bernard Shaw." These are wrong answers but not haphazard ones; they reveal that the mental search required for answering had at least reached the category of playwrights.

These three orders of phenomena—phylogeny, ontogeny, and microgeny—unfold in time, although with great variation in the quantity of time: from periods as long as geological eras in phylogeny, to periods as short as fractions of a second in microgeny. What is of fundamental importance is that the three processes to a large extent follow similar developmental plans. This does not mean literally that in the psyche microgeny recapitulates ontogeny and ontogeny recapitulates phylogeny, but that there are certain similarities in the three fields of development and that we are able to individualize schemes of highest forms of generality which involve all levels of the psyche in its three types of development.[2] We also recognize concrete variants of the same overall structural plans in the three types of development.

The two aspects of the psyche—the organization of forms (a logical order) and the threefold development (a temporal order)—are equally important. Inasmuch as one tends to permanence, the other to change, a double functionality results which is a main characteristic of the psyche.

An important aim of this book is to stress the role of primitive psychological forms, in feelings and external behavior as well as in cognition. This study is relevant not only because it reveals common trends and processes of development, but because these early forms become available again in many conditions of psychopathology and creativity. As a matter of fact, together with a few more mechanisms, such as the excessive dominance or debility of some mature forms, they constitute the essence of all psychological deviances. In Parts II and III, I shall show how unusual sequences and syntheses, and enlargements or declines of psychological forms and stages of development, contribute to the psychopathological and creative processes.

[2] See Huxley (1953) for a similar developmental approach in general biology.

This emphasis on development should not be interpreted as excessive preoccupation with origins and neglect of outcomes; that is, as adoption of the so-called genetic fallacy. Under the influence of early psychoanalytic concepts, some investigators overemphasized early stages of development, bodily needs, instinctual behavior, and elementary feelings that can exist without a cognitive counterpart or with a very limited one. It is true that physiological or simple emotional states—such as hunger, thirst, fatigue, sexual urges, exposure to cold, and fear about one's physical survival—are powerful motivational forces; but by no means do they include all the emotional factors affecting man favorably or unfavorably. It is one of the aims of this book to show that in addition to these physiological states and primitive emotions, important psychodynamic forces exist in man which are brought about by his conceptual life.

Some of the early stages of development referred to above correspond to those included by Freud in the category he termed the primary process; likewise, the subsequent stages correspond to those that he included in the category of the secondary process. Freud's classification will be used in this book together with other terminologies.

Various ways of experiencing the world and the self result from the functioning of different forms and levels. These ways may be in disagreement with one another and produce conflict or confusion. Or they may be in agreement and produce several outcomes, two of which are, I think, of the utmost significance. First, the agreement of the primary and secondary processes may be so devastating to the individual as to bring about a preschizophrenic panic, followed by the dissolution of the secondary process (Chapter 16). Second, it may instead have a useful effect in permitting the emergence of the creative process (Chapters 19 to 24).

Two major authors have followed methodologies that have points in common with the one adopted here. Heinz Werner, who has exerted a strong influence on this writer, opened many lines of inquiry with his developmental approach (1957a, b, 1963). His orientation differs from mine in that it does not make use of the concepts of the unconscious, the primary process, and motivation.

The second author is Jean Piaget, whose investigation is

almost exclusively confined to ontogeny. The phylogenetic and microgenetic developments are not included in his work; nor does he relate his findings to psychopathology or creativity. Although Piaget describes different levels of cognition, he deals only with the conscious secondary process of each level, not with the preceding primary process. In spite of these self-imposed limitations, Piaget's work has yielded highly significant results which transcend the field of child development.[3]

The methodology I have adopted is, on one side, clinical, as it draws data from healthy and ill subjects. On the other side, it is theoretical, as it forms inferences from the clinical findings and searches connections with related sciences. This methodology is thus closer to the one followed in clinical psychiatry and psychoanalysis than to that used by experimental psychologists.

Inasmuch as my orientation is related to Freudian theory, having derived some fundamental concepts from it, a brief review of the Freudian approach is presented in the following section. Rather than going into detail about the basic tenets of the Freudian school, I shall focus on some of the main controversial aspects.

The Freudian approach to the intrapsychic

AFFECT

It is sufficient to think of Freud's contributions to the understanding of anxiety and of unconscious motivation to realize how much he clarified the role played by emotions. And yet, paradoxically, it is in the field of affectivity that we find the most controversial aspects of Freudian theory.

In his early writings Freud gave great importance to affects as direct dynamic forces. He attributed to them what he later thought was the property of psychic energy or libido. He felt that when affects are pent up and prevented from discharge, pathological consequences may result. Release is

[3] For a comprehensive account and evaluation of Piaget's work cf. Flavell (1963).

found through discharge or abreaction (Freud, 1893, 1894)

Later, however, Freud removed affects from the category of primary dynamic forces. He located these forces instead in the instincts or drives, as quantities of libidinal energy. Instincts or drives result from intraorganismic tension pressing for release. Often this bodily tension is not directly observable; it is expressed in the form of a need and is identified by the means taken to reduce the need. If the need is not reduced, a state of tension and restlessness develops which is conceptualized as drive cathexis.

According to Rapaport (1954, 1960) the Freudian primary model of affect consists of the following sequences: drive reaching threshold intensity → absence of drive object → affect discharge. If the drive tension (for instance, hunger) increases and the object which could release the tension (for instance, maternal breast) is absent, a primitive form of conflict is brought about. This is in brief the so-called conflict theory of affect. Affect thus has a safety-valve function of ridding the organism of excessive drive tension.

In the secondary model of affect, the drive tension caused by the absence of the need-reducing object does not end in a discharge of affect. Instead, the affect becomes segregated or controlled by the ego. However, the ego may allow the discharge of small anticipatory quantities of affect which act as signals of the drive tension.

The instinctual drives constitute the id, a part of the psyche which provides energy for the whole mental apparatus. Another part, the ego, deals with perception of and adjustment to reality. The superego is the part which deals with aspirations, moral demands, and prohibitions. In the ego and the superego a hierarchical development of motivations takes place which Freud again sees as consisting of derivatives of drives, predominantly ideational derivatives.

We may conclude that according to Freud's theories (other than his earliest) and those of Rapaport, affects are drive derivatives and mostly have a safety-valve function. They are always seen as something negative, to be removed or "sublimated." The motivational forces remain the drives and the ideational derivatives of the drive. All behavior is ultimately determined (or motivated) by the drives.

Freud's theory adequately explains the driving character-istics of hunger, thirst, and sexual tension, but falls short of explaining the pleasant or positive affects or all affects which are not closely related to these primary physiological states. The motivational function is always attributed to deriva-tives of the presumed libidinal energy. Dynamics are inter-preted in a framework of energetics—the part of psycho-analysis concerned with psychic energy.

Freud and his orthodox followers have often been re-garded by the neo-Freudians as being too biological in their conceptions. Actually, insofar as they follow the libido or drive-cathexis theory, they are not biological enough. The libido theory is not a biological theory; it is an application to the psyche of concepts borrowed from the field of physics. But concepts which are applicable to the physical world (at least, as it was seen by nineteenth-century physicists) are not necessarily relevant to biological levels of integration. In the libido theory, general biology, and neurophysiology are by-passed. The leap is from inorganic physics to psychology.

COGNITION

Freud has made three fundamental contributions to the field of cognition. First, he demonstrated that cognitive proc-esses may be totally or partially unconscious. Second, he un-covered evidence that, at least in dream life and psycho-pathologic conditions, the content of cognitive processes may be symbolic—may stand for something different from what at first it seems to represent. These two contributions are now almost unanimously accepted by psychoanalytic schools and will not be discussed here.

The third contribution, which I myself accept, has not been so widely approved as the other two. It is the proposi-tion, mentioned earlier in the chapter, that there are two fun-damentally different kinds of mental process: the primary and the secondary.

The description of the primary process and its separation from the secondary, as illustrated in Chapter 7 of *The Inter-pretation of Dreams*, remains a classic (1901). Freud called the first process primary because he believed that it occurs earlier in ontogenetic development, not because he thought it more important than the secondary. As a matter of fact, he stressed the point that the secondary process becomes the dominant one in the normal adult.

Freud tried to differentiate the particular laws which rule the primary process. Especially in reference to psychoneuroses and dreams, he described two of its basic mechanisms: displacement and condensation. These mechanisms are now such common knowledge that we forget they were unknown before Freud.

In his first major theory, generally called the topographic theory, Freud treated the primary process as the process by which the unconscious functions. He also considers it to be the form which mental life takes in early childhood before the system preconscious comes into being. In his second major theory, generally called the structural theory, Freud did not limit the activities of the primary process to the id, but extended them to the ego and the superego.

This great breakthrough represented by the discovery and first description of the primary process did not lead to a series of cognitive discoveries by Freud or by the Freudian school. In my opinion, the arrest of progress can be attributed to several factors. Freud did not have a great interest in the primary process as a mode of cognition, but only as a carrier of unconscious motivation. Unconscious motivation is probably the most important aspect of psychoanalysis, and the fact that Freud was so preoccupied with it is understandable. However, since motivational theory in his system came to be studied in connection with libido functioning, the primary process was examined not in a framework of cognition, but in a framework of energetics.

Basically, primary and secondary processes came to be considered not as two different ways of thinking, but as two different ways of dealing with cathexes. In the primary process the cathexis is described as free, that is, easily shifted from some objects to others. Insofar as this shifting may occur from realistic and appropriate objects to unrealistic and inappropriate ones, the primary process becomes an irrational mode of functioning.

This Freudian approach leaves many questions unanswered,

especially those which pertain to cognition. What is over-looked is that a shifting of libido requires the existence of alternative cognitive elements. The psyche must have available the mental representations of the various objects to which the cathexis is shifted. Furthermore, when the libido is shifted to another object, this shifting or displacement is not due to chance, but to a cognitive relation between the original object and the substitutes. For instance, if in dreams the cathexis is shifted from the vagina to a box, this shifting is not casual; it is the outcome of the special type of cognition, which first represents mentally a vagina and a box, and secondly intuits a special relation between the function and shape of the vagina and of the box so that the latter can replace the former. In Freudian theory the displacement is seen almost exclusively as a shifting of mental energy. It is not attributed to a cognitive creation of mental alternatives and to the immediate grasping of a relation between these alternatives.

If the study of the primary process did not lead Freud and the Freudians to additional discoveries in the field of cognition, their study of the secondary process was even less fruitful. They often repeat that the secondary process is characterized by fixed or bound cathexis, or by the fact that there is a delay between the original drive and the thought. The delay is said to be "structuralized," but how this structuralization occurs is not explained.

Although the functioning of the secondary process is not confined to the ego, it is especially in this division of the psyche that one would expect its clearest manifestations. However, when we review Freud's contributions to the understanding of the ego and of the secondary process, we can easily recognize that they are not so significant as those he made in relation to the primary process.

For Freud, the ego is a superficial layer of the id which becomes differentiated. The ego is the perceiver of the external world and the controller of the internal world. Its main purpose is self-preservation. Freud thus defined the principal functions of the ego but did not distinguish the mechanisms that mediate them. Some of his pupils took upon themselves to investigate this part of the psyche. Paul Federn (1952) made such an attempt, but his theories found few followers.[4]

It is Heinz Hartmann who seems to have assumed the leadership in the study of the ego (Hartmann, 1950a, b, 1964; Hartmann and Kris, 1945; Hartmann, Kris, and Lowenstein, 1946). He was one of the first to recognize the importance of the intrapsychic processes attributed to this part of the psyche and to realize that the Freudian concept of the ego needed a more precise formulation. According to him, the ego is much more than a differentiated superficial layer of the id which develops from the impact of reality factors on instinctual drives. Hartmann does not believe that the ego is a structure ontogenetically younger than the id; he contends that id and ego originate at the same time from a common matrix. For Hartmann the ego has many aspects, such as the defensive, the organizing, the rational, the social, etc. Many of the ego's properties are inherited: they constitute its autonomous functions. Among the latter are the "conflict-free areas": the sensorimotor apparatus, the memory apparatus, the functions of adaptation, integration, synthesis, and possibly self-preservation.

Hartmann and other ego psychologists have enumerated these ego functions but have not proceeded to study their formal mechanisms. They have not even touched such important problems as the formal organization of knowledge, affect, and volition. Perhaps in order to remain in what appears to them a psychodynamic context, they have dealt almost exclusively with the metapsychology of energetics. In other words, they have formulated hypotheses about the origin and distribution of the libido necessary for ego functions.

CONATION

Although Freudian psychoanalysis has succeeded in interpreting the behavior of the psychoneurotic and throwing light on actions appearing in dreams, it has not yet adequately explained many aspects of conation. Nevertheless, Rapaport has extrapolated enough ideas from Freud's works to permit the formulation of two models of conation—primary and secondary.

4 Prominent among them is Edoardo Weiss (1960).

In the primary model, the original restlessness of the child, determined by the drive, leads to a specific simple action, like the sucking of the breast. As a result of this simple or reflex action the restlessness subsides, apparently because of tension reduction (or discharge of cathexis). Thoughts and affects do not enter into this type of conation.

In the secondary model of conation there are intermediary stages between the original drive and the ultimate satisfaction. The original drive is replaced by derivative drives, which develop in later stages of phylogenetic-ontogenetic development. Action may thus be triggered by derivative drives.

The derivative drive, however, may be delayed not only in the absence of the object, but also in the object's presence. This delay occurs when the control system follows the reality principle rather than the pleasure principle. It permits a detour from the direct route of gratification. Although satisfaction is ultimately reached, structualized detours permit maintenance of tension.

Again it is only the primary or most primitive type of conation which is clearly explained by classic psychoanalysis. The structuralized delays and detours are seen as defenses against the primary type of conation, and not as something positive in their own right. Moreover, the phenomena of choice and of will receive no consideration in Freudian theory.

sciousness and become more similar to the rest of the functions of the nervous system.

In low species, physiologic sensation is sufficient to elicit a reaction. In more complicated organisms, however, awareness is necessary to elicit more complex responses capable of effecting difficult changes in the environment. The various forms of felt experience, even at the primitive level of sensation-perception, can be easily differentiated. For instance, any normal subject can readily distinguish such varieties of sensation as pain, temperature perception, hearing, vision, thirst, hunger, etc. We shall not study the anatomical or physiological mechanisms which mediate them or the evolutionary steps which led to their development. For our purposes it is important to stress the fact that these sensations (or perceptions) can be considered in two main ways: (1) as subjective experiences which occur in the presence of particular somatic states—for instance, a specific state of discomfort which we call thirst; (2) as reflections (or as production of analogs) of aspects of reality.

Thus at this point we encounter a basic dichotomy. On one side is the awareness of a particular state of the body or part of the body: that is, the experience of an inner status, the experience as experience. Even when this experience is recognized as being of a specific type and therefore is more properly called a perception, it remains fundamentally an awareness of a state of the organism. On the other side, sensations have the function of mirroring reality, a function which generally expands into numerous ramifications that deal with cognition.

Now we can easily recognize that the importance of these two components varies a great deal in the various types of perceptions. The experience of inner status is very important in the perception of pain, hunger, thirst, temperature. It is slightly less important in other perceptions such as touch, taste, and, less obviously, smell; in these the subjectivization of the alteration in the organism still plays the predominant role, but the presence of the external stimulus is generally also acknowledged. In auditory and visual perceptions, however, the experience of a change of inner status plays a minimal role; these perceptions make the animal aware of what

2 ☉ THE EMERGENCE OF FEELING, MOTIVATION, AND OBJECT RELATIONS

Awareness

Feeling is a characteristic unique to the animal world. Although Whitehead has ascribed some kind of rudimentary feeling to the universe, and although the cyberneticians attribute some kind of awareness to machines, at the present stage of our knowledge we must consider these statements either as the personal view of a philosopher or as the enthusiastic attitude of people working in a new field.

Feeling is unanalyzable in its essential subjective nature and defies any attempt toward a noncircular definition. Synonyms of feeling, which are often used in attempts to define the concept, include awareness, subjectivity, consciousness, experience, felt experience. Here these terms will be used synonymously with the understanding that, unless specified otherwise, they refer to a subjective form of experiencing, independent of the many and complex variations that it may undergo.

The simplest form of feeling is sensation. Sensation, however, is phylogenetically preceded by irritability. Irritability is one of the fundamental properties of any living organism, necessary to maintain its intactness in a predominantly inorganic universe which is mostly adverse to life.

With the evolution of the animal scale, the property of irritability is delegated to the nervous system—what is irritability in some vegetables and in very low animal species evolves to the level of sensation. However, a distinction must be made which is of fundamental importance in biology, although it is seldom considered in studies of feeling: the distinction between physiological and psychological sensations.

Sensation, as the word is generally used, implies a subjective experience or awareness. But this element of awareness, which is so important for the psychologist and which is one of the most characteristic properties of animal life, is not a necessary ingredient of physiological sensation.[1] From the point of view of many physiologists and neurologists, sensation is only an impression made on an afferent nerve, an impression which as a rule is transmitted through an ascending tract.[2] This impression and transmission of information may or may *not* be accompanied by awareness. Actually, feeling is associated with only a small part of sensations. The information transmitted by the autonomic nervous system through the afferent parts of the autonomic reflex arcs is not accompanied by subjective feelings. Neither is a large amount of data received by the central nervous system. For instance, the important information transmitted through the spinocerebellar tracts never reaches the level of awareness. Again, only a small part of kinesthetic or proprioceptive sensations reaches consciousness.[3]

[1] Irritability is much simpler than physiologic sensation, inasmuch as it does not require a nervous system. It is probably closer to tropism than to physiological sensation. Physiological sensation is a specific irritability—that of part of the nervous system.

[2] This impression tends to elicit a re-equilibratory reaction through the efferent nerve, the descending tract.

[3] In this book we shall not deal with the unsolved problems of why some colloidal systems acquired irritability of the protoplasm and the power to reproduce, and why some other systems also developed physiological sensation. For some insights into this pioneer field, the reader is referred to the works by Oparin (1938), Blum (1955), and Rush (1957). Equally fragmentary is our knowledge of the neurological substratum which has permitted the emergence of the phenomenon awareness. Until biochemists or neurophysiologists are able to explain this aspect of life, we must resign ourselves to consider basic awareness an unanalyzable phenomenon. Eccles' work may represent steps toward the solution of this problem (1953, 1957).

As long as sensation is only physiological, the organism is not too different from an electronic computing machine or a transmitter of information. Up to this point the cyberneticians have some justification for comparing organisms to machines. However, when sensation becomes accompanied by awareness, a new phenomenon emerges in the cosmos: experience.

Before sensation is associated with awareness, we are still only in the physical (although biological) order of things. One physical event (the stimulus) produces another physical event (although it is in the body of the organism). Awareness introduces the factor of psyche.[4] Physicists, who are interested in the study of things as physical phenomena, try to remove the disturbances produced in their research by this subjectivation; for instance, they are not interested in the subjective experience of a color, but in the wave length which brings about the sensation of that color. But what to the physicist is a disturbing complication is for the psychologist one of the foundations of the psyche. This does not imply that psychological life is confined to awareness; on the contrary, we shall see later that psychological life also expands to the realm of unawareness.[5]

However, already at this point we must stress that awareness, or consciousness, is only one of the many properties of neurological functions and is by no means a constant. As a matter of fact, the majority of neurological functions are unconscious. Moreover, what appear to us as conscious phenomena are only the last steps of a long series of unconscious processes. For instance, a thought or a complicated movement of our hands is the end result of a very long chain of mechanisms, of which only the terminal ones reach consciousness. By demonstrating that some psychological mechanisms are unconscious, Freud made it clear that some of the functions of the nervous system lose this quality of con-

[4] As we shall see in greater detail in Chapter 6, sensation can be divided into two mechanisms: (1) the pathopoietic, which consists of a special neural excitement and of the transmission and elaboration of the excitement; (2) the pathopathetic, which confers to the sensation the subjective feeling of experiencing.

[5] When psychological life expands to the unconscious, the criterion for distinguishing highly complex integrative neurological processes from psychological ones is that the latter have been (or potentially or actually are) endowed with awareness.

2 ⊛ THE EMERGENCE OF FEELING, MOTIVATION, AND OBJECT RELATIONS

Awareness

Feeling is a characteristic unique to the animal world. Although Whitehead has ascribed some kind of rudimentary feeling to the universe, and although the cyberneticians attribute some kind of awareness to machines, at the present stage of our knowledge we must consider these statements either as the personal view of a philosopher or as the enthusiastic attitude of people working in a new field.

Feeling is unanalyzable in its essential subjective nature and defies any attempt toward a noncircular definition. Synonyms of feeling, which are often used in attempts to define the concept, include awareness, subjectivity, consciousness, experience, felt experience. Here these terms will be used synonymously with the understanding that, unless specified otherwise, they refer to a subjective form of experiencing, independent of the many and complex variations that it may undergo.

The simplest form of feeling is sensation. Sensation, however, is phylogenetically preceded by irritability. Irritability is one of the fundamental properties of any living organism, necessary to maintain its intactness in a predominantly inorganic universe which is mostly adverse to life.

With the evolution of the animal scale, the property of irritability is delegated to the nervous system—what is irritability in some vegetables and in very low animal species evolves to the level of sensation. However, a distinction must be made which is of fundamental importance in biology, although it is seldom considered in studies of feeling: the distinction between physiological and psychological sensations.

Sensation, as the word is generally used, implies a subjective experience or awareness. But this element of awareness, which is so important for the psychologist and which is one of the most characteristic properties of animal life, is not a necessary ingredient of physiological sensation.[1] From the point of view of many physiologists and neurologists, sensation is only an impression made on an afferent nerve, an impression which as a rule is transmitted through an ascending tract.[2] This impression and transmission of information may or may *not* be accompanied by awareness. Actually, feeling is associated with only a small part of sensations. The information transmitted by the autonomic nervous system through the afferent parts of the autonomic reflex arcs is not accompanied by subjective feelings. Neither is a large amount of data received by the central nervous system. For instance, the important information transmitted through the spinocerebellar tracts never reaches the level of awareness. Again, only a small part of kinesthetic or proprioceptive sensations reaches consciousness.[3]

---

[1] Irritability is much simpler than physiologic sensation, inasmuch as it does not require a nervous system. It is probably closer to tropism than to physiological sensation. Physiological sensation is a specific irritability—that of part of the nervous system.

[2] This impression tends to elicit a re-equilibratory reaction through the efferent nerve, the descending tract.

[3] In this book we shall not deal with the unsolved problems of why some colloidal systems acquired irritability of the protoplasm and the power to reproduce, and why some other systems also developed physiological sensation. For some insights into this pioneer field, the reader is referred to the works by Oparin (1938), Blum (1955), and Rush (1957). Equally fragmentary is our knowledge of the neurological substratum which has permitted the emergence of the phenomenon awareness. Until biochemists or neurophysiologists are able to explain this aspect of life, we must resign ourselves to consider basic awareness an unanalyzable phenomenon. Eccles' work may represent steps toward the solution of this problem (1953, 1957).

As long as sensation is only physiological, the organism is not too different from an electronic computing machine or a transmitter of information. Up to this point the cyberneticians have some justification for comparing organisms to machines. However, when sensation becomes accompanied by awareness, a new phenomenon emerges in the cosmos: experience.

Before sensation is associated with awareness, we are still only in the physical (although biological) order of things. One physical event (the stimulus) produces another physical event (although it is in the body of the organism). Awareness introduces the factor of psyche.[4] Physicists, who are interested in the study of things as physical phenomena, try to remove the disturbances produced in their research by this subjectivation; for instance, they are not interested in the subjective experience of a color, but in the wave length which brings about the sensation of that color. But what to the physicist is a disturbing complication is for the psychologist one of the foundations of the psyche. This does not imply that psychological life is confined to awareness; on the contrary, we shall see later that psychological life also expands to the realm of unawareness.[5]

However, already at this point we must stress that awareness, or consciousness, is only one of the many properties of neurological functions and is by no means a constant. As a matter of fact, the majority of neurological functions are unconscious. Moreover, what appear to us as conscious phenomena are only the last steps of a long series of unconscious processes. For instance, a thought or a complicated movement of our hands is the end result of a very long chain of mechanisms, of which only the terminal ones reach consciousness. By demonstrating that some psychological mechanisms are unconscious, Freud made it clear that some of the functions of the nervous system lose this quality of con-

[4] As we shall see in greater detail in Chapter 6, sensation can be divided into two mechanisms: (1) the pathopoietic, which consists of a special neural excitement and of the transmission and elaboration of the excitement; (2) the pathopathetic, which confers to the sensation the subjective feeling of experiencing.

[5] When psychological life expands to the unconscious, the criterion for distinguishing highly complex integrative neurological processes from psychological ones is that the latter have been (or potentially or actually are) endowed with awareness.

sciousness and become more similar to the rest of the functions of the nervous system.

In low species, physiologic sensation is sufficient to elicit a reaction. In more complicated organisms, however, awareness is necessary to elicit more complex responses capable of effecting difficult changes in the environment. The various forms of felt experience, even at the primitive level of sensation-perception, can be easily differentiated. For instance, any normal subject can readily distinguish such varieties of sensation as pain, temperature perception, hearing, vision, thirst, hunger, etc. We shall not study the anatomical or physiological mechanisms which mediate them or the evolutionary steps which led to their development. For our purposes it is important to stress the fact that these sensations (or perceptions) can be considered in two main ways: (1) as subjective experiences which occur in the presence of particular somatic states—for instance, a specific state of discomfort which we call thirst; (2) as reflections (or as production of analogs) of aspects of reality.

Thus at this point we encounter a basic dichotomy. On one side is the awareness of a particular state of the body or part of the body: that is, the experience of an inner status, the experience as experience. Even when this experience is recognized as being of a specific type and therefore is more properly called a perception, it remains fundamentally an awareness of a state of the organism. On the other side, sensations have the function of mirroring reality, a function which generally expands into numerous ramifications that deal with cognition.

Now we can easily recognize that the importance of these two components varies a great deal in the various types of perceptions. The experience of inner status is very important in the perception of pain, hunger, thirst, temperature. It is slightly less important in other perceptions such as touch, taste, and, less obviously, smell; in these the subjectivization of the alteration in the organism still plays the predominant role, but the presence of the external stimulus is generally also acknowledged. In auditory and visual perceptions, however, the experience of a change of inner status plays a minimal role; these perceptions make the animal aware of what happens in the external world, thus enabling it to deal more appropriately with the environment.

To a great extent, auditory and visual perceptions become the foundation of cognition. They are elaborated to the levels of apperceptions and become increasingly removed from their sensorial origin. In man they become connected with symbolic linguistic processes. As a rule their importance lies more in their meaning than in their sensorial nature.

Both kinds of experience are needed for the survival of the species. But whereas the experiences of inner status have an immediate and preponderant survival value and are fundamentally not symbolic, the experiences of mirroring reality have more symbolic and less immediate-survival value.

At this point we must indicate that these categories represent an oversimplification. Especially at a human level, any experience is never exclusively of one type or the other, but merely predominantly of one type. Consider, for instance, a pain felt in a part of the body. It is experienced not only as pain but also as an indication that something is wrong in the body and that a doctor should be consulted. The cognitive, symbolic elements, however, are secondary to the experience of inner status. The pain exists as an experience independently of the meaning attached to it. Any meaning attached to pain generally consists of added cognitive processes: "I must go to the doctor."

On the other hand, when we say that a visual perception has a predominantly cognitive function, we do not deny the occurrence of a bodily change. The change can be registered objectively by the electroencephalogram. However, the visual experience as experience is only the initial part of a complicated process. The process becomes symbolic almost immediately because of the cortical associations that it brings about.

Moreover, even if we take into consideration man's most predominantly cognitive experience, reflective or inner thought, we recognize in it the two elements. Not only do we think, but we are aware of our thoughts. To some extent we experience thoughts as auditory images; to a lesser extent, as visual images.

In the rest of this chapter, as well as in Chapters 3 and 4, we shall take into consideration the experiences of inner status.

Lower-level experiences of inner status

Among the simplest experiences of inner status are elementary sensation-perceptions like temperature, pain, touch, etc. As a rule they are easily localizable and have a definite duration. These types of experiences will not be treated here, since they are fully discussed in monographs on perception and books on physiology and physiological psychology. However, there are other experiences of inner status which we must consider. These I have called physiosensations (or physioperceptions, if they are elaborated to the point of perception).[6] They are states of awareness reflecting a particular condition of the organism and are not easily localizable: for instance, hunger, thirst, fatigue, sleepiness, general malaise.

What interests us here is not the condition of the organism (say, the state of dehydration) but the subjective experience (the experience of thirst). Take hunger as an example. Although it is somewhat similar to a simple sensation like pain, it has these specific characteristics: (1) It is experienced more intensely around the gastric area, but is not so easily localized as pain; (2) it is connected with a particular generalized state of the organism, namely, deprivation of food. Like pain, however, hunger is an uncomfortable status.

With small variations, similar remarks could be made about other physiosensations like thirst, sleepiness, fatigue, etc. The physiological mechanisms of these phenomena are not well known. We may assume, however, that in the states of hunger and thirst, for instance, a particular condition or a general state of some mucous membranes of the organism is

6 The names *physiosensation* and *physioperception* are proposed to distinguish this group of experiences from simpler sensations and perceptions. Physiosensation means sensation of a natural somatic state. In certain ways even simple sensations are of this order, but in physiosensations some general regulatory mechanisms of the body prevail. Probably some physiosensations are phylogenetically older than some simple sensations. Some sensations are intermediary between simple sensations and physiosensations —for instance, the experience of one's body temperature.

eventually able to activate some nerve endings. These nerve endings transmit the information to nervous centers, where it becomes conscious. What is a departure from the organism's homeostatic equilibrium becomes a state of discomfort to the psyche. The removal of the discomfort becomes a need. The removal of the need becomes a satisfaction. The discomfort, the need, and the satisfaction are not symbolic. For the biologist, the discomfort is indicative of a threat to the homeostasis, but this is not true for the subject, who experiences the discomfort as an unpleasant state of being.

Do physiosensations require cognitive processes? They do not. They are more or less generalized experiences of inner status. The experience of physiosensation leads, of course, to some kind of activity, which may require learned behavior, but the felt experience in itself does not require any cognitive function. Even when physiosensations are recognized as such, that is, elaborated to the level of physioperceptions, the cognitive element is minimal.[7]

Instinctual experiences

We shall now consider a group of more complicated phenomena which are particularly prominent in infrahuman animals: the instincts. In instincts an external stimulus determines and brings to awareness an alteration of the inner status of the organism. This alteration and, in some cases, its awareness bring about coordinated, purposeful, and generally stereotyped behavior. Sexual activity is a prototype of instinctual behavior.

Instinct may be divided into several components: (1) the priming, or inner state of preparedness, which is based on

---

[7] Considerable evidence is now available proving that physiosomatic states are regulated mostly in the hypothalamus (Cobb, 1950). However, it is more than doubtful that awareness of physiosensations occurs in the hypothalamus. Primitive receptive centers are located in the ventral thalamus, in the pars optica, and in the tuber cinereum. According to Papez (1937), impulses through the ventral thalamus reach the hypothalamus and through the mammillary bodies and the anterior thalamic nuclei go to the gyrus cinguli. It is also possible that what MacLean (1949, 1955, 1960) calls the visceral brain has a great deal to do with the experience of physioperceptions.

hormonal, humoral, or other biochemical excitement imping-
ing on a nervous apparatus; (2) the external stimulus which
is the releasing object—for instance, a member of the opposite sex; (3) a prearranged set of motor and visceral activities which constitute the instinctive behavior; (4) the
subjective experiences which accompany these phenomena.

The study of all these components pertains to ethology
(cf. the works of Lorenz [1937, 1953] and Tinbergen
[1951]). We are interested chiefly in the inner state of readiness which becomes an experience of inner status in the presence of the releasing object. This felt experience of inner
state becomes the trigger for a prearranged set of motor
mechanisms which lead to the extinction of this experience.
In some cases, such as sexual activity, there is an intensi-
fication of the experience before the need is gratified.

How is instinct connected with cognition? Inasmuch as
the instinct needs an external object by which it is released,
perception—and in many cases recognition—of this external
object is necessary.[8] Perhaps conscious recognition is not
necessary in low animal forms.

We see thus a main difference between instincts and physioperceptions. Whereas the experience of physioperceptions
requires little or no cognitive component, instincts need
more. They belong to a more complicated level and represent
one of the first important intrapsychic connections between
cognition and affect.

In low animal species the emotional-cognitive apparatus is
subcortical. In higher species, starting with the amphibians,
the cognitive becomes cortical; that is, the releaser of the
instincts becomes more and more a stimulus which is perceived and recognized by the cortex.

Pleasure and unpleasure

All the experiences of inner status described in this chapter, whether they are simple sensations, physiosensations, or
instincts, are experiences which affect the body; that is, they

---

[8] In man's sexual behavior the stimulus may be replaced by an image or
other mental constructs (see Chapter 8).

are somatic processes. However, inasmuch as they are accompanied by awareness, they also become psychological phenomena. We could call all simple sensations, physiosensations, and instincts by the common name of physiostates.

Although the various physiostates have their own specific characteristics, they can be divided into two broad categories according to their prevalent feeling: pleasant and unpleasant. As a rule, what is pleasant is connected with patterns of behavior which tend to approach and incorporate; what is unpleasant is connected with patterns of behavior which lead to avoidance or to a need-reducing approach (as in hunger, for instance). These two feelings, pleasure and unpleasure, seem to constitute an order of psychological elaboration different from the single experiences of inner status from which they can be abstracted. They are of ancient origin, and as we shall see later in more detail a large part of the lives of animals is based on them.[9]

Although the feelings of pleasure and unpleasure are connected mostly with experiences of inner status, some authors postulate that *"the ontogeny of pleasure* begins with the first manifestations of reflex responsiveness and is related to the satisfaction derived from sensory stimulation and response" (Lindsley, 1964). Displeasure would be associated with sensory deprivation, restricted environment, thwarted activity.

I believe that in every phenomenon accompanied by awareness there is a pleasant or unpleasant tonality (or a mixture of the two). This tonality is particularly strong in some specific experiences of inner status. Feelings of pleasure and unpleasure also accompany the perceptions which become parts of cognitive processes. Visual and auditory perceptions may be pleasant or unpleasant, according to their strength, or to the combination of colors and forms, or to the frequency of the sound waves. Feelings of recognition

[9] Probably in vertebrates there are centers in the medulla oblongata, pons, or mesencephalon which participate in the elaboration of feelings of pleasure and unpleasure. The brainstem reticular system may mediate the experience of pleasure-unpleasure as an elaboration of stimuli which have entered the nervous system through media phylogenetically more recent than the reticular stem. Elaboration in the limbic system may take place.

Ostow in his physio-psychoanalytic studies postulates that "the primary purpose of affect is to label and identify possible objects of instinctual gratification desirable or undesirable" (1955).

or familiarity, and some elementary activities found also in lower animals, like exploratory and gregarious habits, seem to be experienced as pleasant.

Causality and biology

Up to this point we have considered experiences as felt phenomena. We shall now examine how they become connected with such important topics as causality, adaptation, teleology, and motivation.

In the nonbiological world we find endless chains of causes and effects—series of events which determine one another in a regular order. For instance, if the humidity of the air reaches a certain point of saturation, clouds and eventually rain are formed. If the temperature drops below a certain degree, rain changes into snow; if the temperature rises again, the snow changes into water. The water is absorbed by the ground or evaporated, etc. Each element of the series brings about a subsequent one. The chain of causes and effects can extend indefinitely. We do not know the beginning of any series, or the end. What human beings can hope to do is to observe or study segments of these endless chains. With the increase of our scientific knowledge we constantly extend the length of these segments, but that is as much as we can aspire to. The chains, which are typical of what is generally called deterministic causality, have the following characteristics:

1. They are endless.
2. With some questionable exceptions, events regulated by this type of causality seem also to be regulated by the second principle of thermodynamics or entropy; that is, bodies tend to become less organized through the passage of time. A progressive disorganization leads to simple structures.
3. The chains follow the unidirectional arrow of time. In a series $A \rightarrow B \rightarrow C \rightarrow D \ldots$, B follows A, C follows B, etc., indefinitely. A is also preceded by an endless series of antecedents. For simplicity's sake we are

considering only a simple chain series here; but connected systems of causal relationships are the rule.

Now we shall examine what happens in a biological or organic setup. Consider a very primitive organism, which we shall designate as V (from *vivus*, alive). We do not know how V came to be transformed from a colloidal system into an organism. V is subject to all the rules and vicissitudes to which all the entities of the world are subjected, and is involved with segments of deterministic chains of causes and effects. But V has a special characteristic. Among a very large number of different possibilities, it may come into contact with a special substance which we shall call C (from *cibus*, food). C produces a special effect on V, so that V continues to exist as it is, without degrading, and will continue to react in the same way if and when it has a second encounter with another quantity of C. For example, C is like the oxygen which we are breathing in at this moment, and which enables us to breathe again a moment later.

The V-C sequence is a very improbable occurrence, but in a cosmic order of time, among billions of combinations, eventually such an occurrence takes place. Now the relation between V and C can be viewed in the following way:

$$\left(\begin{array}{c} \nearrow\, C \,\searrow \\ \nwarrow\, V \,\swarrow \end{array} \right)$$

—that is, as a circular system. C acts on V, but V will act again on the C which will become available. V will act on C by incorporating it. C will act on V by permitting V's prolongation in time, so that V will be able to react again to C. The chemical essence of C permits V to prolong its entity as V. The survival of V enables V again to react to C in the same way. If, instead of C, any other substance comes into contact with V within a certain period of time, V will decompose or degrade so that it will never again react to C. V will undergo chemical changes which will constitute segments of longitudinal deterministic chains of causes and effects, and not necessarily segments of circular systems.

Now, any form of life can be seen as an enormously complicated reproduction of the cycle. The life of all known organisms does not consist simply of two stages, but of cycles which include perhaps trillions of successive steps which have to occur in a given sequence. Each stage follows the previous one in a deterministic way. Only when the living cycle unfolds in a particular order does it repeat itself, that is, survive.[10] If the stages cease to be in a special sequence, the cycle is interrupted, and each of its elements will have a position only in longitudinal deterministic series.

In the cyclic situation the various stages of the cycle *seem* to have a *purpose*, namely, the purpose of repeating the cycle. The purpose exists only relatively to the preservation of the cycle; actually, each step occurs in a deterministic way. Only we, who are outsiders in relation to the cycle, see a purpose, because we can see the whole cycle. Another hypothetical observer whose life span is shorter than that of the cycle would see only a deterministic sequence. Purposefulness, or, as it is also called, teleologic causality, *in relation to this level of organization,* is only an *outsider's attitude toward a cyclic variation of deterministic causality.* The self-preserving cycle may be interpreted deterministically. Cycles of this type occur not only in living organisms, but in other events of nature (or machines) which we do not take into consideration here.

Deterministic causality may be represented in this way:

Each event (symbolized by a dot) leads to a subsequent event.

Cyclic or pseudo-teleologic causality can be represented in this way:

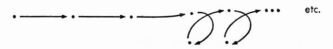

The cycles are part of a deterministic chain. The coincidence of a very improbable set of circumstances permits the cycle to exist and to repeat itself; and when these circumstances

10 For the sake of simplicity we are omitting that extremely important part of the cycle which is concerned with reproduction and which permits the continuation of generations of V's. Reproduction is a subcycle within a cycle.

are altered, the cycle will break. A cyclic system, be it that of the life of a virus or of a solar system, is an interlude in a deterministic succession.

By genetically retaining some mutations, living organisms develop the capacity for *adaptation;* that is, they possess alternative segments of the vital cycle, which make the survival of the whole cycle more probable when unusual circumstances threaten its continuity. For instance, reactions of immunity toward invading germs are examples of adaptational alternatives. These adaptive mechanisms are the result of the long-range molding of the organism by selective evolution through the interplay of mutations and environmental factors.

Motivation

When awareness emerges as a result of complicated and improbable successions of mutations, a revolutionary event has occurred in the universe. No longer does the vital cycle depend exclusively on physicochemical factors or on simple adaptational mechanisms, but on the awareness of what is pleasant (and to be searched for) and what is unpleasant (and to be avoided). As we shall see in more detail later, awareness will direct the organism's responses (which at first will consist of withdrawal or approach, later of much more complicated responses).

A thirsty dog, for instance, is not just thirsty; he is moved by the state of thirst to search for water. Although he is not aware in a cognitive sense of the danger of dehydration, he wants to remove the unpleasant sensation of thirst. If he could not experience thirst, he could die of dehydration. It is obvious that species provided with this type of physiosensation have much more probability of survival than those which are not.

Awareness or subjectivity thus brings about in the universe that revolutionary phenomenon which, according to the various points of view, is called purposiveness, teleologic causality, or motivation. The organism is now equipped with a subjectively experienced purpose and therefore can no longer be equated with a machine or a cybernetic system. The purpose does not exist only for an outsider who contemplates a self-perpetuating cycle, but for the subject which is part of the cycle. We can no longer speak of pseudo purposiveness or pseudo-teleologic causality but of real purposiveness, real teleologic causality, real motivation.[11] Of course, at this level purposiveness is of the most primitive type: the search for pleasure (or the need to seek) and the removal of unpleasure (or the necessity to avoid).

From now on, the universe seems to be regulated no longer only by deterministic (or efficient) causality, but also by teleologic (or finalistic) causality. An aim, that is, something involving something else not yet present (for instance, satisfaction of hunger) is directing present animal behavior. It seems as if—contrary to what happens in the rest of the world, where only the past determines the present—the future too now participates in directing the present.

Purposiveness (or motivation) must be included among the various adaptational modalities of the organism. However, the phenomena of adaptation and purposiveness should not be confused. Adaptation occurs in all living organisms. Purposiveness can occur only in those animal forms which are endowed with feelings.

Some authors have seen in purposiveness the most important aspect of life, even more important than awareness (E. S. Russell [1945]; Du Noüy [1947]; Sinnot [1955]). E. S. Russell speaks of *directiveness,* which he calls an irreducible activity, that is, an activity which cannot be understood in terms of its physicochemical properties or of mechanical deterministic causality.

In my opinion purposiveness, or motivation, as it is more frequently termed in psychological studies, is not in conflict with determinism. To return to the thirsty dog, he is thirsty *now;* his *present* state of thirst determines his forthcoming movements and behavior. He is pushed *a tergo.* However, the *a tergo* pushing becomes connected with a future event and therefore can be considered purposeful. Purposefulness is thus a special type of adaptation which is connected with a

[11] In this chapter we are not considering unconscious motivation, which will be treated in Chapter 9.

feeling that has something to do with the present and future state of the organism.

As a rule (but this rule has a large number of exceptions), what is pleasant enhances survival and what is unpleasant decreases the chance of survival. Pleasantness and increased probability of survival thus become associated, and their association is transmitted from generation to generation. Although this association is imperfect and has many unfavorable exceptions in individual cases, it is a statistically favorable one from the viewpoint of the preservation of the species.

We have taken as examples simple physiosensations, like thirst and hunger, but the same observations could be made about instincts. According to Tinbergen (1951), instincts are the foundation of motivation. They act not only directly but also indirectly—that is, when they are inhibited, they produce a state of discomfort in the animal, so that their motivational power increases. The fulfillment of instincts is a gratifying experience, not only because it leads to the extinction of the need and of the discomfort, but also because it is pleasant in itself—a positive characteristic that is often forgotten in psychoanalytic theories of instinct.

Motivation, as a tendency to search for pleasure and avoid unpleasure, thus becomes a fundamental psychological force. There is no need to believe that this force is a physical energy, libido, or cathexis. It is a readiness to activity which includes some feelings and which is based on the excitability of some parts of the nervous system and on the threshold of this excitability. Physiologists have repeatedly stated that it is not necessary to postulate the existence of a special energy to explain the occurrence of motivation or of other physiological mechanisms (cf., for instance, Lashley and Colby, 1957).

Not all animal functions are motivated. Most of them are the results of physicobiochemical mechanisms which operate in the framework of selective evolution and which are transmitted genetically. The phenomenon of motivation not only enhances survival, but, as we shall see shortly, leads to a gradual enriching of experience by becoming connected with ever more complicated processes.

Object relations

An additional aspect of psychic reality emerges as a consequence of feeling and motivation: object relations. A relationship, or something which can be conceptualized as a tie, develops between the sentient organism and the environmental objects to which it responds.

According to Freud, an object relationship is caused by a movement of libido, a cathectic charge invested in an external object. In this theoretical framework, external objects are seen only as means to instinctual gratification. Fairbairn found this point of view unsatisfactory (1952). According to him, the psyche obtains its fulfillment in object relations. The "central ego" internalizes objects from the environment by actually bringing them into the psyche. In Sullivan's theory, on the other hand, object relations are seen chiefly as interpersonal relations, not as internalizations (1953).

In my opinion, object relationship is at first an organismic change produced by the contiguity or proximity of the stimulus. The source of the stimulus becomes a psychological object when the organism has developed a certain mnemonic disposition toward this source—a disposition which includes feelings, cognitive elements, and motor readiness. Any "tie" between an organism and an external object to which it responds is only a form of influence and should not be conceived or reified as a form of physical energy moving from the organism to the object, or vice versa. Whatever seems to go on between the individual and the object is something which is experienced *in* the organism.

With the development of cognition, the external objects can be represented and therefore replaced by inner objects, which are psychological entities, created and retained by the psyche. Thus object relationship is more adequately studied in subsequent chapters, after we have examined the psychological processes which to a large extent constitute the inner objects.

3 ⊙ SIMPLE EMOTIONS AND SIMPLE BEHAVIOR

This chapter initiates the study of the experiences of inner status which are usually called emotions or affects. Although emotions are experienced within the organism, they cannot be easily localized in one part of the body or another. The main characteristic which justifies their inclusion in the larger category of experiences of inner status is the fact that they occur when a state of the body is subjectively experienced. It is thus not without reason that in English the word *feeling* has a connotation so vast as to include simple sensations as well as high-level affects. It refers to all experiences of inner status.

This chapter treats only the simplest emotions, which I shall call *protoemotions* or *first-order* emotions. Pending further research, I shall divide them into five specific protoemotions: (1) tension, (2) appetite, (3) fear, (4) rage, and (5) satisfaction. Whereas there seems to be no doubt about the existence of fear and rage, the other three types are by no means recognized by all authors as emotions. Future studies will probably reveal that there are not five specific protoemotions but five or more broad categories of elementary emotional experiences. The word *elementary* as used in this context has a relative meaning, because even a simple emotion is a complex phenomenon. Although protoemotions originate at a relatively low level of integration, they retain much importance at all subsequent levels of development.

In a general sense we can say that protoemotions (1) are experiences of inner status which cannot be sharply localized and which involve the whole or a great part of the organism; (2) either include a set of bodily changes, mostly muscular and humoral, or retain some bodily characteristics; (3) are elicited by the presence or absence of specific stimuli, which are perceived by the subject as related in a positive or negative way to its safety and comfort.

TENSION

Perhaps under the large category of tension we can include several relatively simple states of discomfort which tend toward discharge or relief. As long as the discharge is not obtained, the discomfort continues or increases.

Tension is related to the drive tension which Rapaport refers to in his interpretation of Freud's instinctual theory (Rapaport, 1954, 1960). It is also related to the physiostates discussed in the previous chapter. Possibly some authors would be more inclined to consider tension only as a primitive physiological state, not as a feeling.

Following are the most common conditions in which tension is liable to occur:

1. When the nervous system is subject to excessive stimulation without sufficient time for recovery or for adequately organized response; that is, when the input is far greater than the output.

2. When the subject is exposed to simultaneous stimulation from undistinguishable stimuli, so that no adequate response is possible. For instance, an animal will experience tension if, after having been trained to respond positively to a square and negatively to a

circle, it is exposed to a stimulus which is confusing, having some qualities of the square and some of the circle (Gantt, 1936; Hilgard and Marquis, 1940; Liddell, 1938).

3. When instincts or appetites are not consummated (see page 34).

4. When fear or rage is not followed by its usual patterns of response.

5. When the specific satisfying object is lacking in the environment and the subject is in a state of need (for instance, the maternal breast is not available). Rather than leading to a sense of loss, to psychological deprivation, or to a depressed feeling, this primitive state of deprivation seems to result in a special subtype of tension which is a precursor of these feelings.

6. When an unpleasant but vaguely recognized emotion is transmitted from another living organism. The most common example is the anxiety of the mother, which is empathically perceived by the baby and experienced as tension (Sullivan, 1953).

Some authors have also recognized prototypes of conflict in several states of tension (see Rapaport, 1954, and page 9 of this book). However, I prefer to restrict the word *conflict* to the simultaneous occurrence of two or more contrasting emotions, ideas, or motivations. In the state of tension as I am using this term, the discrepancy is between what physical reality imposes and what the organism would require for a state of comfort.

Some tension-producing situations have been intensely studied by many authors. Freud's first theory of anxiety and his concept of actual neuroses as clinical entities different from psychoneuroses have a great deal to do with what is here defined as tension. Freud attributed actual neuroses to such causes as interruption of sexual intercourse, frustrated excitement, and abstinence.

Some people prefer to classify under *anxiety* the primitive emotional states which I have grouped under *tension*. These people also think that anxiety is possible in the first few months of life. It all depends, of course, on the definition of anxiety. As discussed in Chapter 4, I shall use anxiety to imply some symbolic processes which permit the anticipation of danger. These processes cannot occur in the first few months of life because of the immaturity of the central nervous system. The baby, however, may experience tension from birth.

If we were to insist on calling anxiety what is called tension here, we would have to distinguish a *short-circuited* anxiety from a *long-circuited* one.[1] Some authors may see a state of frustration in the situations which I have listed as states of tension. In my opinion the concept of frustration implies an intellectual realization of unfulfillment, which is not possible at a very primitive level. Of course, many states of frustration in humans have connections with, or are elaborations of, the state of tension.

Some kind of elementary learning or recollection of previous experiences seems a necessary precondition for tension. The subject remembers previous situations in which input was followed by a corresponding output, and tension occurs when the learned or previously experienced responses cannot be actualized.

APPETITE

Like tension, appetite is a protoemotion which cannot be easily differentiated or connected with a simple specific situation. Perhaps appetite can be defined as the emotional component of relatively primitive reactions which tend toward an almost immediately attainable gratification.

The main characteristic of appetite is a tendency to move toward, to grab, to incorporate. In my conception, appetite refers not only to a pleasant tendency to eat or drink or copulate, but also includes that emotional state of almost immediate expectancy which Mowrer designated as "hope" (1960a, b). Hope does not seem to me the most appropriate term because it implies an elaborate foresight and an optimistic

---

[1] In some previous writings I have actually used the term *short-circuited anxiety* instead of tension (1947). I decided not to use the term here because I felt that it would lead to confusion with long-circuited anxiety, which is a higher-order emotion. Of course, tension and anxiety are related, and many intermediary stages exist.

conception of the future, neither of which is possible at primitive levels. Certainly the expectancy of something good and the pleasant emotional accompaniment are included in what we call appetite. But they refer to what is about to be present, or to what occurs in the period of time which immediately follows the stimulus. For instance, an infant sees his mother and wants to be nursed; sees a toy and wants to grab the toy. Perhaps a synonym of appetite would be the expression *quick desire.* There is an anticipation of pleasantness which will make the subject strive toward this pleasantness and which, if there is no obstacle, will merge with the pleasantness of consummation.

An appetite can be quickly aroused and quickly quenched. Appetite should not be confused with some physiostates like hunger or thirst, or with some instincts like the sexual urge, although it generally accompanies these states and in many cases needs them in order to be evoked. In infrahuman animals, it is difficult to establish whether what the animal experiences is a physiosensation, an instinctual reaction, or an appetite. We can say this, however: Appetite, even in infrahuman animals, implies some kind of learning. Although the reaction may have instinctual components, a certain amount of learning or of cognitive appraisal of the external stimulus which brings about the craving is necessary. For instance, when children have learned to recognize toys or candies, they develop a strong appetite for them.

The physiology of appetite is not known. The somatic response involves some kind of visceral preparation for what is to follow, and there is some muscular and postural orientation. The physiology of appetite should not be confused with that of the accompanying physiosensations or instinct.

FEAR

Unlike tension and appetite, fear can be defined with relative ease. It is an inner change, subjectively experienced as unpleasant, occurring when the organism has perceived a stimulus which is recognized as dangerous. The cognitive element, which consists of a kind of appraisal of perceptual data, is a specific and important element of fear.

The organism not only perceives and recognizes the stimulus (the feared object), but understands the capacity of the stimulus to affect its existence adversely. Such understanding elicits the unpleasant experience which constitutes the fear.

More clearly than in the other protoemotions already discussed, we can observe in fear the emergence in nature of something of extraordinary importance. An external stimulus which is not in direct physical contact with the organism, and which is not so directly connected with the vital cycle as instincts are, elicits a specific experience of inner status. Fear is registered after what may be compared to a wireless transmission. The unpleasantness and discomfort which are part of the fear experience actually stand for the unpleasantness which the animal would undergo if the fear were to materialize (for instance, if the animal were to become the prey of a bigger animal).

Fear thus *seems* to be symbolic. It also seems purposeful, because no matter how unpleasant it is, it is less harmful and less unpleasant than the feared event would be if it happened. Fear is a warning of the probability of danger. Nevertheless, the experience of this protoemotion is *not* symbolic; it is present, actual—a subjective unpleasant reality. The protoemotional state is a signal to act on; although brought about by an external stimulus, it becomes an *intraorganismic* communication. The part of the organism which experiences the altered emotional status impels the whole organism to be ready for a specific action: *flight*.

Thus whereas feelings of general unpleasantness lead to motor responses which may be called general withdrawal or avoidance of the unpleasant stimulus, fear leads to the specific withdrawal of flight from the stimulus. Flight has to be initiated right away. The fleeing response, however, is not so immediate as it seems; for between the stimulus and the response there is a brief interval, which may be too short to be appreciated, during which the response is microgenetically organized. The experience of fear and its specific response, flight, are a parsimonious pattern of response developed in evolution. In fact, the situations which bring about fear are many and very different, but the responses are similar or identical.

The microgenetic psychology of fear is unknown, but we

have some knowledge of the physiology. In mammals, the neocortical network which mediates the appraisal of the fearful situation is connected with a network in the limbic system and with lower subcortical structures, including the reticular system. After the emotional flavor of the experience has been mediated, probably in the limbic system, the response is organized in the hypothalamus. This hypothalamic response coordinates all the visceral, humoral, and muscular reactions which lead to that specific behavior which will eliminate the source of fear. For instance, the excitement of the autonomic nervous system in its turn affects the endocrine system. A discharge of adrenalin occurs, which causes a constriction of the blood vessels. "Cold feet" and cold hands, characteristic of the state of fear, are a consequence.

RAGE

In rage, relatively simple cognitive processes lead the animal to the perception of a danger which has to be overcome not by flight but by fight. In many cases it is difficult to determine if the reaction is instinctive or if learned cognitive processes make the subject realize that the danger is not great and that fight will overcome it. Perhaps both processes and a combination of them are possible, or perhaps gradual changes from instinctive to learned reactions occur in the phyletic scale.

In rage the predominant feeling is not terror, but a violent attitude toward the stimulus, which has to be attacked or chased away. Although a stirring up and a discharge mechanism seem the most important elements in rage, the signal quality and the defensive purposes are also significant aspects.

In rage the excitement of the autonomic nervous system does not predominantly involve the sympathetic branch as in fear, but possibly the parasympathetic branch is engaged to an equal degree. Salivary output, secretion of hydrochloric acid, and peristalsis all increase, and the blood vessels dilate so that the muscles receive an increased blood supply. All these changes improve the animal's ability to fight.

SATISFACTION

It is likely, although by no means certain, that satisfaction is a distinct protoemotion. A state of satisfaction seems to require: (1) the consummation of all appetites and the extinction of all unpleasant experiences of inner status—pain, hunger, thirst, fatigue, other kinds of physical discomfort, fear, rage, tension, higher-level unpleasant emotions, etc. (2) some kind of protracted pleasure in experiencing physiological functions.

Sullivan (1953) has described the state of satisfaction as occurring when all bodily needs have been gratified. If satisfaction is only the absence of unpleasantly experienced needs, then it cannot be considered as something which exists in a positive sense. However, as more and more data are accumulated on the encephalic organization of pleasant emotions, it is more and more difficult to rule out the existence of satisfaction as a specific state of being. Some psychiatric patients have reported an intense feeling of satisfaction in dreams as well as in states of intoxication and drug addiction.

When satisfaction is felt, the organism does not experience the urge to mobilize mechanisms to preserve the homeostasis. The organism functions at its best, as if its homeostasis would not be threatened. When the newborn baby is in a state of health and in a perfect environment, provided for by a loving mother, he is presumably in a state of satisfaction. The insecurity brought about by higher-level emotions does not set in.

General characteristics of protoemotions

In the nature and complexity of the somatic response, most protoemotions (certainly fear and rage, and probably appetite and tension) are related to physiostates. In some cases a physiostate (for instance, hunger) and a protoemotion (appetite) coexist and overlap. An important difference between the two is that protoemotions require the appraisal of an external stimulus. A cognitive element—some kind of learning, even if minimal—is necessary.[2] This cognitive component, however, is relatively minor in comparison with the affective element. We could even say that since the cognitive component is so undeveloped in protoemotions, the affective part has to be intense to enable the animal to survive. And with the possible exception of satisfaction, protoemotions are intensely felt experiences. The protoemotion "informs" the subject that something is happening or about to happen inside it or in its surroundings. The information is transmitted as a feeling state and becomes a strong motivational force.

Protoemotions appear to be concerned with the present time: they seem tied to a present stimulus or to one which follows with a very short interval. Actually, this brief interval always exists between the stimulus and the protoemotional response. (In contrast, the organism experiences no interval in simple sensations and physiosensations—for instance, a pain or a burning sensation is felt as an immediate occurrence.) In protoemotion there is a state of expectancy, very short, often a small fraction of a second. This little temporal interval actually may be a matter of life or death for the animal which has to appraise the emergency and organize a quick response consisting of behavior valuable for its survival. That such a temporal interval can exist is very important not only for evolution in general but for the evolution of the psyche in particular. This brief temporal delay opens the door to cognitive elaboration of the stimulus and to the organism's assessment of the future. At the protoemotional level of development, however, the future is merging with the present; for instance, the danger is about to materialize right away, or the desired object may be available only for a fleeting moment.[3] The stimulus which elicits the protoemotions may be replaced by a signal of the stimulus.[4] And of course, at the human level protoemotions may be elicited by language too; for instance, the word "Fire!" shouted in a crowded theater may evoke immediate fear. Language is not

[2] Mowrer gives great importance to protoemotions in his learning theory (1960a, b).
[3] The importance of protoemotions in the state of emergency has been illustrated by Cannon (1929, 1939).
[4] But not necessarily by a verbal symbol (see Chapter 7).

mandatory, however. Protoemotions in humans may also be stimulated by images (see Chapter 5).

It has been asked whether protoemotions can be used as a form of communication: that is, as a method of transmitting to other organisms a certain way of being or some kind of message. The communicative aspect of emotions has been stressed by some authors. Although emotions, especially those of a high order, have definite communicative elements, they are originally intraorganismic phenomena. Communication is only a by-product. This is particularly true of protoemotions. Protoemotional behavior, however, may occur in some animals as a form of imitation. In humans a protoemotional communication undoubtedly exists in the infant-mother relationship. What is often referred to as *empathy* is probably a pleasant communication occurring chiefly at a protoemotional level, without the partners involved intending to communicate.

Another important question, which we shall discuss again in Chapter 6, is whether protoemotions can exist in a state of unconsciousness. It is a characteristic of protoemotions that the organism seeks their immediate discharge or extinction rather than repressing them. However, as Chapter 6 will show, they may become associated with or transformed into higher emotions which can be repressed.

Although all types of emotions *seem* to be experienced in their totality as general feelings not susceptible of division or of scientific analysis, this impression is not correct. The following questions differentiate some characteristics of emotions with which we shall be concerned:

1. Is the emotion pleasant (P) or unpleasant (U)?
2. Is it quick to originate and to extinguish, or does it have a tendency to last for a moderate or a long time? We shall use the symbols Q, M, and L.
3. Does it have an impelling tendency toward action and discharge (I), or toward self-perpetuation (p)?
4. Is it centripetal, centrifugal, or reflexive? A *centripetal* emotion is experienced as something directed from the stimulus to the organism—for instance, fear. A *centrifugal* emotion is experienced as directed toward something outside of the organism—for instance, rage.

A *reflexive* emotion seems to reflect back to the organism experiencing it—for instance, tension and satisfaction. We shall use the symbols ← for centripetal, → for centrifugal, and ⊕ for reflexive.

5. Is the emotion potentially an increasing one, or is it self-contained? We shall use the symbol < for increasing and *O* for self-contained.

These are not *objective* aspects of emotions, like somatic, motor, or verbal responses, but only qualities of the subjective experience. Undoubtedly other qualities of emotions could be differentiated. Following is the list of protoemotions characterized by the symbols specified above. Needless to say, these symbols offer only "profiles"; they do not stand for the emotional states the way chemical formulas represent chemical substances.

Tension	$UMI \ominus <$
Appetite	$PQI \rightarrow <$
Rage	$UQI \rightarrow <$
Fear	$UQI \leftarrow <$
Satisfaction	$PMp \ominus O$

The importance of these basic protoemotions varies with various species and with individual members of a species. When they are not well balanced by other emotions, they determine in humans a fundamental disposition toward a type of personality. Thus there are some human beings in whom fear (later changed into anxiety) is the predominant emotion. Depending on its interaction with their other emotions and on the prevailing type of their interpersonal relations, these people may eventually become either detached (that is, withdrawing from fearful stimuli) or compliant (placating the source of fear). People in whom rage is the predominant emotion tend to be aggressive and hostile. People in whom appetite is the principal emotion tend to become hedonistic. When tension predominates, the individual is likely to be hypochondriacal and more interested in his body than in the external environment. When satisfaction is the principal emotion, the person's predominant outlook is conservative, centered on the *status quo*.

In the ontogenetic development of man, protoemotions

lose importance as they are gradually transformed into higher types of emotion. Interpersonal relations, especially those with the mother or a mother substitute, are indispensable in helping the child evolve toward higher forms of emotional life. In some psychopathological conditions, especially drug addictions and psychopathic personality forms, there is a re-emergence of the importance of protoemotions. For instance, people in whom rage is the preponderant protoemotion are predisposed to the aggressive variety of the simple psychopathic personality type (see Chapter 15).

The protoemotional level of motivation

Feelings exist in the evolutional scale as preservers of the intactness of the animal organism. In most protoemotional states, feelings reflect external events, and by the manner in which they do this they are easily recognized as directly connected with what is indispensable for survival. It is obvious by now that although I too consider feelings as qualitative states of consciousness, my approach differs from the phenomenological-existentialistic one in that I study them also as motivational factors.

Motivation is subjectivity diverted from the inner feeling to a relation with the external world or its symbolic equivalents.[5] It is an expectation of an affective change, which in certain situations the subject itself can at least partially implement. It may also be considered a directional attitude toward this affective change: generally the removal of the unpleasant and/or the acquisition of the pleasant. But what is pleasant or unpleasant differs at various levels of motivation. At the level of protoemotions or simpler experiences of inner status, motivation seems to consist predominantly of the attainment of either a state of sensuous pleasure or a state of satisfaction. The removal of pain, discomfort, hunger, the sexual urge, etc.—as well as the removal of the unpleasant protoemotions such as fear, rage, and tension—is the goal.

Using Freud's terminology, this level can also be called the level of the pleasure principle, in which a hedonistic attitude

[5] In this chapter we are not considering unconscious motivation (see Chapter 9).

prevails. Actually, from an evolutionary point of view, a motivation based on the pleasure principle is not unrealistic. As Spencer (1899) wrote, pain is generally the correlative of what is immediately injurious to the organism, whereas pleasure is correlative of what is often conducive to its welfare. The species generally manages to survive if the motivation is regulated in accordance with the pleasure principle, although individual members may perish. This type of motivation focuses on the soma, or, more exactly, on the soma's search for pleasantness and avoidance of unpleasantness. The elementary needs for survival are generally respected by an organization centering on the pleasure principle, although survival is not a conscious purpose of the individual members of the species. Attainment of pleasure and avoidance of unpleasure are generally achieved by the living organism which has the necessary physical equipment. In case of competition, the strongest or the fittest wins.

When human beings reach higher levels of integration where more complicated forms of motivation predominate, the pleasure principle still has an important role, and in some pathological conditions assumes supremacy. As we shall see later, it is normal for a human being to behave in accordance with the protoemotional level of motivation, if such behavior is not in conflict with higher levels.

The exocept

We have spoken of the protoemotional level of the psyche, as if only feelings and emotions were involved. Obviously cognitive and conative functions too are necessary and are integrated with the other functions.

At this level, perceptions and experiences lead to a quick response. The response actually follows an inner preparation —a mental construct or inner representation which is subsequently embodied in movement or action. The inner representation, which I call *exocept* and which resembles what some neurologists call engram, is one of the early constructs which eventually lead to the formation of concepts. Until the exocept is translated into motor behavior, it is only an internal and unconscious representation of motor behavior. In this construct there is no clear-cut differentiation between cognition and conation. Perhaps we can state that in the exocept there is a primitive preconceptual meaning, which is inherent in the response and in the response to the response. For instance, in a dogfight, dog A responds to dog B. Dog A's response affects dog A and dog B. Dog A's exocept includes the anticipation of its own response and the response of dog B to A's response.

To some extent many exocepts, especially in subhuman animals, are innate—that is, they are learned by the species, not by the individual. In other words, only those organisms which had a congenital readiness to some adequate motor responses survived and transmitted it genetically.

In subhuman animals exocepts play a very important role, being intimately connected with physiostates, instincts, and protoemotions. For instance, in fear, rage, and appetite, the response consists of sensation → perception → recognition → protoemotion → exocept → motor response. Thus in a physiosensation like hunger, the experience of inner status elicits an exocept which leads to a motor response (search for food). If the motor response consists almost exclusively of motor engrams which have been transmitted genetically, then perhaps we can talk more specifically of instinctual reactions. Often, however, a learned element enters into instinctual responses also, and we have a mixture of congenital and acquired schemata. At times the learned experience disturbs the instinctual response, as in the phenomenon of imprinting, described by Lorenz (1953). If at a certain period in the life of a gosling a man and not a goose displays a maternal attitude, the gosling reacts to the man as it would instinctively react to a goose. Thus it would seem that for the organization of some instinctual exocepts, the proper stimulus has to occur at a certain stage of development.

Primitive exocepts tend to remain connected to specific stimuli, so that a certain rigidity of behavior results. This rigidity has overall beneficial effects as far as the survival of the species is concerned (especially in transmitting from generation to generation adequate responses to physiosensations, instincts, and protoemotions), but it may be inappropriate in some circumstances. Rigidity of behavior, however, may also be part of learned behavior. For instance, a dog learns to recognize the footsteps of his master who is coming home. As soon as he hears them, the dog runs to the door to "greet" the master. The stimulus activates in the dog a series of exocepts, all of which have to be actualized into overt behavior. The dog has no choice: he cannot stay still.

Exocepts in their more primitive forms represent motor behavior which, relatively speaking, is not complicated. The subsequent behavior leads to avoidance of danger, to fighting behavior, or to immediate possession or incorporation of the needed object, if such an object is available. At these primitive stages of development there seems to be a strict coordination between stimuli (of inner or external origin) and subsequent behavior. If the subsequent behavior consists of incorporating an object or of a special type of relation with an object, the relationship remains external; no internalization of such relationships occurs until the organism reaches higher levels of development. We cannot yet talk of a mental representation, except the specific representation of the exocept. Thus we may say that at this level, cognition, conation, and object relationship coincide, or almost coincide. Exocepts also include mechanisms for exploratory behavior and games.

Although so far we have spoken of exocepts in subhuman animals, actually they play an important role in human life too. In the human being the learned part of the exocept outgrows the congenital. Exoceptual activity is particularly dominant in the first two years of life and corresponds to what Piaget calles sensorimotor intelligence.[6] In adult life, exoceptual mentation recedes to a more modest role. However, it remains important in some aspects of human life, especially in games, sports, and other predominantly motor activities which do not require high symbolic levels. When the tennis player responds to the stimulus ball, he manages most of the time to produce an adequate response. He creates exocepts by their similarity to previous exocepts.

People who do manual work or operate machinery also expand their exoceptual life.

The role of the exoceptual forms of life should not be

[6] The phylogenetic or ontogenetic acquisition of exocepts will not be described in this book. For a neurological point cf view, see Schlesinger (1962); for a psychological, Piaget (1952) and Gesell (1945).

underestimated. We know that most mental life, no matter how complicated, ends sooner or later in overt behavior and therefore requires exocepts. Nevertheless, to consider only the exocept without the antecedent steps, or to think of a life limited to the exoceptual pleasure-principle level, is an unwarranted simplification. This is the mistake made by the behaviorist school of psychology.

Behaviorism does not even deal with the exocept, which is a mental construct, but with external, objective, and, in many instances, measurable behavior. The acme of this tendency is seen in Watson's attempt to reduce thinking too to implicit motor behavior. Attempts to explain mental life predominantly in terms of motor behavior (or in conceptualizations similar to the exocept) are found in the works of many important exponents of psychology and related sciences. Even such a great thinker as George H. Mead, who was certainly aware that the mind consists of much more than motor behavior, tried to explain psychological phenomena predominantly in behavioristic language (1934). His explanations referred often to such topics as gestures, games, and dogfights, because such phenomena are characteristic of a type of psychological life where motor behavior, or interaction through motor behavior, predominates.

Other authors have given great importance to what I call the exocept. For Morris, "meaning" is a disposition to act (1946). More recently, Becker has spoken of dependable responses by which the subject tries to overcome problematic situations (1962). These responses are internalized and become converted into what he calls *external objects.* Following Mead and Morris, Becker stresses the external aspect of the interactions of the individual with the world. Actually, what he calls external objects are inner constructs and internalizations of certain responses. They constitute one of the simplest types of object relations.

Exocepts are also given prominence in some philosophies, where they are seen as depositories of most of what is meaningful in man. For instance, in Zen Buddhism the exocepts necessary for the art of archery or other motor activities are seen as a perfect embodiment of human life.

Exocepts acquire a predominant role in some pathologic

conditions, such as some cases of schizophrenia and some psychoneuroses (see Chapters 16 and 17). In one form of art —dance—exocepts also have the central role (see Chapter 21).

A last important consideration is whether exoceptual behavior can acquire the quality of unconsciousness. It can, but not with the mechanism of repression described by Freud, which applies only to higher levels of integration. Loss of awareness in the phenomenon of habituation is a parsimonious device used constantly by the nervous system. It applies to exoceptual behavior too, even when the individual develops beyond the exoceptual level. In our daily living we focus our attention only on a relatively small range of our perceptions, thoughts, and feelings. The rest is unattended or at the periphery of our consciousness. When we walk, when we perform habitual acts—even acts which were once difficult, like the use of complicated instruments—we become progressively unattentive. Finally the acts become automatic. If we were conscious of everything which impinges upon our senses, we would not be able to focus on what we are mostly concerned with at one time. Thus a great deal of our functioning is simply automatized or nonattended. What is nonattended, however, can easily come back to consciousness; it belongs to the periphery of consciousness, or to what Freud calls the preconscious.

There is also a special large group of psychological phenomena which are *subliminal:* they occur at the sensorimotor level and are not accompanied by awareness. In these cases stimuli come from the external world, or are enteroceptive; but either because they have not reached a certain threshold, or because the sensitivity of the individual is diminished, they are not followed by a subjective experience. They are registered by the organism, but there is no awareness of the registration. That perception may be subliminal there is ample proof which does not need to be repeated here.[7]

[7] For a good account of research on subliminal perception see Miller (1942).

The primordial self

Is it possible at this sensorimotor level to experience a sense or awareness of the self, which includes and integrates the functions that we have studied? If by "self" we mean a living subject, then of course we can state that at this stage the self is an organism operating at a protoemotional-exoceptual level. If by self we mean the individual as he is known to himself, then we must say that this state of consciousness is rudimentary. It probably consists of a bundle of simple relations between physiostates, perceptions, proto-emotions, and exocepts—relations which at first involve some parts of the body, particularly the mouth. However, as patterns of motor behavior develop in relation to external objects, a kind of primitive motor identity, as well as awareness of the totality of one's body, probably evolves even in subhuman animals.

The important relations that at this level the baby already establishes with other persons will not be discussed here. We must mention, however, that feeling of "omnipotence" which has been described by many authors in children at this early stage of development. When the concept of omnipotence is used in reference to the young child, it is to be understood as a feeling that the expected pleasure is about to be consummated. It is more a state of the organism and an exoceptual readiness than a cognitive construct. Ferenczi, in describing the feeling, writes that at this stage of development there are no inhibiting, postponing activities (1913). The pleasure-fulfilling movement occurs spontaneously and unhesitatingly as "an averting movement away from something disagreeable, or an approach towards something agreeable."

4 ⊚ PERCEPTION AND RESPONSE: PART AND WHOLE

Protoemotions and exocepts, which were discussed in the previous chapter, presuppose the experience of perception, which we shall now examine from a cognitive point of view. No attempt will be made to summarize the extensive studies which have been carried out on perception. Instead, this chapter develops a topic which is of basic importance in our inquiry: the perception of part and whole.

From primitive unity to whole

The problem of the part versus the whole extends over the whole field of cognition, from the simplest perception to conceptual thinking. In Chapter 2 we saw that when a small organism V responds to an environmental substance C, it separates C from the rest of the world. C becomes differentiated and finite, although it may remain indefinite; thus C becomes a unity. Perhaps the unity does not exist so much in the external object itself as in the response or the reactivity of V. The reactivity of V to C constitutes a unity because it is a distinct episode in the life of V. The external object C may consist of several parts, just as a molecule of water or of glucose consists of several atoms; but V reacts to C in a unitary way, as it reacts to whole molecules of water or of glucose. Unity is thus at first a psychological construct, the reaction of the organism to a fragment of the external world. This fragment becomes differentiated by the reactivity of V. It becomes an object. An object is something having a unity.

In Chapter 2 we also saw that V will continue to respond in the same way to subsequent exposures to C. When organisms develop a nervous system, this generalization of responses becomes the well-known S-R process. The organism will respond to stimulus A in a certain way. By responding to A, it will continue to separate A from the rest of the world. We could be tempted to say that the organism "recognizes" A, except that recognition implies an experience endowed with consciousness. To respond to A and be aware of one's response to A (that is, aware of separating A from the rest of the world) is a very complicated mechanism. It presupposes the perception of unity as an act of consciousness. The perception of unity is actually the fundamental base on which the whole field of cognition rests.

We can only speculate on the perception of unities in simple organisms. When irritability has evolved to the level of sensation, then in many instances stimulation, either simple or multiple, produces in the organism a subjectively felt discontinuity—a temporary change from the previous state. *When this discontinuity is not felt* (as in many physiologic and practically all homeostatic processes), *we do not have experiences directly related to cognition.* When there is a felt discontinuity, no matter whether it was provoked by what appears to us a simple stimulus or a constellation of stimuli, a psychological unity is formed. At first, however, a unity is an experiential phenomenon, not something located in the external environment. Later, what originated as an internal organismic effect is projected, and the perception is experienced as external. Only those species which could project the perception could survive and evolve into higher forms.

When is an experiential phenomenon perceived as a unity? Is the perception of unities inborn or learned? There seems to be no doubt now that some perception of "primitive unity" (for instance, the discrimination of the figure from the background) is innate. Even Hebb (1949), who, in contrast to the gestaltists, gives much more importance to the learned part of perception, admits that a primitive unity is not learned. Probably only those species which had the ability to discriminate figures from backgrounds could survive and transmit this ability genetically. Such primitive differentiation seems to be a prerequisite to more advanced forms of perception.

At this primitive level, however, the animal does not perceive the figure-ground differential at all clearly. Only the most primitive differentiation seems innate. The total response is experienced both as an inner change and as a trigger to some motor or visceral change. Whatever is experienced deeply and leads to the main motor response is part of the figure; whatever is less strongly perceived and leads to weaker motor responses is part of the background. The figure, in contrast to the background, seems to have a compelling quality, or a releasing quality, inasmuch as it elicits the strong response.

It is difficult to anticipate what will remain relatively undifferentiated and part of the background, and what instead will be part of the unity. Indeed, one of the most arduous struggles of animal evolution is to determine what belongs to the unity and has to be differentiated from a more or less indefinite background. In fact, many species of animals respond to what seem to us parts, not unities or wholes.

Tinbergen has illustrated some interesting mechanisms. For instance, certain fish like the sticklebacks, in fighting competitor male fish which invade their territory, react only to the red color of the competitors' bellies (1951). Since they react to only a part of the total environmental situation and neglect the other parts, they can make mistakes: artificial red objects introduced by the experimenter elicit the same fighting response. Yet the sense organs of these fish are able to perceive the whole situation, and it is the total situation which is important for the fish—the chasing away of male competitors. Nevertheless, it is a part, the red color, that is perceived as a unity, recognized and identified, and responded to with fighting behavior. The perception of the stimulus red as a unity here seems certain. It would be too much to ascribe to the fish the capacity to abstract the red from the environment. These animals do not abstract; they respond in a primitive way only to a simple stimulus, which is differentiated from the background.

Tinbergen adds that these situations where only a stimulus, like the red belly, is the releaser of the response are actually quite rare. Other configurational or concomitant elements, such as the movement and appearance of the water, contribute to a certain gestalt which triggers the specific behavior. However, a stimulus, like the red color, is the essential element; it is the releasing mechanism, clearly perceived against a less differentiated background.[1]

In animal psychology there are many examples of responses to a fragment of a situation, or to a quality of the background, with disregard of the whole situation. All of us are familiar with the fact that moths are attracted by light even though they may burn themselves to death in contact with powerful electric bulbs. The reactivity to one element is often used to trick and kill insects. In the case of flypaper, the fly, which reacts only to the sweetness of the paper, is caught by its stickiness. It would seem that, early in phylogeny, the organism reacts predominantly to a releasing element, which is seen as a whole; it reacts in a very weak fashion to the rest, which is experienced as undifferentiated or fragmented.[2]

Higher in the evolutionary scale the perceived object becomes more complicated, consisting of more than the releasing element, although the releasing element still has the most

[1] Tinbergen warns that we should not confuse gestalt situations with chain reactions. The secondary elements which are necessary to elicit the instinctual behavior are reacted to individually, just as the red belly is; but all these additional reactions occur in a chain of events which is very rapid and gives the observer the impression of one gestalt.

[2] Fragmentation is a form of perception difficult to conceive because it presupposes wholes which are later fragmented. The term *fragmentation* is suggested by experiences occurring in psychopathological states, as we shall see in Chapter 16. Actually, something similar may occur in early infancy: the perceptual background may consist not only of undifferentiated parts but also of parts which have not been organized to form wholes. These parts may appear to *adults* as fragments.

important perceptual role. Additional parts are detached from the background and become part of the figure or of the whole.

Thus objects that appear to us as wholes have not always been experienced as unities, either in phylogeny or in ontogeny. What corresponds to our part perception is at first the main perceptual method of experience. Later the releasing element, or main part, remains the most important among the various parts of the object. Finally the releasing element is perceived as only one of the many parts of the unity. Riesen (1947), using mammals raised in darkness, and Von Senden (1960), using adult humans who were operated on for congenital cataracts and were learning to see, have demonstrated how part perception precedes the total perception of the object. In each study a serial apprehension of the parts was a prerequisite to perception of the whole. The shortest time in which a congenitally blind person approximated normal perception was about a month.[3]

In the psychoanalytic literature Melanie Klein has given great importance to part perception in infants. According to her, objects which are perceived (or introjected, as she says) are at first partial objects. For instance, the mother is not seen as a whole, but as a breast (Klein, 1948a, Klein, Heimann, and Money-Kyrle, 1955).

Corroboration of this point can also be obtained from the experiments of Pritchard, Heron, and Hebb (1960). Following previous work by Ditchburn (1961) and Riggs and Tulunay (1959), they confirmed that movements of the eyeballs are necessary for normal perception. If the eye movements are made impossible and an image is thus stabilized on the retina, an abnormal, presumably primitive, form of perception occurs. Pritchard and his associates attached to the eyeball itself a special device consisting of a contact lens and an optical projector. With this device the image remains fixed on the retina and does not move with the movements of the eyeball. The authors found that with this procedure a complex image, such as the profile of a face, may vanish in fragments, with one or more of its parts fading independently.

[3] Hebb has used this material of Von Senden to support his neurophysiological theory of learning.

Some fragments remain in perception. This fragmentation seems to correspond to an original part perception. For some fleeting periods of time, parts remain aggregated but do not form wholes.

In tachistoscopic and other subliminal experiments, parts alone are often registered (Werner, 1956). In subliminal experiments, some parts which were apparently not perceived were registered, as demonstrated by the fact that they appeared in subsequent dreams. Fisher (1954, 1960, Fisher and Paul, 1959) has done interesting work in this respect by continuing and expanding experiments originally devised by Pötzl (1917, Pötzl, Allers, and Teler, 1960). The subject is exposed to a visual image which lasts only $\frac{1}{100}$ second. No conscious perception is possible at such speed; what does occur is a subliminal and incorrect perception of which the subject is unaware. Fisher has been able to demonstrate that parts of the exposed pictures, which were not consciously perceived, appeared in dreams or in drawings made by the subjects. It is evident that tachistoscopic perception is part perception.

Some neurological conditions, such as visual agnosias, also induce a return to part perception. The literature on visual agnosia is abundant. To the author's knowledge, one of the most accurate reports is that by Alexandra Adler on the disintegration and restoration which occur in visual agnosia (1944, 1950). Adler described, among other things, the alternation in visual perception experienced by a 22-year-old woman who was injured in the famous fire at the Cocoanut Grove night club in Boston in 1942. At first the patient was totally blind; after two days she could distinguish white from dark but could not recognize colors. She presented also a picture of pure subcortical visual alexia, Wernicke type. The diagnosis was lesion of the brain, probably caused by carbon monoxide fumes.

After her injury, this woman was no longer able to perceive wholes. She had to add part by part in order to reconstruct wholes and recognize objects. Often she recognized parts and guessed the rest. She could not identify the figures 2, 3, 5, 6, 8, and 9 because she could not make out the direction of the curves of which these figures were composed; but she was able to recognize 1, 4, and 7 during the second week of her illness because she could guess where a straight line was going. Since this patient recognized objects "by tracing the contours, by adding the parts and by making conclusions from all she had perceived, she had to take more time than did the normal person, who recognizes all the parts, in the main, simultaneously" (Adler, 1944).

Some neurologists (Brain, Nissl von Mayendorf, Poppelreuter, all cited by Adler, 1944) have suggested that a patient's inability to perceive the whole might be caused by a defect in the visual fields. Some controversy has arisen on this subject—for instance, that provoked by a famous case, described by Goldstein and Gelb (1920), of a man whose brain was injured during combat in World War I. This man lost the capacity to recognize by a simultaneous act of visual perception the whole of a figure—the gestalt. Goldstein (1939, 1943) and Adler herself (1959), supported by observations made by other authors (Jossman, 1929; Wilbrand and Sanger, 1917; Wolpert, 1924), could disprove the interpretation that a defect in visual fields might be involved. The conclusion reached was that in certain pathological conditions, parts instead of wholes are all that can be perceived. A tendency exists, however, for the patient to reconstruct wholes, which at times are inappropriate ones only loosely related to the original.

Response to the part and to the whole

So far we have focused on the perception of the part versus the perception of the whole. Actually, this topic cannot be separated from that of the response to the part versus the response to the whole.

Although a low organism responds only to a part, in a way which seems erroneous to our human intellect, the species survives and transmits its capacities when the partial response fits the whole most of the time. For instance, although the stickleback reacts only to a red color, its reaction is useful and appropriate to a larger situation which favors the survival of the species. Outside the man-made laboratory situation, the stickleback has little chance of being exposed to extraneous red objects and therefore little chance of wasting his reactions on a part-object.

We can say that, at least potentially, two types of responding exist in nature: to the part (or to a releasing element) and to the whole. Each of these types is generalized; that is, the organism tends to respond in the same way to different examples of the same stimulus, irrespective of whether the stimulus is what we consider a part or a whole. The stickleback generalizes its reaction to all red parts; the cat generalizes its reaction to all mice.

Generalization is a process applicable to a group of stimuli —either a group of what seem to us parts or a group of what seem to us wholes. Generalization probably leads to recognition. Although at a mature level the animal responds to an object after it has recognized the object, very early in phylogeny and ontogeny the animal probably recognizes the object because it has first recognized its own response. It is likely that the baby first recognizes his response to the maternal nipple before recognizing the existence of the maternal nipple and breast. Recognition will open the road which leads to class formation; that is, to formation of groups of objects. The group may consist of objects which have just a part in common or, as we shall see later, objects which have a whole in common. In the first case the processes eventually lead to formation of primary classes; in the second case they lead to formation of secondary classes (see Chapters 7 and 8). It is thus necessary to examine more accurately some examples of generalization of responses. We shall first take into consideration the phenomenon of generalization as studied by Pavlov.

If it is similar to a conditioned stimulus which has been reinforced, a new stimulus, not reinforced, may elicit a conditioned response even the first time it is presented to the subject. For instance, an animal which has been conditioned to respond in a certain way to a tone will produce the same response when presented with a tone of slightly different frequency. The frequency can be gradually changed; the generalization is at the level of nondifferentiation, so that the reactions are not very specific. The responses are to a part or quality: the buzzing tone.

With the Pavlovian technique, a second type of generalization occurs as a result of discrimination. If the two stimuli are somewhat distinguishable (that is, similar but not identical), the organism can be taught to respond to one of them and to inhibit the response to the other. This is done by regularly reinforcing one of the stimuli and not reinforcing the other. In other words, at first the two stimuli are equivalent. They evoke the same response because they have a characteristic (or part) in common: they belong to what we consider the class of buzzing tones. Later only the class of tones of a certain frequency evokes the response. Thus the response has been generalized to a whole formed by at least two qualities, the buzzing tone and a given frequency.

This second form of discrimination suggests that wholes are formed by contiguity, when the contiguity has a reinforcing effect. Presumably the capacity to perceive contiguities as wholes has not been consistently transmitted in phylogeny. What has been more universally transmitted is the capacity to perceive those wholes which, by being perceived as such, increase the survival value of the animal. This increased survival value is probably due to the fact that the perceptions of these wholes are more or less accurate representatives of external reality. The holistic effect is not produced artificially, but is the outcome of evolutionary laws: effects which have survival value are much more likely to be transmitted genetically. That is, in a succession of environmental opportunities, animals endowed with holistic faculties (or capacity to respond to wholes) have been the more efficient reproducers among the available genetic alternatives.

There is a certain circularity in these concepts. It would seem that the effect (survival of the species) is the cause, whereas we are accustomed to think of the cause as occurring before the effect. This circular or servomechanism, similar to those studied in cybernetics, has only phylogenetic value: it applies to the species as a whole, not necessarily to the individual. Similarly to what Thorndike described in the learning of the individual, the phylogenetic effect is revealed in the probability of occurrence of the response, when the situation occurs again for different members of different generations. If it has the power of increasing the chances of survival, the capacity for that effect will be genetically transmitted.

In summary, it seems that contiguity and similarity play a crucial role in the perception of wholes. The parts that eventually form wholes must be in contiguous spatiotemporal relations; but among all spatiotemporal contiguities only some are selected to form wholes, probably because of their survival effect and, by implication, because they correspond more closely to "external reality." The other fundamental property of the nervous system, the appreciation of similarity, leads to the recognition of the whole through recognition of the organism's response to the whole.

Phylogenetically, the prevailing trend has been toward the perception of wholes and responses to wholes. Such a mode of perceiving and responding has eventually led to the acquisition of concepts, as we shall see in later chapters. However, a tendency to respond to the part persists in all animals, and is particularly accentuated in pathologic conditions.

In the field of comparative psychology, Klüver has done very important work on equivalents, that is, on stimuli which are able of eliciting the same response (1933, 1936). He found that pronounced changes in the stimulus often leave the animal's response unaltered. What seem to the human observer to be heterogeneous stimuli (for instance, a meshed wire, a floor brush, a live rat, a toothpick, etc.) elicit the same response from certain cebus monkeys. Klüver attempted to specify the factors responsible for particular types of equivalence, but often was able to define them only negatively (1936). In other words, after eliminating one factor after another, he demonstrated that "various common properties or sets of properties found in a given group of equivalent stimuli play no role in bringing about the same behavior."

Klüver feels that the common property is not necessarily responsible for the same response. We have seen, however, that in low forms (for instance, the stickleback) it is definitely the same property which elicits the same response. Of course, a "common property" does not necessarily mean a property of various stimuli which affects our human senses or intellect in the same way. It may be a multitude of factors which are experienced in the same way at a primitive level of nervous integration.[4] Again we have to invoke a circular process which may be applied to some animal species: does the organism react in the same way because the stimuli have something in common, or do they have something in common because they are reacted to in the same way? Another possibility may also be that the common property is a complicated relation which cannot easily be detected or abstracted by the observer.

"Imprinting," as described by Lorenz (1956), may be a similar phenomenon. A gosling learns to react to a man as it would react to the mother goose, apparently because at a certain period in the development of the gosling the man disclosed maternal qualities and released filial instinct. This behavior of the gosling becomes imprinted, that is, becomes a basic pattern of behavior which is irreversible. An important aspect of the phenomenon is that the gosling does not learn to respond in this way to the special man who takes care of him, but "to Man, with a capital, as a species. . . . The irreversible imprint refers to the species and not to the individual. We have no explanation of this at all" (Lorenz, 1953). The response is to a primary class which had the maternal attitude that was the releasing element, but this primary class of response does not include all objects with maternal attitudes (because, in that case, geese too would be included). It includes another less primitive class, although a wrong one.

As we shall see later in detail, there are many types of primary classes, more or less primitive. Their formation is not necessarily connected with imprinting. Imprinting is the perpetuation of a primary class which leads to a specific and unalterable response. The imprinting as described by Lorenz is a pathological phenomenon. Perhaps homosexuality is based on it.

[4] Probably related to the same category of phenomena are the observations made by several authors (Lacey et al., 1953, 1958, Wenger et al., 1957, 1961) that some individuals respond to different stimuli with a fixed patterning or some hierarchy of responses of the autonomic nervous system.

In conclusion it may be stated that life organized at the level of protoemotions and exocepts, or at even lower levels, does not require a definite distinction of part from whole. The part which constitutes the releasing element elicits a certain type of behavior just as the whole does.

5 ⊚ THE PHANTASMIC WORLD OF INNER REALITY

At higher levels of integration motor responses are delayed or inhibited and mental representations of the external world are organized. At first these representations consist of images and primitive forms of symbolization and are accompanied by second-order emotions. They constitute a world of inner reality which, because images prevail in it, I shall call phantasmic.

The image

An image is a memory trace which assumes the form of a representation. It is an internal quasi reproduction of a perception which does not require the corresponding external stimulus in order to be evoked. Although we cannot deny that at least rudimentary images occur in subhuman animals, there seems to be no doubt that images are predominantly a human characteristic. In fact, we can affirm that images are among the earliest and most important foundations of human symbolism. If, following Susanne Langer, we use *symbol* to mean something which stands for something else which is not present, the image must then be considered one of the first symbols.[1] For instance, I close my eyes and visualize my mother. She may not be present, but her image is with me; it stands for her. The image is obviously based on the memory traces of previous perceptions of my mother. My mother then acquires a psychic reality which is not tied to her physical presence.[2]

Image formation is actually the basis for all higher mental processes. It introduces us into that inner world which I call phantasmic. It enables the human being not only to re-evoke what is not present, but to retain an affective disposition for the absent object. For instance, the image of my mother may evoke the love I feel for her.

The image thus becomes a substitute for the external object. It is actually an *inner object*, although it is not well organized. It is the most primitive of the inner objects, if, because of the exocept's ambiguous position, we exclude that construct from the category of objects. When the image's affective associations are pleasant, it reinforces our longing or appetite for the corresponding external object. The image thus has a motivational influence in leading us to search out the actual object, which in its external reality is still more gratifying than the image. The opposite is true when the image's affective associations are unpleasant: we are motivated not to exchange the unpleasant inner object for the corresponding external one, which is even more unpleasant.

Images permit a type of interpersonal relations that is of much greater significance than those occurring at a protoemotional-exoceptual level, which are relatively underdeveloped and not always necessary. Interpersonal factors at a protoemotional-exoceptual level involve only the present or the immediate future, and the other person or animal is im-

---

[1] In her early writings, however, Susanne Langer had not recognized that the image is a symbol (1942).

[2] In this chapter the word *image* is used to mean simple or sensorial images, which tend to reproduce perceptions. It does not refer to those much higher internalized constructs which represent whatever we connect with a person: for instance, in this more elaborate sense, the image of my mother would mean a synthesis of what I think, feel, and know about her.

portant only to the extent that it changes the individual's present state. For instance, a cat may be important to a mouse, but only inasmuch as it may change the status of the mouse, and not in itself. The mother may be important to a newborn baby, but only inasmuch as she may give pleasure or displeasure to the baby.

Images soon constitute the basic level of the inner psychic reality, which in human psychology is as important as, and in some respects more important than, external reality. Imagery helps the individual not only to understand the world better, but also to create a surrogate for it. Whatever is known or experienced tends to become a part of the individual who knows and experiences. Cognition can no longer be considered a hierarchy of mechanisms, but a psychological content which retains the power to affect its possessor, now and in the future.

We should not believe, however, that images have the ability to evoke the same kind of behavior that the corresponding perceptions do. They generally elicit a more delayed and less direct action. Only sexual images can evoke instinctual urges approximating in intensity those elicited by the presence of the sexual object.

The particularly strong effect of sexual images cannot be considered just a casual anomaly. This phenomenon must be connected with the fact that whereas mammals below the primates restrict their genitocopulatory activities to the times when the female is capable of conceiving, in primates there is a tendency toward removal of the sexual rhythm. Although particular states of the sexual glands or concentration of sexual hormones increases the sexual appetite, human beings do not require the occurrence of a specific state of the female hormonal cycle in order to be sexually aroused.[3] Except when they have been satisfied shortly before, young adults can have sexual relations at any time, although they prefer not to have them during menstruation. Inasmuch as a sexual partner is not always available, imagery which is sex-

[3] Some infrahuman primates—for instance, chimpanzees—have been observed in copulatory activity even when the female was not in a state of fertility (Ford and Beach, 1951). In relation to this characteristic too, they can be considered as holding an intermediate position between man and pre-primates.

ual in content can be elicited and can actually replace realistic contacts. This happens, for instance, in masturbation. Although masturbation without accompanying images may occur in a sort of mechanical way in human beings and in animals, the possibility of evoking sexual images increases this practice. Most psychiatrists feel that normal masturbation must be accompanied by appropriate erotic images, and that masturbation which is not accompanied by them is indicative of pathologic repression or suppression.

The psychosexual mechanism may operate in the opposite direction: sexual desire is frequently experienced because sexual imagery keeps the sexual instinct awake, even when there is no external sexual object. Thus a reciprocal synergism seems to exist in human beings between genital physiology and sexual imagery. This particular synergism can at least partially account for the great role of sexuality in human psychology. Freud, who was the first to recognize the magnitude of this role, interpreted it in relation to libidinal energy only, and not also in relation to the cognitive level of imagery.

Unfortunately, we know practically nothing of the neurophysiologic mechanisms which retain memory traces and elaborate them to the level of images. We must make a distinction, however, between the function of memory and the function of imagery.

Memory is phylogenetically very ancient, so that in a certain respect we can even talk of a protoplasmic memory. At the human level, however, the memory traces needed for subsequent symbolic processes seem to be deposited in the cerebral cortex. The following cortical mechanisms appear to be necessary for a proper memory function:

1. Prefrontal mechanisms by which attention is focused on a stimulus (Malmo, 1942).
2. Consolidation of the memory, for which the functioning of at least one of the two hippocampal areas is necessary. In fact, in cases of bilateral hippocampal lesions, no memory is possible (Milner, 1958, 1959; Penfield, 1958; Penfield and Milner, 1958).
3. Deposit of memory traces in the temporal lobes (Penfield and Rasmussen, 1952; Penfield, 1958).

4. Reactivation of memory traces in some areas adjacent to the sensory areas during the process of recognition. (According to Nielsen, recognition of visual perceptions occurs in area 18 of the occipital lobe [1946].)

Voluntary recall is different from recognition. If I want to recall the image of my mother, this mechanism is much more complicated than recognizing my mother when I see her. According to Nielsen, visual voluntary recall occurs in area 19. When this area is impaired, the patient is unable to recall objects, although he can recognize them. Recall is effectuated through images.

The phenomenology of images

In the last fifty years images have lost the important position they occupied in the old books of psychology. This loss of popularity was possible because their most important functions (maintenance of motivation for absent objects, transformation of emotions, symbolic formation, building of inner reality) had not yet been recognized. Their study consisted purely of a static description which did not lead to fruitful results. Not only were they more difficult to study than sensations and perceptions; but when they seemed to be valuable for the understanding of the psyche, they proved to be accompanied by other mental processes, like thinking and language, which could be examined independently with clearer results. Even the affects that accompany images were found impossible to study unless the subject was able to verbalize his introspections.

In spite of these considerations, I believe that the phenomenology of imagery can no longer be ignored. Following is a summary of what is known about some of its main characteristics. I hope that future work in the field will soon make this summary obsolete.

Images may occur spontaneously. They are facilitated by (1) inhibition of motor reactions and (2) elimination of external stimuli. People differ in their ability to produce images. Some, especially scientists or individuals given to abstract thought, are poor in imagery; others, like artists and poets, are rich.

There are many types of images—as many as there are types of sensations—and in most persons one type of imagery predominates. The two prevailing types are the visual and the auditory. The role played by language in human mental activity complicates the study of imagery, since most people think in words which are generally experienced as auditory images. If we eliminate verbal images, we can easily recognize that in most people the visual type plays the predominant role.

In special cases images appear in unusual forms. They may be so vivid as to look like photographic reproductions of previously perceived objects: these are the eidetic images, first described by Jaensch. Other types are the hypnagogic, often wrongly called hallucinations. They are fleeting images of auditory or visual types occurring in some people while they are about to fall asleep. Hypnopompic images are those which occur to some people while awakening from deep sleep. Images are, of course, used in dreams and hallucinations, where they acquire the characteristics of perceptions.

Images have other important characteristics:

1. They are fleeting. A person can retain an image for only a very short period; when he re-evokes the image, it appears in a slightly different form.

2. Most of the time images are hazy, vague, and shadowy. Exceptions are some special forms, like the eidetic, hypnagogic, and hypnopompic images mentioned above, and like those appearing in dreams.

3. Unless a strong voluntary effort is made, images cannot be seen in their totality. For instance, if a subject tries to revisualize his kitchen, now he reproduces the breakfast table, now a wall of the room, now the stove. It is very difficult, often impossible, to visualize the whole room at once.

The last characteristic is very important, because it seems to indicate that in imagery, just as in primitive perception, part-object representation is a major factor (see Chapter 4). Consciousness shifts rapidly from one part of the image to another, with an uncertain visualization of the whole. In the mind of the person, however, there is no doubt that although he focuses only on one part, he is mentally in a total situation. For instance, in the kitchen example above, the subject knows that he visualizes his kitchen; the part is enough for him to infer the whole.

Images may undergo many private alterations, for only eidetic images seem to be similar to photographic reproductions. This alterability or volatile character makes images at times difficult to express in words. They may also be difficult to express because they may not correspond to schemata accepted by a social group, or by the individual's entire social milieu. Furthermore, the fluid changes that they undergo make them dissimilar to previous occurrences. Thus they are difficult to commit to memory.

Most images lead to associations with other images by the mechanism of contiguity. However, some images have a salient part which corresponds to the releasing element of primitive perception (see Chapter 4). The releasing element may lead to associations with other images which have the same element. In some other images there is no releasing element or hierarchical organization of the parts, but rather a concatenation or chain of parts which can easily displace one another.

Images do not have the relative stability which is characteristic of perceptions. Perceptions seem to arrest the flux of the external world, or to transform it into apparently fixed representations, which are kept in the storage of memory traces. But when the memory traces are activated into images, they prove not to be immutable historical archives. They resume a state of flux, which seems to be even more unstable than that of the external world. Furthermore, whereas perceptions are projected to the external world, images are experienced as occurring inwardly. The normal person knows that they are produced by his mind and do not necessarily have a simultaneous equivalent in the external world.

It is possible that the mechanisms of image formation can be retraced in some works of art, especially in primitive art and children's art. In infantile drawings a part, like an arm or an eye, may be a dominant element around which the rest of the picture is centered. In primitive sculptures some parts of the body, often the female breast or the penis, receive prominence. At times the rest of the body is like a frame or an entourage for the prominent part. In humorous art or carica-ture drawing, a part or a feature also acquires salience.

A return to a level of imagery occurs in states of relaxation, states of sleepiness, and periods of introspection and medita-tion. Some people, especially after prolonged solitude, revert to a level of mental activity in which imagery predominates. Primitive imagery is more likely to occur in certain cases of intoxication, like those due to mescaline and lysergic acid.

The paleosymbol

The next stage of cognitive development is represented by the *paleosymbol* (Arieti, 1955).[4] The paleosymbol is a par-ticular mental cognitive construct which stands for some-thing that exists in external reality. Thus it has symbolic value, but this value remains private to the individual who experiences it. It cannot be shared with anybody else, unless it is translated into other cognitive forms; and yet, contrary to the image, it has an external counterpart.

To a limited extent, paleosymbols exist in apes too. The psychologist Kellogg has reported that his little female chim-panzee was so attached to him that whenever he left the house, she became very despondent (Kellogg and Kellogg, 1933). She would go into a tantrum of terror and grief. If, however, he gave her his coverall at the time of his depar-ture, she seemed placated, showed no emotional displeasure, and carried the coverall around with her as a fetish. As Langer pointed out (1942), this is probably one of the first manifestations of high symbolization of which animals are capable. The coverall represented the master. It acquired the property that the master had, in that it would satisfy the ape emotionally as he did. In other words, it was a symbol, but it was a symbol which needed a concrete and present segment of reality. Perhaps it retained the smell of the master or was perceived as part of the master. Actually, it was more than a sign of the master; it was identified with him. We could say

---

[4] For a comparative analysis of different classifications of symbols, see Goldman (1961).

that a special external object, the coverall, evoked an image or a series of images in which the master was involved, or at least activated emotions and behavior connected with previous perceptions of the master. This relatively complex mental construct, consisting of a perception, images, and emotions, formed a paleosymbol—that is, an inner object, a unity of the animal's inner reality, which stood for Kellogg.

Let us assume theoretically that at the same time Kellogg trained this ape, he trained two other chimpanzees with potentialities similar to hers. When Kellogg would leave the house, assume that the second chimpanzee found comfort not at the sight of his coverall, but at the sight of one of his tools, while for the third chimpanzee his pipe was the paleosymbol of the master. Thus we have three chimpanzees who use three different things as symbols of the master. In such a hypothetical case, obviously there must have been some incidental events specific in the lives of the chimpanzees which caused them to respond to different objects as equivalents of the master. Although the three chimpanzees might show concordant behavior in respect to their master when he was present, they could not agree on a symbolic representation of him. When a symbol does not receive consensual validation or is not shared by others, it tends to retain its primitive forms and can only be corrected with great difficulty. As we shall see later, in many psychopathologic conditions, especially in schizophrenia, higher levels of symbolism tend to revert to the paleosymbolic type. This is the phenomenon that Bleuler called autism (1913).

In comparison with the development they have in man, these preconceptual levels of cognition undoubtedly are rudimentary in apes. We must remember that man's preconceptual levels are fed not only by his lower levels but also by his highest. He has not only a tendency to transform perceptions into concepts, but also a countertendency to transform high concepts and verbal expressions into paleosymbols and images. This second tendency cannot occur in apes because they are deprived of language and concepts.

Second-order emotions

An organism which cannot develop beyond the level of the pleasure principle does not experience feelings more complicated than protoemotions. As Chapter 4 discussed, the cognitive component of these feelings consists only of the perception of a definite and circumscribed set of stimuli. At a level which includes imagery and paleosymbols, however, more complicated emotions—which I shall call second-order emotions—are experienced. Some of them can be differentiated: for instance, anxiety, anger, wish, security, and perhaps, in a rudimentary form, even love and depression. In this chapter the word *emotions* refers to these second-order emotions and not to protoemotions, which will always be designated as such.

Second-order emotions are not elicited by a direct or impending attack on the organism or by a threatened immediate change in homeostasis, but by cognitive processes, the simplest forms of which are images and paleosymbols.[5] By making possible an emotional response to what is not present, images add a temporal dimension. They actually permit the evolutionary process to advance from the level of the protoemotion to that of the emotion. For instance, the presence of a wild animal may elicit the protoemotional experience of fear. The image of this animal, occurring when the animal is not present, elicits not fear but *anxiety*, which will enable the subject either to avoid such encounters or to prepare defensive measures to be used if they should occur. Anxiety is imagined fear. In the same way, the image of what generally evokes appetite tends to evoke a feeling better designated as a *wish*. There is no wish without the possibility of anticipating (through imagery or other symbolic processes) what is wished for.

Experience has only one tense: present. As we shall see in subsequent chapters, one of the functions of cognitive processes is to permit the experiencing (and therefore transporting into the present) of what belongs to the past and to the

[5] Perceptions and signs, too, may elicit emotions, provided they are followed by images, paleosymbols, or higher constructs.

future. To a considerable degree this already occurs at the level of images and second-order emotions. This possibility fosters prolonged, not just immediate, survival, because past dangers and their future reoccurrences can be mentally represented so that attempts can be made to avoid them.

Another temporal characteristic that distinguishes emotions from protoemotions is that they last longer. Whereas protoemotions are extinguished in a few seconds or minutes and are quickly converted into visceral and motor outlets, emotions linger as experiential states.

Emotions and protoemotions differ in another important aspect: the somatic response. We have seen how rich protoemotions are in endocrine, muscular, and visceral responses. Although somatic responses occur in emotions too, especially in anxiety, they are far less intense than in protoemotions.

Our knowledge of the neurophysiology of emotions has been increased by the works of Papez (1937), MacLean (1949, 1955, 1957a, b), and many others.[6] Today it is generally considered that the part of the limbic system which for a long time has been called the archipallium plays the crucial role in the neurology of emotion. A neopallial network produces a cognitive content, which becomes associated with an archipallial network. The latter gives the emotional flavor to the cognitive content.

The archipallium originated in evolution as the center of olfaction, but was later converted into an emotional center when the importance of the sense of smell declined in the highest animal species. Although the neopallium is the part of the central nervous system that has undergone the most conspicuous growth in the human species, the archipallium is also larger in the human species than in any other. The neopallium would not have expanded to its present size in humans if it had not been accompanied by an expansion and reorganization of the archipallium, for there is a functional equilibrium between archipallium and neopallium. In schizophrenia this equilibrium is altered (Arieti, 1955, 1956b; Gerard, 1956).

[6] For a comprehensive account of the neurology of emotion, see the excellent two-volume work by Arnold (1960).

As mentioned above, the archipallium has the function of giving an inner affective tone not only to some of the lower experiences of inner status, but also to the cognitive processes. Thus an emotional experience is not the result of a changed status in the soma and should not be confused with the somatic resonance of the James-Lange theory. It is mediated by a central excitement of the archipallium. If the emotional experience seems to involve the soma, it is not only because any central experience has to be projected either to the soma or to the external world,[7] but also because phylogenetically there is an attempt in emotion to mimic the lower forms of experiences of inner status which are replaced by the emotion.[8]

If it is difficult to classify protoemotions, it is much more so to classify emotions. Being subjective experiences and in many cases poor in somatic responses, emotions cannot easily be delimited and differentiated. Furthermore, several emotions often coexist or overlap, producing unusual and possibly infinite combinations, perhaps as colors or musical notes do. Also, because they are associated with cognitive elements in an almost limitless variety of ways, emotions acquire numerous and in many cases indeterminable nuances.

We shall now examine four important second-order emotions. Undoubtedly many others could be distinguished, but much more study and research would be needed even for a preliminary report.

ANXIETY

Since the advent of the psychoanalytic school, anxiety is the emotion that has received the greatest attention in the psychological and psychiatric literature. If anxiety's impor-

---

[7] For instance, when I see a book in front of me, the visual experience of the book occurs around my calcarine fissure, but I project the existence of the book into the external world. I project other experiences to my soma.

[8] Seeing the totality of the emotional experience as "central" means considering the phenomenon as another example of what neurophysiologists call encephalization. This name designates the process by which functions that in lower species are mediated by lower or more caudal centers shift toward higher centers. In encephalization, higher levels not only "go beyond" lower levels, but in a certain way they also "mimic" the lower levels.

tance has been firmly established, however, its definition has not been so widely agreed on. Freud himself changed his early view of this emotion. At first he felt that anxiety is the state of not being gratified. He later abandoned this definition, which in my classification has been termed "tension," [9] and described anxiety as the emotional response to a situation of danger. Although I believe he was correct in stating that anxiety is an emotional response to a situation in which, consciously or unconsciously, danger is perceived, a more specific definition is required to enable us to distinguish anxiety from fear. Freud was not concerned with fear, as he did not differentiate protoemotions from complex emotions.[10]

Goldstein, on the other hand, does distinguish fear from anxiety. According to him, whereas fear is the reaction to a definite well-perceived danger, anxiety is the reaction to a vague threat. Goldstein believes that anxiety can be produced by a variety of events which have one common element: a discrepancy between the individual's capacities and the demands made on him (Goldstein, 1939, 1940).[11] Goldstein also describes anxiety as lacking in object; the person who experiences it is not aware of what he fears.

To my way of thinking, anxiety is the emotional reaction to the expectation or anticipation of danger. However, the danger is not immediate, nor is it always well defined. Its expectation is not the result of a simple perception or signal. Images and paleosymbols may enable the person to antici-

---

[9] As explained in Chapter 3, tension replaces the term "short-circuited anxiety," which I used in earlier writings.

[10] According to Freud, anything more primitive than the ego-controlled emotions must be of id derivation. But in his theoretical framework, only the instincts come from the id (*Eros*, which to a certain extent corresponds to our appetite, and *Thanatos*, which has some similarity to rage). Thus there is no consideration of fear, and psychoanalytic literature in general often confuses it with anxiety.

[11] Goldstein describes what he calls "catastrophic reactions," which occur in infants and, more conspicuously, in brain-injured patients when the individual is not able to master a task. It seems to me that the "catastrophic reaction" or diffuse sense of disorganization, as described by Goldstein, is similar to what I have called "tension" or to Freud's first concept of anxiety, except that it must be intense to a pathological degree. The patient is not able to organize or mediate the excitement, and he reacts in a catastrophic way. Many brain-injured patients do not seem to be able to experience long-circuited anxiety. Also, patients who underwent psychosurgery showed a symptomatic improvement, probably because they were no longer capable of experiencing long-circuited anxiety.

pate a future danger and its dreaded consequences even though he does not expect it to materialize for some time. As we shall see in subsequent chapters, the danger is often represented by sets of symbols, which are more complicated than images. Some of these symbols may become unconscious (see Chapter 6), so that the anxiety seems to have no object. Anxiety is elicited not only by threats to one's physical existence, but by threats to the values and meanings given to one's existence.

It is not the knowledge of a definite danger which distinguishes anxiety from fear. For instance, I may be anxious over the fact that my country may go to war and that my and my family's lives may be in danger. It is the complexity of the cognitive mechanism that distinguishes anxiety from fear. Inasmuch as this mechanism involves a future, which cannot be predicted accurately, it leaves room for a sense of uncertainty, which is also a characteristic of anxiety. Neurologically speaking, more of the cortex and less of the autonomic system is involved in anxiety than in fear.

Anxiety is unpleasant and, together with depression, is often referred to as mental pain. These two emotions in some respects are indeed similar to pain. The fact that the word *pain* connotes both physical and mental pain is not a peculiarity of the English language. In all the languages with which the author is familiar, the word for pain has these two meanings.

Physical pain is the result of a direct attack on the continuity or intactness of the organism. As a rule it can be localized.[12] Mental pain stands for such a physical pain; in a way, it is physical pain's emotional equivalent. Like physical pain, mental pain demands that the organism find it unacceptable and remove it. Unless it is pronounced to a pathological degree, anxiety leads to responses which are beneficial for the organism. It is a message of warning as well as an experience of discomfort.

Anxiety, at least in its primitive form, is as important for survival as fear is. Psychiatric books emphasize only the negative aspects of anxiety; actually, it is the emotional reaction

12 An exception is thalamic pain, which cannot be localized and is in some ways similar to an emotional experience.

to the visualization of future dangers that compels men to take steps for future survival. Anxiety does not lead to immediate flight or fight, but to a more or less prolonged and coordinated action aimed at removal of the forthcoming danger or danger equivalent. Especially at higher levels, it may take a long time to remove the danger, and the discomfort caused by anxiety will remain for the entire period.

A large literature deals with the somatic processes accompanying anxiety; for example, see works by May (1950), Arnold (1960), Hillman (1960), Grinker (1961). Grinker points out that the mobilization of adreno-corticotropic hormone from the pituitary body is a signal analogous to anxiety. This adreno-corticotropic hormone in its turn stimulates the secretion of 17-hydroxysteroid from the adrenal gland. Mixed chain reactions with mixed psychic and biochemical elements may originate.

In addition to being unpleasant, anxiety is impelling (although it may be of moderate duration), is centripetal, and tends to expand. Thus it could be represented by the following symbols: $UMI \leftarrow <$.

ANGER

Although we know much less about anger than about anxiety, the following observations seem well founded. Anger can be seen as directly related to rage, just as anxiety is related to fear. Anger is *imagined rage;* that is, rage sustained by images. Whereas rage usually leads to immediate motor discharge, generally directed against the stimulus which elicits it, anger tends to last longer, although it retains an impelling characteristic. The prolongation of anger is possible because it is mediated by symbolic forms, just as anxiety is.

Anger tends to accumulate and to seek outlets when a certain reservoir of it has formed. Although it may be discharged through muscular responses, it is predominantly expressed in symbolic forms: an angry voice, angry gestures, angry facial expressions, and, at higher levels, angry words. Anger has a delayed reaction in comparison with rage, but because of its impelling quality, it cannot be contained for a long time. Containing it produces a state of tension which adds to the unpleasantness of anger. The somewhat pseudo-pleasant feeling that the angry person experiences in letting off steam is to some extent due to relief of tension. Anger is usually centrifugal; that is, directed not against the self but against somebody else. It can be represented with the symbols $UMI \rightarrow <$.

If rage is useful for survival in the jungle, anger was useful within the first human communities to maintain a hostile-defensive attitude toward the enemy, even when the latter was not present. Anger also has practical value in that the anticipation of it in others may deter the individual from doing what moves others toward aggressivity. Anger may be harmful, however, when it is excessive, elicited by wrong stimuli, or used not as a form of defense but as a way to obtain pleasure. When anger remains the predominant emotion or is excessive, it distorts the whole personality, just as rage does.

WISHING AND LIKING

Wishing (which includes liking) is an emotional state which, except where it has been confused with appetite, has received little consideration in psychology. By wishing we mean a pleasant attraction toward something or somebody, or toward doing something. Contrary to appetite, wishing is made possible by the re-evocation of the image or other symbols of an object whose presence is pleasant. The mnemic image of an earlier pleasant experience—for instance, of the satisfaction of a need—evokes an emotional disposition which motivates the individual to replace the image with the real object of satisfaction. A search for the real object is thus initiated, or at least contemplated. This search may require detours, since a direct approach is often not possible.

A wish may be as strong as an appetite or as intense and potentially unlimited as love. On the other hand, it may appear in mild forms. Liking is in fact a moderately felt form of wish: a wish to be near the wished object in order to enjoy its qualities. Friendship is a typical expression of liking.

In comparison with other emotions that we have examined and that we shall examine later, liking seems rather lukewarm. It is because of these lukewarm qualities, apparently unimportant in situations of emergency, that its study has been neglected. Actually, however, the consequences of liking are enormous. Although less intense than love, it may apply to far more situations and objects. It is a very common emotion and a strong source of human motivation. When a person's range of liking is limited, the whole personality is restricted or impoverished.

The following symbols describe liking: $PLp{\rightarrow}O$.

SECURITY

The affective state which, following Sullivan (1953), I shall call security is much more difficult to describe than the previous emotions. In fact, we must ask whether such an emotion really exists. Just as in the case of satisfaction (Chapter 3), it can be argued that security is either the lack of unpleasant emotions or else purely a hypothetical concept.

By definition security is a self-contained emotion: a person who feels secure does not need to increase this feeling. Self-contained emotions are more difficult to recognize, since they do not lead to quick discharge, nor do they have the impelling quality that, for instance, anxiety and anger have.

However, security does not seem to me to be characterized only by negative qualities. It does not consist only of removal of unpleasant emotions or removal of uncertainty, but also of pleasant anticipation, a feeling of well-being, a trust in people and in things to come. All these seem intellectual concepts; and undoubtedly there are important intellectual elements in this feeling, especially at higher levels. Actually, however, security seems to be experienced by year-old children in their contacts with the mother, if she is not anxious, hostile, or prevented by other causes from mothering the child. The baby expects to be taken care of, to be fondled, to be on his mother's lap. The mother expects the child to become a healthy and mature person. The child later perceives his mother's expectation and accepts it, just as earlier he accepted in a reflex-like fashion being nursed, being fondled, etc.

This feeling of security, at least in its early stages, corresponds to what Erikson (1953), Buber (1953), and Arieti (1957b) have in different contexts called trust or basic trust. Basic trust or security is a feeling which is elicited in proximity to some other human beings. Although it is elicited by interpersonal relations, it is experienced intrapsychically. Its different manifestations occur in connection with various interpersonal relations which are beyond the scope of this book. Security is perhaps fully experienced later in childhood, when higher cognitive processes permit reflected appraisal and the building of self-esteem.

As mentioned before, security is self-contained and therefore at times is almost imperceptible. In some dreams, however, it occurs in pure form, so that it is immediately recognized and strongly experienced as a pleasant feeling which does not overflow into a state of euphoria or joy.

Security is an emotional state that tends to last, is not only conflict-free but also distinctly pleasant, and is reflexive and self-contained. Thus it could be represented by the symbols $PLp\ominus O$. Although it does not seem to be necessary in a state of emergency, it is a prerequisite for the normal development of the child. The tenuous equilibrium on which the cycle of human life is founded needs the reinforcement offered by this emotional state. Lack of security is the critical factor in many psychopathologic conditions, ranging from minor to major disorders.

EARLY GERMS OF DEPRESSION AND LOVE

Although they are not fully developed, some feelings of depression and love can be traced as far back as the level of images and second-order emotions. We have seen that at the protoemotional level, the subject feels deprived only insofar as he experiences tension or discomfort caused by the absence of the needed object or by the impossibility of satisfaction. But at the second-order level of emotions, deprivation can be cognized as an image which reproduces the loss of the wished object—a loss which affects the present and the near future. To be deeply felt, however, depression requires a certain stability and duration of mental constructs, which is not yet possible at this stage.

Similar remarks can be made about the feeling of love at the second-order level. To love requires not only a strong wish to be with the loved person, but the ability to enjoy the presence of the loved person as a *separate* object. This ability first develops at the second-order level. The reassurance and pleasure conferred by the proximity of the wished object constitute the first elements of love. Although nothing could be more pleasant than the presence of the loved object, the mere image of the object produces a somewhat pleasant effect. However, at the second-order level the image of the loved object can produce anxiety too, when the individual recognizes that the image cannot be equivalent to the actual presence of the object.

The phantasmic world

We have seen that in the phantasmic world, the parameter of motivation is no longer restricted to protoemotions and physiostates, but includes anxiety, anger, wishes, and the search for security. Wish fulfillment and the feeling of security become the main positive motivational factors. Anxiety and anger are the negative second-order emotions which strengthen the effect of negative protoemotions and physiostates. Love and depression are experienced only in rudimentary forms.

Images and paleosymbols not only enlarge the scope of external reality but tend to replace it, and, because of their multiple representations, enrich man's existence enormously. At the same time, however, they cause complications and important intrapsychic conflicts. Let us imagine an individual in whom the subsequent levels (to be described in the next two chapters) have not yet evolved. Assume that he is an early hominid, and assume that these hominids have developed only to the phantasmic level. We can make inferences about this level just as Von Uexküll could do for the *Umwelt* of subhuman animals in his classic studies (1957). Our task is more complicated than Von Uexküll's, however, since he was dealing almost exclusively with the relatively simple level of perception.

A hominid arrested at the phantasmic level would have great difficulty in distinguishing images, dreams, and paleo-symbols from external reality. He would have no language and could not tell himself or others, "This is an image, a dream, a fantasy; it does not correspond to external reality." He would tend to confuse psychic with external reality, almost as a normal man does when he dreams. Whatever was experienced would become true for him by virtue of its being experienced. Not only is consensual validation from other people impossible at this level, but intrapsychic or reflexive validation cannot even be achieved. The phantasmic level is characterized by *adualism,* or at least by difficult dualism. As Baldwin analyzed it in young children (1929) and as I have described it in schizophrenics (Arieti, 1961c), adualism is lack of dualism: lack of the ability to distinguish between the two realities, that of the mind and that of the external world. This condition may correspond to what orthodox psychoanalysts, following Federn (1952), call lack of ego boundary. However, our preverbal hominid would have had at his disposal a method for at least partially correcting the unreality of his inner life: the possibility of plunging himself into the earlier level of exocepts, the "realistic" sensorimotor stage.

Another important aspect of the phantasmic world is the lack of appreciation of causality. The individual cannot ask himself why certain things occur. He either accepts them, in a sort of naïve acausalism, as just happening, or he expects things to take place in a certain succession, as a sort of habit rather than as a result of causality or of an order of nature. The only phenomenon remotely connected with causation is a subjective or experiential feeling of expectancy.

A world limited to exocepts, images, and paleosymbols and deprived of the concept of causality is of necessity a restricted one. Nevertheless, it permits the individual to re-experience important occurrences through images and paleo-symbols. It enables him to re-evoke pleasure and suffering, as well as to acquire the knowledge and fear of death from his observations of animals and people.

As already mentioned, images with pleasant connections motivate the individual to search for the equivalent external objects. Unpleasant images and paleosymbols, however, tend to remain durable inner objects. Thus, unless the circumstances of the external life are so satisfactory that they prevent disagreeable imagery, inner life is predominantly unpleasant at this level. To make matters worse, images are adualistically confused with reality. And since they are not inhibited by higher levels, they probably recur very frequently, being evoked by perceptions or emotional states with which they are associated. Accordingly inner life at this level consists chiefly of clusters of images that are accompanied by unpleasant emotions. No matter how dangerous the life of the jungle is for a subhuman animal, it is not so psychologically traumatic as the life of a human being at a phantasmic stage of development who has to contend with the unpleasantness of his images. The animal in the jungle has realistic fears; the phantasmic individual has to contend not only with such fears but with anxiety as well.

The phantasmic level is very difficult to evaluate ontogenetically, for in normal children it is very soon followed and transformed by other levels. Some children start to talk by the end of the first year of life. Only in children whose psychological development is delayed or modified by adverse circumstances can the phantasmic level be discerned underneath the influences of the rapidly emerging subsequent levels.

The few-months-old human baby cannot experience images other than kinaesthetic ones, or paleosymbols, because the required cortical areas are not yet fully myelinized and are not functioning (Arieti, 1961c). Probably the very young infant cannot even dream with images other than kinaesthetic ones—nor, contrary to what is often assumed, can he hallucinate. If he were able to hallucinate (for instance, when he is deprived of the maternal breast, as Freud thought), such hallucinations would not enhance his survival or the survival of the human race. When the baby experiences hunger, he cries—a realistic and appropriate response.

It is only toward the seventh month that the child starts to experience images. For instance, if he is able to look for a rattle when the rattle has been hidden under a pillow, presumably he can carry in his mind the image of the rattle.

Although no language is used at this age, some kinds of primitive communication are possible—both empathic forms and forms of learning by imitation.

In their interpretation of man's childhood and of psychopathological conditions, Melanie Klein and Fairbairn have given great importance to the phantasmic world. However, they have not described the single formal elements of this inner reality in a comparative developmental frame of reference.

The child who is raised in normal circumstances is generally capable of overcoming the difficulties of the phantasmic stage of development. He will learn to see himself not exclusively as a cluster of feelings and of self-initiated movements, but also as a body image and as an entity having many kinds of relations with other images, especially those of the parents. Inasmuch as the child cannot see his own face, his own visual image will be faceless—as, indeed, he will tend to see himself in dreams throughout his life. He will wish, however, to look like people toward whom he has a pleasant emotional attitude or by whom he feels protected and gratified. The wish tends to be experienced as reality, and he believes that he is or is about to become like the others or as powerful as the others. Because of the reality value of wishes and images, the feeling of omnipotence which has been carried over from previous stages will be reinforced (see the section on The Primordial Self in Chapter 3).

A child who is exposed to unpleasant experiences during this period may be delayed in reaching subsequent levels of development. Consequently he may learn to interpret the world predominantly through the distortions that this level of immaturity and the disagreeable interpersonal surroundings bring about. He may experience his parents as clusters of unpleasant images, which subsequent levels of development will transform into terrifying fantasy figures. He may not wish to be or become like the parents, and he may develop an awareness of himself as an entity that is victimized, ignored, hated, or manipulated by other images.

When the phantasmic level is too difficult for the child to bear, several consequences may follow. As we shall see in Chapter 28, he may escape again into the exoceptual world and become hyperkinetic. He may also repress the images from consciousness, perhaps by transforming them into endocepts (Chapter 6). However, the effects of a too disturbing phantasmic level may not be easily kept in a state of unconsciousness. They may re-emerge, even much later, in dreams, schizophrenia, and states of intoxication.

Images and paleosymbols remain normal constituents of the psyche throughout the life of the person. Their importance decreases, however, as other psychological forms emerge. In the normal adult they are inhibited to a large extent by the perceptual stimuli of external reality. In their purest forms images belong to the primary process. But in the normal adult's waking life, they are almost always under the control of the secondary process, which initiates, controls, screens, and inhibits their occurrence.

6° *THE ENDOCEPT*

Nonrepresentational experience

If in the last few decades little attention has been paid to the image, even less has been given to the intermediary stages between the image and the concept. The workers of the Würzburg group were among the first to indicate that there are some mental processes which occur without representation (that is, without images) but which are not at the level of mature thoughts. Surprise, hesitation, doubts have been depicted by Marbe as "experiences which cannot be closely analyzed" (*Bewrsstseinslage,* 1901). Ach wrote of "the actual presence of knowing without images" (1935).

What is less known is that at the same time the Würzburgers were drawing these conclusions, the French psychologist Binet developed a similar point of view (1903, 1911). For him some forms of thought are completely without images; the intention, not the image, is the foundation of psychic life. This intention is related to what the Würzburgers called the *Aufgabe* of thought.

At the level of the psyche which we are now considering there is a primitive organization of perceptions, memory traces, images, and exocepts. This organization results in a construct which is not representational. In a certain way it transcends the image, but inasmuch as it does not reproduce anything similar to perceptions, it is not easily recognizable. On the other hand, it is not an engram or exocept which leads to prompt action. Nor can it be transformed into a verbal expression; it remains at a preverbal level. Although it has an emotional component, it does not expand into a clearly felt emotion. I have proposed the name of *endocept* for this intermediary construct (Arieti, 1965).[1]

The endocept is not, of course, a concept. It cannot be shared. We may consider it a disposition to feel, to act, to think, which occurs after simpler mental activity has been inhibited. The awareness of this construct is vague, uncertain, and partial. Relative to the image, the endocept involves considerable cognitive expansion; but this expansion occurs at the expense of the subjective awareness, which is decreased in intensity.

The content of an endocept can be communicated to other people only when it is translated into expressions belonging to other mental levels. Expressing endocepts is much more difficult than describing psychological experiences like sensations, emotions, images, etc. This is because the endocept is an intermediary construct, which cannot be represented by actions, words, images, or clear-cut emotions. It cannot be represented even by paleosymbols.

At the present stage of knowledge, we cannot obtain empirical proof of the existence of the endocept. However, in the course of this chapter we shall see that there is some evidence, both deduced logically and gathered from clinical observations, of its existence. Perhaps what I call an endocept will eventually be found to consist of numerous steps or mechanisms which are even susceptible to neurophysiological interpretation.

Although the endocept does not reach the verbal level, men give names to experiences which retain mostly endocep-

[1] Extrapolating from the word "conceive," I have also suggested the verb "to endoceive" and, in relation to the exocept, "to exoceive."

tual characteristics. At times the endocept seems to be completely unconscious. At other times the individual refers to the endocept as to something which is felt as an atmosphere, an intention, a holistic experience which cannot be divided into parts or words—something similar to what Freud called oceanic feeling. At other times there is no sharp demarcation between endoceptual, subliminal experiences and some vague protoexperiences. On still other occasions, strong but not verbalizable emotions accompany endocepts.

Endoceptual knowledge not only cannot be compared with the experiences of other people; it cannot even be intrapsychically validated, because the individual cannot compare his endocepts with his other psychological processes. Endoceptual life does not permit reality testing, since such a test requires a dialogue with oneself. If some endocepts retain some awareness, the awareness is dim, and has a global or diffuse quality which does not lead to fine discrimination. All these characteristics add to the confusion of our knowledge of the endocept.

People vary in relation to their endocepts. Some persons deny that they occur; others easily admit them. As in the case of imagery, we find that with the exception of what happens in periods of creativity, people devoted to scientific work or to the application of logical thinking focus on concepts and are hardly aware of endocepts. People with "artistic temperaments" are more given to endoceptual experiences. At times we encounter intelligent and well-educated people, inclined to logical, deductive thinking, who nevertheless seem "too-dimensional," lacking in depth. These people stick to fact; they are indeed *factual.* Their intelligence shows a mechanical quality which has a pragmatic value in some aspects of life but is disagreeable in many others. Since early life these people have been trained (or because of the nature of their anxiety have trained themselves) to experience only concepts and to suppress and repress endocepts totally. Actually their conceptual life too is limited, as we shall see later, because it is not enriched by endoceptual sources. Endoceptual processes, although indefinite, tend to accrue. They are self-enlarging and self-enriching; they add new dimensions, even when higher levels of mentation are present. To a large degree, however, endocepts are repressed or suppressed in every adult human being.

Patients under psychoanalytic treatment often mention some endoceptual experiences which occurred in early childhood, from ages 2 to 4, before the acquisition of adult language. The following is an example:

> In my grandparents' home there was an extra living room, "the red living room," reserved for big occasions—parties, celebrations, and so on. We children were not allowed to go into that room. Occasionally I would sneak into it, to give a quick look, afraid of being caught there. The room had an aura of solemnity. It was like a sacred, holy room. There were the pictures of our great-grandparents—pictures to revere, like those of saints. The furniture was covered in gold and had red upholstery. There was a red carpet on the floor. The wallpaper was red. The whole room had an aspect of austerity.

This is a memory from the third to the fourth year of life, when the patient probably had not yet acquired the concepts or the words "aura," "austerity," "sacred," "solemnity." How is one to interpret this memory? The first interpretation, of course, is that we are dealing here with retrospective falsification: the patient attributes to his memories concepts and words which were not available at the time of the original experience. But if such concepts were not available, how was the memory of the experience carried through the years? Obviously the memory consisted of more than a conservation of visual images; the patient also remembered an affective state and a certain behavior or at least motor disposition: desire to sneak into the room, and inhibition of actions because of the fear of being caught. In other words, in addition to visual images, endocepts were retained. During the analytic session the original endocepts were translated into words congruous with the patient's present understanding of the memory. He said that he had experienced the feeling of "sanctity, austerity," etc. Sanctity means the state of being sacred, or free of impurity. The child knew that the room was only for big occasions, and he experienced that situation as an inner state, a state which later he attributed to the room and called "sanctity." He also described the room as having an aura of austerity, although it was richly furnished, the walls were red, and the furniture was beautiful. According to Webster, *austere* means "severe, stern, harsh, rigorous, morally strict; abstinent, ascetic, lacking ornament." Apparently the fact that the room was restricted to adults made the child experience something which he later referred to as its "austerity." These inner experiences which could not be verbalized presumably were endocepts.

Similar phenomena occur in dreams. In several types of dreams, verbal expressions and other kinds of communications are present and may even play an important role. We are all aware, however, of another large group of dreams into which language does not enter. The dreamer experiences the dream in an intense way, yet with no words. When he is asked by the analyst to give details or to describe what he felt in the dream, the patient uses many words of which he was not conscious while he was dreaming. For instance, he may say that he was experiencing a mixture of joy, fear, and anxiety such as he has never felt in waking life. He may describe the dream as having an atmosphere of mysteriousness and yet hope that everything would turn out all right. Thus the patient who is now awake tries to translate into words the experience of the dream or, rather, the memory of the experience. But while he was dreaming, he was not thinking in words; his experiences were endocepts. As a matter of fact, the dreamer often states that his account of the dream is at best approximate. It is difficult and always inaccurate to translate endocepts into concepts.

There are other situations in which the person is aware of the discrepancy between his endocepts and his verbal explanations. He says, "I know what I mean and feel, but I can't explain." In certain situations with intense emotional content, such as being in the company of a loved person, or intense artistic appreciation, such as seeing a beautiful landscape, endocepts play an important role. Often people who try to verbalize these experiences say that "words spoil the feeling." Some lovers in the midst of their loving experiences like to say and hear endearing words and other expressions exalting the beauty of the shared experience. However, other lovers do not want any verbal accompaniment to their physical or spiritual pleasure. Again the feeling is that words "spoil everything. Beauty must remain unsaid." In some poetry, the words which are used suggest much more which remains unsaid and is experienced endoceptually. Another feeling is that words "put on a strait jacket" or "crystallize the experience." The experience tends to be "an unending phenomenon" to which "words put an end." Indeed endoceptual experiences, as clusters of nonverbalized associations, tend to expand in indefinite ways. All this is reminiscent of artistic or aesthetic experience, as we shall see in Chapter 21.

Endocepts may remain endocepts. However, in both ontogenetic and microgenetic development they tend to undergo various transformations: (1) into words, that is, into various preconceptual and conceptual forms, (2) into exocepts and actions, (3) into more definite feelings, (4) into images, (5) into dreams and fantasies.

Endocepts are important constructs not only because they are developmental ontogenetic and microgenetic stages toward full conceptual forms, but also because a great part of our conceptual life tends to fuse with the endoceptual counterpart, or to return to an endoceptual level when focal attention is defective. Empathy is a type of communication based to a large extent on a primitive understanding of one another's endocepts. Some people who operate at a predominantly endoceptual level experience strong empathy for others. In most cases, however, the individual who operates endoceptually appears to be objectless. He is not really so, but he seems unmotivated because he has difficulty in experiencing images or attachment for external or internal representational objects. He discloses only the form of diffuse intentionality or affective tone that we have mentioned.

At times, especially in creative moments, an endocept is immediately converted into a verbalized statement, or into some kind of external act (painting, for instance). We speak then of intuition or of inspiration. Intuition appears to be nonmediated knowledge, or an immediate method to obtain knowledge. Actually there is no such thing as a nonmediated acquisition of knowledge; the knowledge does not seem to have been mediated because the subject was unaware of the antecedent microgenetic stages. It is my belief that at least part of the intuitional knowledge to which Spinoza and Bergson have given so much importance is endoceptual knowledge which is promptly translated into a conceptual form.

Endocepts and the state of unconsciousness

Using Freudian terminology, we can call some endocepts unconscious, others preconscious. The quality or state of unconsciousness of the psychological processes will be discussed in detail in Chapter 9. Chapter 2 has already pointed out, however, that only a small number of the functions of the nervous system are endowed with various degrees of consciousness. The most vivid awareness is found in sensations, physiostates, protoemotions, and emotions. Cognitive constructs do not possess similar vividness.

Generally when we refer to unconscious processes in psychoanalytic terminology, we mean processes which could be conscious, or those which used to be conscious and no longer are. In the last case, we say that they have undergone repression. In the transition from the image to the endocept, however, we cannot properly speak of repression. What probably takes place in many cases is an inhibition of the simpler image-producing mechanism. In other cases the image is not inhibited but isolated from its endoceptual elaborations or derivatives. Finally, images and endocepts coexist in both dreams and waking life, but the endoceptual part of the experience remains difficult to communicate.

In subsequent chapters we shall see that cognitive processes which are generally conscious and communicable may acquire endoceptual forms. A large number of schizophrenic patients live at a predominantly endoceptual level. In normal persons, too, an intermittent reversion of concepts into endocepts takes place. What was formerly the conceptual material becomes part of what are often called the unconscious and preconscious systems. Such a reversion, which generally occurs when consciousness is unpleasant, may in many instances be the phenomenon usually referred to as repression.

Also, a part of conceptual life tends to assume endoceptual forms when attention is defective. However, it is very doubtful that what is not under the scrutiny of one's attention always recedes to an endoceptual level.

7 ° THE ORIGIN OF LANGUAGE, VERBAL THINKING, AND HIGH EMOTIONS

The various forms of cognition may be experienced as static or mobile, as external or internal, as constructs likely to change into others belonging to lower or higher levels, and as phenomena whose subjective quality is of much more or much less importance than their cognitive content.

Thus according to this schema, a visual perception tends to be experienced as a process that has immobilized the flux of nature into an apparently static mirror image, as something related to the external world, as a construct that tends to be elaborated into higher cognitive forms, and as a phenomenon whose cognitive element is more important than the subjective. To take another example, an image changes the trace of a perception into something which is again in a state of flux and of perennial becoming even more pronounced than that of the external world. It is experienced as internal and tends to become transformed into higher constructs. A paleosymbol is an inner construct, but in its typical forms, an external object is needed for the endocept to evoke it. An endocept is even more closely bound by the inner world than the image is, for the endocept seems unrelated to external reality.

A symbol, although endowed with an internal psychic life, needs to be externalized and to be understood by others in order to move to progressively higher levels of complexity. This chapter will deal predominantly with externalized symbols.

The first symbolic externalizations of primordial man consisted of finger pointing and gestures. Finger pointing is at first an exocept; then it becomes an action with symbolic characteristics. The pointing individual adopts some attributes of the sign itself: he becomes a person who makes a sign with the finger. The movement of the finger replaces a general movement such as grabbing, mouthing, or reaching to touch. Unlike these, it does not incorporate or establish physical continuity with the object, but rather acknowledges the object's presence at a distance. This movement becomes refined and usually limited to the index finger. It may become accompanied by gestures, that is, by other movements which have a symbolic value.[1]

The origin of language

Finger pointing and gestures are phylogenetically followed by vocalization which requires specific movements of the larynx and the oral cavity. Finger pointing and vocalization, at least in their primitive forms, are not acts of contemplation of distant objects. They express an affective disposition, and indicate to another human being that some kind of action is to be taken. They are thus among the first symbolic activities which become connected with man's social life. Some vocal sounds become what Werner calls words-of-action: they lead immediately to movements.

In an excellent scholarly book Diamond (1959) has given

[1] Gestures have been studied intensively, but for the sake of brevity I shall not discuss them here. As verbal language gradually becomes dominant, gestures lose their importance. In people who cannot use verbal symbols, like deaf-mutes, gesture language reacquires prominence. Some of us remember silent movies in which gestures were again stressed or exaggerated to convey meaning. I shall also omit from the present study references to other languages, such as musical language, olfactory language, bee language, etc.

convincing evidence that primitive words conveyed a request for action or for participation in an action. The first words were "imperative verbs," corresponding to our "look-hit-kill-run-strike," used by primitive men to obtain help from other humans in overcoming the difficulties of nature. They contained a conative element, a sense of striving. According to Diamond the vocal sound was accompanied by an automatic movement of the arm. Of course, we have to take the designation of these primitive words as "verbs used in the imperative sense" with caution. These words did not have a universal meaning like verbs used later, nor a definite tense. Probably they were a mixture of an exclamation, a signal to action, a command, a gesture. They referred to a specific concrete situation, which required a given position or attitude of the soma.

If we compare the acquisition of the first words in phylogeny and ontogeny, we realize that today's children do not learn their first words as Diamond has described. This is by no means a surprise. There is no reason to suppose that ontogeny should mirror phylogeny in the learning of language. The central nervous system of a 1- to 2-year-old is quite different from that of primordial man. The infant has a genetic potential for language which will be actualized if maturation is unimpeded and the proper environmental stimuli are present. We cannot postulate that primordial man had a similar potential. In the former case the process is one of normal maturation, while in the latter it is one of emergent evolution. There are additional reasons why the two processes are not analogous. For at least a million years, generations of human babies have been in situations completely different from that of primordial man when he first acquired the faculty of speech. When the baby has reached an age suitable to the acquisition of language, he is handed it "on a silver platter," as a tool ready to be used, a product of the largest part of human history. It is true that the baby is only gradually exposed to the complexities of language. Nevertheless we must recognize that he is taking a very accelerated "course."

Diamond's theory of the origin of language seems to me a plausible one. Some additional evidence and some revisions can be offered. Not being a neurologist, Diamond does not present the neurological facts that actually support his theory. For there is indeed a neurological connection between arm-hand and language functions. In spite of recent controversial reports (Zangwill, 1960), most neurologists and neurophysiologists agree that there is a direct relationship between handedness and language centers. In right-handed people the language centers are in the left cerebral hemisphere, and in left-handed people they are in the right cerebral hemisphere. It seems that the exocepts related to the movements of the preferred hand awaken the language centers in the corresponding cerebral hemisphere. The motor areas presiding over the movements of the hand and the oral cavity and over the center of motor language (Broca's area) are contiguous in the frontal cortex.

My own modification of Diamond's theory of language concerns the fact that in addition to the automatic movement of the arm, made in order to participate in the action, the arm and hand become important in pointing and in making gestures. Moreover, there are other important functions in which the exocepts of the hand and of the mouth work synergically: sharing food and eating. These collective actions probably were accompanied by vocal sounds which became words.

Other somatic factors, outlined by Langer (1962), are prerequisites for language: (1) a larynx capable of sustaining relatively simple sounds, which gibbons also possess; (2) an epicritical ear capable of distinguishing one sound from another and not merely of perceiving sounds as noises; (3) the ability to imitate sounds. Some prehuman animals possess one of these characteristics but not all of them.

Many theories of the origin of language have been advanced. Below are brief reviews of the most important ones, which are usually referred to by their nicknames.

The *bow-wow theory* assumes that primitive words were onomatopoetic or imitative. For instance, man imitated the natural sound of an animal, like the barking of a dog, and that sound became the word designating dog. Although it is true that in some primitive languages a small number of words seem derived from animal sounds, the complexity and social aspect of language are not explained by this theory.

In the *pooh-pooh theory*, the hypothesis is that the first words were emitted during expressions of sensations or emotions, like pain or anxiety. Darwin supported this theory and tried to give it a physiological interpretation. According to him, interjections like *pooh!* and *pish!* occur as expressions of contempt or disgust, resulting from blowing out of the mouth or nostrils. This theory has been criticized on the ground that there is a wide chasm between interjections and words: interjections are used when words cannot be used. The theory does not seem to me completely unplausible, however. Sounds which were at first emitted as exclamations in specific situations may later have become indicative of these situations.

A third theory, proposed by Max Müller and nicknamed the *ding-dong theory*, advocates a mystical resonance between a substance and a sound.

Noirè's theory, which is called the *yo-he-ho theory*, suggests that during muscular effort it is a relief to breathe strongly and repeatedly, in such a way that the vocal cords vibrate and emit sounds. When actions were performed by a group of primitive humans, some sounds may have been associated with the idea of the act performed and eventually became a name for it. The first words thus would represent muscular efforts. Noirè's theory has the advantage over the previous ones that it gives importance to the sharing of an experience and thus adds an interpersonal factor. Noirè, however, did not realize that his theory implied the neurological importance of the movement of the hand. To some extent, his theory is compatible with Diamond's and with my modification of Diamond's theory.

Susanne Langer (1962) has adopted and expanded a theory previously proposed by John Donovan: the *dance theory*. Langer recognizes the fact that the situation which stimulated speech must have been one where members of a human group were together. A situation of communion must have existed before it became one of communication. According to the Donovan-Langer theory, in the development of the tribal dance all individuals of the primitive horde became familiar with the sounds that were associated with the various steps and gestures of the dance. By the process of association of images, those sounds became associated with other things and came to constitute an important group of primordial words.

It may very well be that many words were added to the small vocabulary of primitive tribes by the act of the communal dance. But this type of dance, performed to celebrate a ritual or a holiday, seems to me to presuppose a level of societal organization which is inconceivable without the previous acquisition of some words. The main weakness of this theory, however, lies in the prominence it necessarily gives to the movement of the leg. Although movements of other parts of the body are involved in dances, especially in those of primitive people, it is the leg which plays the predominant role. The neurophysiological facts which have been mentioned point instead to a much closer association between the movements of the arm and hand and those required for language. The hand as the pointer, helper, and toolmaker becomes the main auxiliary of man, whereas the leg (used, as in subhuman animals, for presymbolic actions like moving away or moving toward) does not achieve such an important role. It is thus doubtful that the leg rather than the hand is the main stimulus to the acquisition of language.

Primitive words

In studying the development of language it is a useful procedure to distinguish a series of stages. It must be understood, however, that these stages are abstractions and reconstructions. Although in a gross fashion they may represent the gradual growth of language, they may never have existed in pure form. Many stages appear to overlap, with one of them predominating. Even at the most advanced stages we can find residues of the primitive, and at the most primitive we can find precursors of the advanced.

What kind of words were the first ones used by primordial human beings? According to Diamond they were requests for action or anticipations of action, and they represented shared actions, as well as the accompanying emotions.

However, other authors have emphasized the occurrence

of a second type of words in primitive languages. Werner (1957a) and Jespersen (1922) have reported that in primitive languages many words possess complicated meanings which, when expressed in modern languages, require long sentences. Language at the very primitive level does not really have a concentration of communicable meaning. Syncretism, or concentration of meaning, is an aspect of language that occurs at a somewhat later stage. At the very primitive stage, words which do not refer to actions have a diffuse, almost endoceptual referent and are extremely difficult to define. Later such a primitive word comes to represent either a diffuse experience or the salient part of the experience. In other words, eventually it is one of these two aspects of the experience that is permanently attached to the verbal expression. If the salient part is an action, a verb originates. Later the reference may shift from the action (or verb) to the object or situation which stimulates the doing. The word is then connected to only a fragment of the original parameter: it is attached to an external object or external behavior and becomes a noun. A great change has occurred indeed from the stage at which the sound made by the subhuman animal conveyed only knowledge of a subjective state or of an experience. This linguistic connection with the external world, which is experienced as separate from the individual, occurs especially at the stage of denotation.

The stage of denotation

At this stage of development the forms of cognition lose more and more of their diffuse characteristics that are difficult to communicate. Names of actions and things accumulate at a great rate. Endoceiving, pointing, grabbing, and moving away are replaced by the uttering of a name which refers to external objects and actions. In its periodical pendulum-like course, cognition now externalizes again and tries to crystallize into static entities the flux of nature as well as the flux of inner reality. These relatively static entities are the names of things, for at this stage language consists mostly of naming.

Names are more reliable constructs than the flickering images, the unshareable paleosymbols, or the obscure endocepts. The process of denoting reinforces the external character of reality and diminishes the importance of imagery. Except in some situations where it is purposely used to evoke an image, as in poetry, the name is a substitute for the image and may even inhibit the production of the image. If I want to talk or think about my friend George, I may simply think or utter the word *George;* but if I want to re-evoke a nameless object, I must re-evoke its image. The denotative stage is the realistic stage par excellence. It actually helps primitive man to structure reality. It may deal only with a limited reality, but in its limitation it is safe. This is the stage to which modern "practical" people also want to stick.

One characteristic of the denotative stage has been reported by many linguists in primitive languages: words for specific things or actions abound, but generic words are lacking. For instance, some primitive languages have a word for each species of bird known in their environment, but do not have a generic word for *bird*. In Cherokee language there is no word just for washing; different words are used according to what is washed—one's head, somebody else's head, clothes, tools, etc.—and according to the particular action used for the washing and the concrete environmental situation.

The cognitive revolution produced by the stage of denotation has been better understood since some similarities between the functions of electronic computers and the functions of the brain have been recognized. There are two types of computers, analog and digital. In analogic codification, the symbols which represent events or things attempt to reproduce or copy these events or things. A relation of likeness between two entities must be established. The two entities (the thing and its representative) are comparable, but not identical. To some extent the human brain acts as an analog computer (Ruesch, 1961). In spite of the doubts that philosophers have imparted to us about the reliability of our perceptions in "copying" the external world, perceiving must be considered a type of analogic codification. So must imagery. The brain has other analogic codifications which are not so

obvious: for example, organismic responses, including alterations of the homeostasis and emotional responses. With the
formation of the endocept, however, analogic codification becomes more and more inadequate in representing experience.

With the advent of language, the constitution of the brain
changed radically: from an analog computer it became more
and more a digital computer. Whereas an analog computer
deals with a continuous function, like the emotional state of
the organism, a digital computer deals with discrete step intervals. No transition exists between one sign and the other.
The digital computer lacks the analog computer's simultaneity of input and output, but it is much more flexible. A
system of arbitrary signs allows enormous expansion of the
amount of material handled.[2]

When language enters into human cognition it is no longer
possible to separate cognitive processes from language; they
are all intimately interconnected. For instance, language as a
carrier of thought cannot be distinguished from thought itself. Moreover, as we shall see later in this chapter and in
Chapters 8 and 9, language becomes not only a carrier of
emotion but also a source and a transformer of emotion.

As for the comparison that can be made between the
human brain and computers, it also illustrates the difference
between them: one is endowed with awareness and the other
is not (see the first section of Chapter 2). Thinking machines
can reproduce some thought equivalents and use them, but
they are not aware of what they are doing.

We can roughly divide the process of verbal thinking, not
only at a denotational level, but at every level, into two
parts: the "noupoietic," or the part which produces the
thought processes, and the "noupathetic," which permits the
awareness of them. The rather lowered intensity of the
noupathetic part, in comparison with that of other subjective
experiences, contrasts with the expansion of the noupoietic
part. These two parts of cognitive processes occur simultaneously or almost simultaneously in normal conditions, and
perhaps they are the characteristics which give the human
being the unique quality of self-reflection. By means of this

---

[2] Von Neumann was among the first to compare the characteristics of the
brain with those of a digital computer (1958).

double mechanism, the individual can carry on a dialogue with himself. Although the dialogue presupposes an inter-personal process (because it is from other people that the human being first obtains the symbolic tools necessary for thinking), it soon becomes purely intrapsychic. We have here one of the highest capacities of the human psyche: the transformation of the interpersonal into the intrapsychic.

In microgenetic development the stages other than the terminal do not have a noupathetic mechanism. In some pathologic conditions like epilepsy, the noupathetic mechanism is occasionally lost, and cognitive dissociation occurs. For instance, in epileptic fugues and their psychomotor equivalents, a patient may display rational behavior (avoiding traffic and other dangerous possibilities, paying carfare, etc.) and yet be unaware of what he is doing.[3]

Opposite use of words

An important characteristic of the denotative stage, as well as of some subsequent stages, is that words often denote or connote opposite things or actions. Freud dealt with this phenomenon when he realized that things which appear in dreams may mean their opposites (1910). He also found that the word *no* does not exist in dreams. Contraries are combined in a unity, and any element can be represented "by its wishful contrary."

In investigating this topic, Freud turned to the work of the philologist Karl Abel, who had observed the same phenomenon in Egyptian hieroglyphics (1884). Abel wrote, "Man has not been able to acquire even his oldest and simplest conceptions otherwise than in contrast with their opposite; he only gradually learnt to separate the two sides of the antithesis and think of the one without conscious comparison with the other." [4] Freud, again quoting Abel, posed the question of how people listening to these primitive words would under-

---

3 This may not actually be the mechanism involved, at least in some cases. The patient may be aware of what he is doing in that instant, but the next minute he may not remember what he did. This phenomenon would thus be due to impairment of memory and not to an impairment of consciousness.
4 Abel, quoted by Freud (1910).

stand which one of the opposite meanings was intended. In Egyptian hieroglyphics this difficulty was remedied by a picture which accompanied the alphabetically written sound. For instance, when the written sound *ken* means strong, it appears with the picture of an upright armed man. When it means *weak*, it is accompanied by a "crouching, weary man."

Freud, like many other authors, accepted the fact of the antithetical character of primitive words, but could not explain the phenomenon. Undoubtedly, forerunners of opposite meanings are included in the endoceptual type of organization; but why, out of the many undefinable components of endocepts, should two antithetical components eventually be reunited in the same verbal expression? To explain the phenomenon by saying that the human mind searches for or is attracted by opposites is circular reasoning.

I should like to suggest a hypothesis which, since it depends on some concepts discussed in Chapter 12, will be treated in more detail there. Briefly, the two basic conative movements of the organism are to advance or move toward, and to retreat or move away. We have seen that many primal words probably indicated not only a certain disposition toward an object, but were also accompanied by a movement either of the whole body or of the hand. In some cases a primitive sound may have referred only to a disposition—for instance, to go—while the movement indicated whether the going was toward or away.[5] All words had a positive meaning. There was no "no moving toward" but rather "retreat" or "withdrawal." There was no "no withdrawal," but rather "advance." The same endoceptual disposition could become connected with the two basic opposite movements, so that eventually the corresponding verbal symbol could have opposite meanings, according to the basic movement or action with which it was associated.[6]

The two movements are both positive and fundamental for the organism. It is on these "biphasic processes underlying approach and withdrawal" that Schneirla has based a great

[5] Darwin (1873) and Spitz (1957) have written about the antithetical meaning of gestures.
[6] A segment of the primary aggregation, which will be discussed in Chapter 7, may also become associated with the two basic directions of the biphasic primary conation.

part of his evolutionary and developmental theory (1939, 1949, 1959). Schneirla deals with the elementary processes of simple organisms and therefore is not aware of how well the biphasic approach, which he has so clearly illustrated, may also describe the primitive stages of human cognition. We have seen that at the stage of the exocept, cognition is not differentiated from conation (Chapter 3). At the stages that we are taking into consideration now, cognition is not independent of conation but is still strictly connected with the two basic positive conative dispositions.

Freud too, in his paper *Negation* (1925), states that the first function of judgment is concerned with two sorts of decision. It may assert or deny that a thing has the particular property of being good or bad, useful or harmful. Freud writes: "Expressed in the language of the oldest, that is, of the oral, instinctual impulses, the alternative runs thus: 'I should like to eat that, or I should like to spit it out,' or carried a stage further, 'I should like to take this into me and keep that out of me.' That is to say: 'It is to be either inside of me or outside of me.'" In Freud's view too, the association of primitive words with primary conation (approach and withdrawal) is implicit.[7]

The stage of verbalization

Following, though to a large extent overlapping, the denotative stage of language is the stage of verbalization. The word, or the verbalization, now acquires an importance of its own over and above that of merely denoting the thing it stands for. In some primitive societies the word becomes either an essential part of the thing, or actually equivalent to the thing it stands for. That is, the word is no longer just a symbol of the thing, but becomes the thing itself, or at least

---

[7] It may be remembered that an important part of Pythagorean philosophy was based on the concept of "opposite." Socrates too, in the words of Plato, thought that one thing originates from its opposite.

Aristotle (in *De Interpretatione* C7, from 17 to 38) wrote that opposites are two propositions which affirm or deny the same predicate in a universal sense. In "Categories," Aristotle stated that two concepts are opposite when, in referring to the same content, they express the two extreme degrees.

acquires the power of the thing. This is the origin of "word-magic" and of some religious practices involving names (Werner, 1957a). As described by Werner, a "physiognomic" quality, which can be assigned to the denoted thing, is also attributed to the word itself. The word may be experienced as beautiful or ugly, soft or strong, fitting or unfitting. This animation of the word is probably at least partially due to the fact that it has become connected with the image of the thing it stands for and has in a certain way acquired the characteristics of the image. As a matter of fact, the word can be used to elicit that image. The thing itself is thus by-passed.

Concern with words as words, that is, as phonetic products independent of their meaning, develops further during this stage and remains to some extent during subsequent connotative stages. The sound of the word, its musicality, rhythm, assonance or rhyme in relation to other words, and its repetition, all acquire great importance. The characteristics of this stage of language resume prominence in literature, especially in poetry (Chapter 21).

Connotation

Language reaches its greatest cognitive importance when words acquire connotative power. The connotation is the definition or the concept of the thing. A word acquires connotation when it can stand for a concept. For instance, at this stage the word *table* no longer indicates just this or that table, but a table in general—an article of furniture consisting of a flat top that stands on legs.

Various degrees of connotation are acquired at different times. Each word has a long connotative history, with many stages of development.[8] The steps by which a word acquires

[8] When does a word start to have connotation? Susanne Langer (1962) believes that the concept of the thing which is denoted and verbalized is inherent in the act of denotation; that is, a thing will be connoted as soon as it is denoted. She writes: "Several eminent psychiatrists to the contrary notwithstanding, primitive denotation was not like using a proper name. When words took shape, they were general in intent from the beginning: their connotations *inhered in them, and their denotations were whatever fitted this inherent sense.*" [Italics added.]

connotation or meaning are numerous, and many of them are completely unknown. In some cases we can only infer them.[9]

Langer thus makes two statements in support of the immediate origin of connotation: The first argument is that the original word applied to the whole class, and not to the specific embodiments, as proper names do. There is no doubt that the original word in many cases applied to what is for us a whole class. However, giving a name to each member of a class does not imply having a concept of the class. It could be that the difference between Langer's position and mine is only one of semantics. I am more inclined to believe, however, that we differ on what is meant by "concept," probably because Langer does not use the notion of endocept.

Naming an object means first recognizing the object, and second applying a name to what is recognized. Subhuman animals probably "recognize" by reacting in a specific way. For instance, a cat recognizes a mouse, insofar as he reacts to a mouse always in the same way. The cat does not possess the platonic universal of mouse or "mouseness." The primitive class "mouse" that we attributed to the mentality of the cat is not the field of applicability of the concept "mouse," but the field of applicability of a response, or, at most, the field of applicability of a recognition or of a preconceptual subjective experience. No concept is really involved. We have seen, as a matter of fact, that the range of applicability of the response varies with the phenomenon of the equivalence of stimuli (Chapter 4). Stimuli may be equivalent, although their concepts may differ. Human beings probably recognize a thing by comparing the external object with an inner image of that object. The perception "mouse" is replaced by the image "mouse." Now, an image does not necessarily have a connotation, even if it is connected with a verbal sound.

Let us now consider Langer's second argument: "When words took shape, they were general in intent from the beginning; their connotations *inhered in them*, and their denotations were whatever fitted this inherent sense." [Italics added.] Langer thus states that whenever an object is denoted, there is an accompanying inherent sense. I agree, but it seems to me that this "inherent sense" is not necessarily a concept. At least, it is not a concept in the ordinary sense, if by concept we mean not an experiential phenomenon but a definition of an object, or an idea which applies to the whole class, something which can be communicated and on which most people agree. Concepts also imply a grasp of a definite relationship between parts. All this is not necessarily a part of the inherent sense which accompanies primitive denotation. This "inherent sense" is something between the image and the connotation. It may be evoked by (1) the perception of the object, (2) the response to the object, (3) the image of the object, (4) the denotation of the object. It is what I have called the endocept. Naming an object actually makes the endocept even more inaccessible to one's consciousness.

[9] Morris' approach should be briefly considered at this point (1946). According to Morris, a word is a sign when it "disposes" certain human organisms to make responses which have previously been made by means of the object which the word stands for. For instance, the word *knife* disposes the hearer to cut, because previously he cut by using the object *knife*. Words represent things because they more or less reproduce the actual behavior elicited by these things. For Morris, the meaning of the sign is the disposition toward a certain behavior elicited by the sign.

My objection is that disposition toward behavior is not necessarily a connotative experience. When we say "disposition toward behavior" the emphasis should be on the disposition, not on the behavior, which may never materialize. The possibility of the nonoccurrence of the behavior, as

The primary aggregation

Conceptual organization follows a definite course, which can be divided into several stages. Werner wrote that "Wherever development occurs it proceeds from a state of relative globality and lack of differentiation to a state of increasing differentiation, articulation and hierarchic integration" (1957b). Constructs like images, endocepts, exocepts, and denotative words become associated to form the *primary aggregation* (Arieti, 1962a).[10] The primary aggregation does not have a definite holistic organization, except in a general and very loose way. It differs from the endocept in that it contains verbal elements and can therefore be externalized. This externalization usually consists of the verbal expression of an element of which it is composed. The element then comes to represent the whole primary aggregation. At times the primary aggregation seems a strange agglomeration of disparate things put together, as they are in a collage. At other times it may be recognized as an embryonic structure from which conceptual structures eventually emerge. Or in some cases it may even embrace a field which at higher levels of development corresponds to a highly abstract concept.

How a primary aggregation is formed is difficult to say. Often the grouping of the elements is naturalistic, reproducing the contiguity found in the external world or the chronological continuity of some experiences. Among the many examples given by Werner (1957a) is the expression *tu ku eng*, which the Bakairi Indians of Brazil use to designate the colors emerald green, cinnabar red, and ultramarine. These

---

a matter of fact, emphasizes the symbolic aspect of the word. The disposition toward a certain behavior may be experienced even when an endocept is translated into an exocept.

The organization of meaning actually tends to have an effect opposite to what Morris suggests. It transforms objects from things-of-action into objects of knowledge and feeling. There is a gradual shifting to a contemplative attitude. Any contemplation eventually leads to action through intermediary stages, which may vary considerably both in number and quality. Between the baby who responds immediately to a toy by reaching for it and a philosopher who before acting has to ponder whether external reality is or is not, there is an elaborated gamut of cognitive possibilities.

10 The primary aggregation corresponds approximately to what Schilder called "the sphere" (1953) and Linn "the cluster" (1954).

colors are found in the feathers of a parrot called *tu ku eng*. Also according to Werner, water and thirst are called by the same name in the language of the Australian aborigines because they are both elements of the same global construct involving relations and attitudes toward water.

When children learn to talk, at first they extend the meaning of a word to all the experiences which are associated with it, thus forming a primary aggregation. For instance, the same babbling sound may mean glass, water, milk, to drink, being thirsty, etc. Many examples of a return to the level of primary aggregation are found in patients suffering from organic diseases of the central nervous system. In aphasic patients, Bouman and Grunbaum (1925) considered the basic change "an arrest at an earlier stage of development of a mental process, which normally proceeds in the direction from amorphous total reaction toward differentiated and definite forms." Conrad (1947) describes this phenomenon as an arrest at a pregestalt level. Werner (1956), following Lotmar (1919), speaks of a level where "spheres of meaning" rather than specific concepts are apprehended. In many such organic conditions, the patient does not use the appropriate word but one that belongs to the primary aggregation. The same phenomenon may occur in normal persons who are momentarily distracted. In these cases any element of the primary aggregation may reach the level of consciousness. Almost always the element, though not the right one, is more or less related to the right one. The relation between the two elements originated in their contiguity either in external reality or in subjective experience. As we shall see in Chapter 16, typical cases of primary aggregation are also observable in patients suffering from advanced schizophrenic regression.

A primary aggregation is not an assembly of organized elements; each element assumes an equivalence to the whole which is not acceptable at higher levels of the mind. This equivalence of the part to the whole has also been described by Cassirer (1955, vol. 2). He writes that in mythical thinking "The whole is the part, in the sense that it enters into it with its whole mythical-substantial essence, that it is somehow sensuously and materially 'in' it. The whole man is contained in his hair, his nail-cuttings, his clothes, his footprints." At the level of the primary aggregation, however, there is no conception of "whole" as an organized entity.

Perhaps even in simple conditioning a similar process of equating part and whole takes place. In the classic Pavlovian experiment, the dog responds to the ringing of the bell as he responds to the food; that is, in this situation a part which has been aggregated by temporal contiguity has the same effect that the whole has. Physiologically the dog identifies the ringing of the bell with food.

Although the primary aggregation seems an unsatisfactory form of cognition, it represents some evolutionary progress from the level of the endocept or of simple denotation. In the endocept, the sphere of meaning is completely unverbalized, as some of a child's knowledge is, and cannot be translated from an experiential to an externalizable form. In simple denotation, the emphasis is more on indicating and reacting than on conveying meaning.

Primary identification and organization of classes

As thinking progresses from the level of primary aggregation and becomes more and more organized, it eventually reaches that order of organization which is called logic or Aristotelian logic. I have given the name *paleologic* (which etymologically means ancient or archaic logic) to the stage which precedes the Aristotelian (Arieti, 1948, 1955). Although paleologic cognition is illogical according to Aristotelian standards, it is not haphazard or senseless. It can be interpreted as following special laws of organization, or a "logic" of its own. This organization consists of connections between different elements which eventually lead to the formation of "classes." Classes are divisions and groupings of ideas which facilitate the response of the individual. In fact, the individual will tend to respond in the same way to each element of the class. Class formation is thus a parsimonious device.

At this level of organization, the individual tends to register identical segments of experience and to build a conceptual organization based upon the identical segments. We find many residues of this type of organization in primitive societies. Lévy-Bruhl, reported by Werner, writes: "A Congo native says to a European: 'During the day you drank palm wine with a man, unaware that in him there was an evil spirit. In the evening you heard a crocodile devouring some poor fellow. A wildcat, during the night, ate up all your chickens. Now, the man with whom you drank, the crocodile who ate a man and the wildcat are all one and the same person.'" Obviously a common characteristic or predicate (having an evil spirit) led to the identification. Werner rightly states that "this kind of interpretation is rooted in an altogether different mental pattern, a differently constituted faculty of conception, from that exhibited by the scientifically thinking man." He adds that this primitive mode of thinking is neither illogical nor prelogical; it is logical in a different sense. In my view, the logical process is arrested at a stage where a common characteristic (in the quoted example, having an evil spirit) leads to the identification of different subjects. The different subjects (the man, the crocodile, and the wildcat) become equivalent. The total identification leads to the same response: to keep away from the man, from the crocodile, and from the wildcat.

From many examples reported in Werner's book, we learn that young children too have the propensity to identify objects which have elements in common. Levin has also made these observations in children (1938). For instance, he reports that a child 25 months old was calling anything which was made of white rubber a *wheel*—as, for example, the white rubber guard which is supplied with little boys' toilet seats to deflect urine. The child knew the meaning of the word *wheel* as applied to the wheel of a toy car, and he had many toy cars whose wheels, when made of rubber, were always of white rubber. Thus he came to think that the word *wheel* included not only wheels but also anything made of white rubber. His mental organization could not go beyond a stage where an identification had occurred because of the same characteristic, "white rubber."

In the writer's experience, children have a special propensity to indulge in paleologic thinking from age 1½ to age 3½ or even 4. There is a great variation, however, in the amount of paleologic thinking from child to child. Some children around 2 years of age will quite often say "Daddy" if shown a picture of a man and will say "Mommy" if shown a picture of a woman, no matter whom the pictures represent. A girl 3 years and 9 months old saw two nuns walking together, and told her mother, "Look at the twins!" The characteristic of being dressed alike, which twins often have, led to the identification with the nuns.

This does not imply that children or people belonging to some societies must necessarily think paleologically. Only very young children are incapable of full conceptual thinking. Slightly older children, still of preschool age, tend to think paleologically when inability to evaluate all the elements, or strong wishes toward certain conclusions, or lack of familiarity with other important notions does not permit them to reach higher levels of thinking.

The confusion occurring in paleologic thinking between similarity and identity can be stated as a principle which was first enunciated in a slightly different way by Von Domarus: "Whereas in mature (or secondary process) thinking identity is accepted only upon the basis of identical subjects, in paleologic (or primary process) thinking identity is accepted upon the basis of identical predicates" (1944). The predicate which leads to the identification is called the identifying link or identifying predicate.[11]

This type of thinking is of very short duration in normal ontogenetic development. It reacquires predominance in certain situations: in the mental processes which accompany prejudices, in crowd thinking, in some creative processes, or wherever emotions prevail over the normal progression of thinking.

Instances from psychopathology which occur when the microgenetic development is arrested at the paleologic level disclose typical characteristics. For instance, to the question "What city is the capital of France?" patients with organic

[11] At this level identity cannot be based upon identical subjects, because logical "subjects" are in reality only concepts, and clear concepts have not yet been formed. Clear concepts must include *all essential predicates* (see Chapter 8). "Subjects," however, may have a clear-cut denotational or verbal identity, even when they do not have a conceptual one. Preconceptual confusions may lead to denotational confusions (as in the case of the nuns called twins) and at times even to perceptual confusions.

impairments and also some regressed schizophrenic patients give such replies as "London." Although the answer is incorrect, it is not haphazard; obviously the patient has constructed the category of "capitals" or "European capitals." But the thought is arrested at this level, before all the capitals are microgenetically scanned and the right one selected. An organic patient reported by Linn (1954) called her wheelchair a "chaise longue." Hughlings Jackson was one of the first authors to report similar examples in aphasics (1932a).

The paleologic mode of thinking can be interpreted with formulations which apparently differ from Von Domarus' principle, but which actually infer the same mechanisms. We can say that at the paleologic level special classes are formed. I shall call these classes primary classes, because they belong typically to what Freud called the primary process. I shall call secondary classes those that belong to the Aristotelian level of thinking, which corresponds approximately to Freud's secondary process.

As we shall see in Chapter 8, a *secondary class* is a collection of objects to which a concept applies. For instance, Washington, Jefferson, Lincoln, Roosevelt, Truman, et al., form a class of objects to which the concept "President of the United States" applies. A *primary class* is a collection of objects which have a predicate or part in common (for instance, possessing an evil spirit), and which, by virtue of this common part, become identified or equivalent. Whereas the members of a secondary class are recognized as being similar (and it is actually on their similarity that their classification is based), the members of a primary class are freely interchanged. Not only are they all equivalent, but one of them may become equivalent to the whole class. To recapitulate: Whereas a secondary class is characterized by the recognized similarities of the members, by the concept of a whole, by the possible abstraction of an essential predicate, and by the separation of the subject from all predicates whether essential or nonessential, all these properties are lacking in a primary class.

It is not too difficult to understand some characteristics of primary classes. For example, the common element (the part or predicate) is dominant because it is the only element to which the organism readily responds. All the rest is not intensely experienced or reacted to. Maybe it is the organism's propensity to respond to a part that makes different subjects cling together and form a primary class. In some cases, if the response is delayed, the individual may recognize that the class is primary and proceed to the formation of a secondary class. A primary class may be also a secondary class, or vice versa. For instance, "London, Paris, Rome," etc., usually form a secondary class, but when the patient interchanges the members (say, Paris with London, as in the example given above), then they constitute a primary class.

At this point it is possible to see a parallel between part perception, as described in Chapter 4, and the formation of primary classes. It is also possible to see a similar parallel between whole perception and the formation of secondary classes. It seems that at the levels both of perception and of thinking, the human mind operates by the two forms of generalization discussed in Chapter 4. What in primary generalization is the releasing element corresponds to what in paleologic thinking is the identifying predicate.

Von Domarus' principle and the similar principle of the formation of primary classes are also typical of cognition in dreams. Symbolic thinking, as Freud described it in *The Interpretation of Dreams,* may be seen as expressing the paleologic level of cognition. The Freudian symbol is not only something that stands for something else, but also something that has at least a common characteristic (predicate) with the thing it symbolizes. A person may dream that a king is talking to him. Analysis of the dream will reveal that the king stands for the dreamer's father. Here it is the similarity of the cognitive content (person in authority) that leads to the identification of father with king. After this paleologic identification has taken place at the level of thinking, the thought itself is perceptualized and a visual image of a king appears.[12]

[12] A similar mechanism operates in hallucinations (Chapter 16).

Teleologic causality

We have seen that the phantasmic world, which was described in Chapter 5, is acausal. Occurrences of things and events are accepted without the individual being able to ask "Why?" This is no longer so when man is endowed with language.

The person who thinks exclusively paleologically can ask himself why certain things happen; but the answer he gives is always an anthropomorphic or personal one. He thinks of all events as being determined by the will of men or by anthropomorphized forces. In other words, he explains them in terms of teleologic causality.

Teleologic causality is valid in many instances. It is the explanation many historians give to certain social events, and psychologists and novelists to personal occurrences. For example: This man drinks *because* he wants to quench his thirst; I read this book because I want to learn Spanish; Caesar went into politics because he wanted to satisfy his ambition. All these "becauses" mean "for the purpose of." The purpose is carried out by a will. Ancient people, however, resorted to this type of explanation even when it would seem to us unwarranted. If it is not human will, it is divine will which has caused an event. Apollo, god of the sun, is tired and goes to sleep; that's why night occurs. You are sick because your enemy wants you to become sick. Mythology is to a large extent an attempt to interpret nature in accordance with teleologic, not physical, causality. Trees, rivers, lakes, seas are anthropomorphized. Epidemics and droughts are the result of the anger of personal gods.

The concept of teleologic causality becomes confused with the concept of responsibility, as we shall see in more detail in Chapter 12. Examples of this type of causality are commonly seen in children, irrespective of the culture in which they have been raised. For instance, if a child bumps into a chair and hurts himself, he wants to hit the chair because it has inflicted pain on him. He sees the chair as responsible for being hard and for having inflicted pain. In two important books, Piaget (1929, 1930) describes teleologic causality in children. He calls this cognitive function "precausal think-ing" and attributes it to "egocentrism." [13]

It seems reasonable to suppose that the young child moves from acausality into teleologic causality by the agency of in-terpersonal relations. Before the surrounding human beings assume symbolic importance, the child's life is almost en-tirely governed by reflexes, conditioned and unconditioned, and by autonomous mechanisms. He takes simple associ-ations for granted: hunger, for instance, is followed by the appearance of the mother's breast. Events seem to occur just by temporal or spatial contiguity, in a sort of natural se-quence.

Somewhat later, but still before the child has acquired the ability to speak, he can already sense some kind of vague intentionality in the surrounding adults. For instance, he un-derstands in a primitive way that it is up to Mother to feed him, to keep him on her lap, to fondle him. Through imag-ery, he can even expect these things to happen and anticipate them. However, this vague intentionality cannot be ab-stracted or conceived as a causal factor or as an act of will, until the child can use words to represent people and actions and to detach them from the total situation in which he finds himself. When he acquires a rudimentary language, he learns to interpret everything in a teleologic way—every-thing depends on the will or actions of others. The child

[13] Piaget divides this precausal thinking into different stages. The first is phenomenism: just a naïve connection between phenomena which are con-tiguous in space or in time, or between facts which bear resemblance or relation. It corresponds to my "acausality." Four following stages (finalism, artificialism, animism, and dynamism) represent different degrees of tele-ological or volitional causality. For details, the reader is referred to the original works of Piaget, and to the recent book by Laurendeau and Pinard (1962). Laurendeau and Pinard discuss the criticisms to which Piaget's works have been subjected and reaffirm the validity of his conceptions.

In the child, this precausal thinking is gradually replaced by physicalistic interpretations of the world. Accession to a higher level presupposes a partial withdrawal from the preceding level, but transitional stages and overlap occur. The impact of school, culture, and environment in general helps the child to proceed to higher levels.

Piaget, Laurendeau, and Pinard imply that precausal thinking is the expression of a level of maturity or immaturity of the child. Immaturity can explain why higher levels are not accessible to the child, but cannot explain how he proceeds from phenomenism to animism, from *acausal* to *causal* connection, from seeing an association between A and B to thinking that A *wills* B.

makes a generalization and comes to conceive everything in nature as consequence of a will. In some instances it will be very difficult to relinquish such a belief later. However, school and life in general in a civilized world will help the child to proceed to another order of causality; and in most cases the transition will be rapid because the child is offered, ready made, new concepts and systems of symbolism with which it will be relatively easy to grasp new concepts of causality. Here too, as in the acquisition of language, we find that high levels of cognition cannot occur without concomitant interpersonal processes.

We could postulate similar occurrences in phylogenetic development. Presapiens humans who did not develop beyond the level of images certainly expected things or events to occur, but they could not yet attribute teleologic causality or personal responsibility to others. They became able to do so when they developed the function of language. Later in phylogeny, it was equally difficult to acquire the concept that not all causality is teleologic. Eventually, however, teleologic causality was recognized as playing only a small role in the cosmos known to man (see Chapter 8).

Third-order emotions

When man reaches the level of primitive language and paleologic cognition, evolutionary changes occur in emotional life too. The protoemotions and simple emotions described in previous chapters continue to be experienced in their original forms, but they exist side by side with some transformations imparted by the new forms of cognition. They become more and more involved with language processes and long-circuited mechanisms. For instance, anxiety and wish are no longer determined exclusively by images or by external stimuli accompanied by images, but also by simple words. Such words as "Fire!" or "The enemy is here," may elicit a gamut of second- and first-order emotions.

In third-order emotions, language plays a greater role. The temporal representation is enlarged in the direction both of the past and of the future: both become more significantly present. We shall now take into consideration some of the specific emotions which occur at this level. Some of them— depression and love, for example—already existed in rudimentary form at the level of images, but they attain great development at the third-order stage.

DEPRESSION

Depression has been the object of more psychiatric attention and research than any other emotion except anxiety. Indeed, before the psychoanalytic era it received even more consideration by psychiatrists than anxiety.

As a subjective experience, depression is difficult to define or even describe. It is a pervading feeling of unpleasantness, often accompanied by bodily symptoms such as numbness, paresthesias of the skin, changes in the muscular tone, and decreases in respiration, pulsation, and perspiration. The head of a depressed person has a tendency to bend, the legs to flex, the trunk to be tilted forward. In severe depression the face has a special expression, with more wrinkles than usual and slightly swollen eyelids. Movements and thoughts are retarded, and the person has a general feeling of weakness. Contrary to what happens in anxiety, in depression there is no feeling that a dangerous situation is going to occur. The dangerous event has already taken place; the loss has been sustained.

It is thus evident that depression is consequent to cognitive processes, such as evaluations and appraisals which require verbal expressions. For example, a person is told of the sudden death of a friend. He evaluates the news. He promptly understands what it means to his dead friend— and to him too, as the survivor, who will be deprived of the friend's company. All these processes would not be possible without language. Linguistic forms evoke surprise, evaluation, and an unpleasant feeling called sadness or depression. This feeling tends to linger.

Although it appears to serve no purpose, depression, like anxiety, has survival value. Like other unpleasant sensations and emotions, it preserves life inasmuch as it stimulates the person to nonacceptance of this emotion—that is, to its removal.

How can depression be removed? Let us take again the person saddened by the death of someone close to him. For a few days all thoughts connected with the departed person will bring about a painful, almost unbearable feeling. Any group of thoughts even remotely related to that person will elicit depression. The survivor cannot adjust to the idea that the deceased does not live anymore. But since the deceased was so important to him, many of the survivor's thoughts or actions are directly or indirectly connected with the deceased and therefore elicit an unpleasant reaction.

Nevertheless, after a certain period of time, the survivor becomes adjusted to the idea that the deceased is no longer present. The unpleasant, unacceptable sadness is removed because it has forced the person to reorganize his thinking, to group his thoughts into different constellations, to search for new directions. He especially needed to rearrange the ideas which were connected with the departed. This rearrangement can be carried out in several ways, according to the person's mental predisposition: he may no longer consider the deceased indispensable; he may associate the image of the dead person mainly with the qualities of that person which elicited pleasure, so that the image no longer brings mental pain; or he may think of the deceased's life as not really ended, but as being continued either in a different world or in this world, through the lasting effects of the deceased's actions. Whatever the ideational rearrangement, there is no moving away from a physical source of discomfort, as in pain, or from the source of threat, as in anxiety. The moving away is only from depressive thoughts. When this process fails, another slightly less normal mechanism occurs. The depression, rather than forcing a reorganization of ideas, slows the thought processes which bring about mental pain.

Depression is neither a centrifugal nor centripetal emotion, but reflexive. It may be represented by the following symbols: $ULp \odot <$.

HATE

Hate is so closely related to rage and anger that perhaps they might all be grouped together under the common head-ing "hostility." There are gradations, however, between these three feelings. Rage impels the organism toward immediate motor discharge which aims at destroying or impairing the external source of the emotion. Anger, although not tending toward such immediate discharge, is still impelling and, in accordance with the subject's level of development, manifests itself in gestures, sounds, or verbal expressions. Hate lasts longer; it has the tendency to become almost a chronic emotional state, which is sustained by special thoughts. Although hate too eventually aims at some motor actions, a feedback mechanism is established between the sustaining thoughts and this emotion. Hate leads to calculated action, and at times to premeditated crimes.

At first it would seem that hate possesses only a negative quality, but actually it has a great deal of survival value. In primitive societies men learned that other human beings could be harmful if they were enemies of the tribe. When the enemies were present, the tribe confronted them with rage and anger. However, a negative feeling toward them had to be sustained even when they were absent, so that the tribe could maintain vigilance and a destructive propensity necessary for future defense. Hate thus enables people to cope with the enemy by long-delayed actions. It is a lasting, unpleasant, centrifugal, and potentially progressive emotion. It may be represented by the symbols $ULP \rightarrow\, <$.

Unfortunately, hate exists in modern societies too. It is artificially kept alive and nourished by well-organized hostile propaganda for the purpose of facilitating the destruction of adversaries and the acquisition of power. Furthermore, the complexities of living together at a human level engender hate directed not only toward recognized enemies, but often toward people who live in our immediate environment and even members of our own family. Since hate is supposed to be reserved for "enemies," conflictful situations emerge which arouse other unpleasant emotions, such as anxiety and tension.

LOVE

At least since the beginning of historic times, love has been the most celebrated of all emotions; yet even today it is one of the least understood. The wealth of artistic and literary works that deal with love contrasts with the scarcity of pertinent psychological studies. The few which have been reported are so influenced by art, literature, philosophy, and ethics as to give the impression that these are better approaches to an understanding of this feeling than a scientific methodology.

Few people except inveterate cynics would deny the reality of love's existence. And if this affect exists, we must believe that sooner or later psychologists will develop ways of studying it.[14]

With the word *love* people generally refer to a very intense and pleasant emotion experienced toward persons and, less frequently, toward groups, institutions, or ideals. Love may be felt for anything on which our happiness depends. Although springing originally from physical needs (for food and shelter in familial love, for sexual gratification in erotic love, for physical and mutual protection in neighborly love) it transcends the original need: it becomes a need in itself. You do not love the person you need, but you need him because you love him. Thus love enhances survival of the species, because a person wishes to protect his love object. As in many other cases in evolution, however, what starts as a means to an end becomes an end in itself and expands in unpredictable directions and to unpredictable proportions. Mature love is not based on physical dependency, but feeds, so to say, on itself and on the love exchanged with the loved person.

As mentioned in Chapter 5, love does not require the presence of the loved object to be experienced. The image, the

[14] Some difficulties connected with the study of love are semantic. In some languages—for instance, English and French—the verb *to love* (*aimer*) is often used indiscriminately for the verb *to like:* for instance, "I love ice cream." In other languages—for instance, Italian—the verb *to love* (*amare*) has such strong emotional associations as to allow a very sparing use of it. Italian parents generally do not use this word in reference to their children, and even lovers use it only in the acme of their passion.

thought, and the verbal symbol of the loved object are pleasant in themselves. Nevertheless, they motivate the lover to search for the loved object. Proximity, or a sense of participation, belonging, and unity with the loved object, seems to represent the crux of love and to be the condition necessary for experiencing this emotion intensely.

Mature love is at the same time centrifugal, centripetal, and reflexive: centrifugal in that it is experienced as directed toward the love object; centripetal in that it is reciprocated from the loved object; reflexive in that it is experienced as something which remains in the individual himself. Love may be represented by the symbols $PLp\rightleftharpoons<$.

JOY

Another emotion which is difficult to study is joy, not only because of its rare occurrence but also because it is not part of psychopathology. The euphoria and the elated excitement of the manic patient or of the expansive general paretic are hardly more than a bizarre caricature of joy.

Joy has agreeable antecedents and is accompanied by a pleasant anticipation of the future. Extended cognitive elements are thus prerequisites to joy. Whereas in depression the antecedent consists of the knowledge that something adverse has happened and that the sustained loss is not going to be made up, in joy the antecedent consists of the knowledge that something good has happened and that its pleasant effects extend from the present into the future.

Joy is experienced as a feeling of well-being; it seems to flood the body, not to be directed toward something or away from something else. It is a reflexive emotion. Tasks no longer appear burdensome; the individual feels adequate and capable, without necessarily experiencing feelings of pride and power. His initiative, mobility, and thinking are increased and facilitated, but are not uncoordinated. Joy is a potentially lasting emotion, and contrary to security, it is not self-contained but can expand. It may be represented by the symbols $PLp\ominus<$.

The paleologic world

Whereas the phantasmic world is mainly visual and is populated by images and ghosts, the paleologic world is predominantly auditory. Language makes its entrance at this point, expanding man's inner reality beyond comparison. The acquisition of language, at the denotative stage, increases his understanding of the external world, inasmuch as it gives definite labels to things and makes communication and consensual validation possible. It also permits sequences of thoughts or associations of ideas to unfold more easily than they could at preverbal levels. Since a verbal representation of a *sequence* of events is now possible, a temporal dimension is added: man acquires his first understanding of the past and the future. Although long periods of time cannot yet be measured exactly, the past and the nonimmediate future emerge as full temporal dimensions.

One might be inclined to think that when man acquired the faculty to denote, he would find it easier to understand reality and to establish a correspondence between external and inner reality. But such is not the case. The newly developed paleologic world is a world of transformation. Things are experienced as undergoing metamorphoses, because they are easily identified with other things when they have one or only a few characteristics in common.

A paleologic ideation brings to a much more advanced degree the mental internalization of external objects—or, in other terms, the creation of inner objects—which had already started at the phantasmic level. Melanie Klein would say that the external objects are incorporated, their mental representation being the equivalent of oral incorporation. Whether we accept this theoretical conception or not, we must recognize that motivation, which in the most primitive stages was directed toward incorporation of external objects, is now partially concerned with internal objects. But these introjected internal objects undergo transformations, and these transformations are projected back to the external objects, so that the latter appear changed too.

These metamorphoses are possible because at the paleologic level, contrary to the phantasmic level, man has the capacity to abstract. He can separate similar data from the manifold of objects and can build up categories or classes of objects. The process of abstraction, however, is far from complete. Either the abstracted part is confused with the whole, or else different wholes to which the similar parts belong are misidentified.

Ontogenetically this type of cognition makes a very rapid appearance in childhood, sometimes being followed so quickly by the next stage that it is almost unnoticeable. The language and thinking of children do reveal traces of it, however. An important consequence of this cognitive stage is that during it, children are likely to make generalizations which follow a primary-class formation and that these generalizations are often retained even much later in life. For instance, the basic attitude that a person has toward women throughout his life may be determined by the experiences he had with his mother during the paleologic stage of early childhood, and by the generalizations he made then. The person forgets the origin of these paleologic generalizations, which psychologists at times refer to as unconscious assumptions.[15]

The organization of the self also becomes more complicated at the paleologic level. The child discovers that his own identity is not only a group of images or feelings but also a name, or the pronoun "I." This discovery, however, does not lead him to an awareness of himself as an enduring and consistent entity. His sense of self undergoes paleologic metamorphoses in accordance with wishes and fears. In unhealthy interpersonal situations, even his sexual identity may be uncertain or unstable.

Phylogenetically, the paleologic world corresponds in many ways to the mythical world of ancient people and to some cultural institutions of various aboriginal societies today. The philosophers Vico (1744) and Cassirer (1955, vol. 2) have given us the best descriptions of the mythical world

---

[15] It is regrettable that after Chapters 5 and 7 have described these primitive worlds, the phantasmic and the paleologic, they do not deal with their populations (the persons of the external and inner reality of the growing person). As mentioned in Chapter 1, however, the topic of interpersonal relations is beyond the scope of this work.

of the ancients, characterized by metamorphoses, equivalence of part and whole, and interchangeability of objects.

Anthropologists have at various times reported that in some aboriginal cultures, paleologic thinking prevails over other types, and that in general it is much more common in primitive societies than in Western cultures. Paleologic thinking seems to be behind many societal or collective manifestations (rituals, magic, customs, and beliefs) that are transmitted from generation to generation and accepted without any inquiry as to their validity (Arieti, 1956a). These findings mean only that some cultures tend to retain paleologic characteristics in some forms of *collective behavior*. In Western societies too, collective manifestations of paleologic thinking can be found, even in our times.[16] In a not too distant past, the Western world too was permeated by paleologic thinking. In his admirably scholarly book, *The Waning of the Middle Ages* (1924), Huizinga clearly described the prevalence of this type of thinking in medieval Europe, although, of course, he did not use the word *paleologic*. Differences in the amount of paleologic thinking in various eras and various countries are due to different *historical*, not *biological*, factors. Even Lévy-Bruhl, one of the most misunderstood authors in this field, referred only to collective manifestations and not to the individual native when he was describing "the prelogical functions" of aboriginal societies (1910).

It could be that some presapiens species of hominids, such as *Homo Erectus*, were obliged by the limitations of their nervous integration to think paleologically. This possibility may explain why they eventually perished. No man living today belongs to a presapiens species, and every existing man who is in a state of health and more than 3 years old is at least potentially capable of thinking in accordance with the Aristotelian laws of thought.

---

[16] Paleologic processes also occur in some habits of Western man, and are much better recognized as such by non-Westerners. For instance, in many Western restaurants waiters are reluctant to serve white wine with meat and red wine with fish. They feel that red wine belongs with meat, white wine with fish. Actually there is no biochemical or other scientific reason for these associations. Meat can taste well with white wine too, and fish with red wine. The association is purely due to a paleological identification with the redness of the meat and the whiteness of the fish.

Thus two important points must be kept in mind: (1) The frequency of paleologic thinking in some human societies neither implies that their individual members are mentally inferior, nor calls into question the moral and spiritual equality of man; (2) the fact that paleologic thinking may have first appeared in some presapiens species and may have remained the preponderant form of thinking for that now-extinct hominid does not mean that people who think or act paleologically are in other respects like presapiens men. Moreover, from a biological point of view a structure or function which has appeared earlier in phylogeny may be of the same evolutionary relevance as one which appeared later. The chronologic order is not necessarily an order of value (Arieti, 1950). Also, as we shall see in Part III, paleologic thinking resumes an important role in that high faculty which is the creative process.

Like other types of cognition, the paleologic mode tends to invade both prior and subsequent levels. In a certain way it gives a structure to the phantasmic and oneiric worlds. Dreams consist of images which transmute in accordance with paleologic cognition. The phantasmic world of the young child, even in the descriptions of Melanie Klein and Fairbairn, would remain almost structureless if it did not follow paleologic modes. Once images become connected with names, they become associated, interchanged, or organized according to paleologic modalities. Similarly, paleologic mechanisms tend to impinge on higher levels, especially when emotions become very strong—for instance, in the experience of prejudice. It is one of the functions of the higher levels to inhibit paleologic forms of thinking.

Paleologic cognition brings major changes in the affective life, in motivation, and in object formation. In fact, verbal representation which is now possible continues and enormously expands the emotional transformation already started at the level of images. An important question is whether ideas can be removed from consciousness at this stage, in accordance with Freud's process of repression. It seems to me that the word *transformation* more accurately describes the phenomenon involved in paleologic mechanisms. Unacceptable reality can be transformed because members of primary classes can be freely interchanged. If this transformation is not sufficient, a regression to endoceptual forms takes place. Positive and negative emotions are the motivational forces behind the mutability of the inner objects: a new attempt is made to move toward what is pleasant and away from what is unpleasant.

We have thus the following paradox: At the paleologic level the individual starts to think categorically or in terms of classes. But these categories are not reliable; being primary classes, they are at the mercy of emotions. The paleologic thinker wants to transcend the particular, but his attempts lead him not to platonic universals but to transmutability.[17] In its extreme forms, this transmutability has two almost opposite effects. First, if the individual believes that things change in accordance with his own wishes, he strengthens and transforms the feeling of omnipotence which had already appeared at earlier levels (Silverberg, 1952). Or second, if the individual believes that things change contrary to his wishes, anxiety increases. If transmutability is not sufficient to bring him emotional relief, the emotion is then attacked directly. We shall study this possibility in Chapter 9.

Primitive man tries to counterbalance the transmutability of the inner reality by again plunging into external reality, this time not by quick sensorimotor reactions, but by collecting and possessing. The volume and plurality of external objects will be the best antidote to the uncertainty of the inner objects, since what is familiar by volume and plurality will be less likely to transmute. Primitive men thus became hoarders and collectors. In addition, collecting food will be useful for future needs, which can be envisioned at the paleologic level. Collecting without immediate consummation also intensifies a sense of distance between the person and the external object and counteracts the last vestiges of adualism.[18] A hoarding period has been described in children, too, at a

[17] Benedetto Croce (1947) wrote that in his conclusions about the studies of ancient people, Vico had changed Plato's universals into "phantastic universals" (corresponding approximately to the contents of our primary classes).

[18] Hoarding habits that occur in some subhuman animals are more primitive instinctual manifestations and should not be confused with paleologic tendencies.

certain level of development. The orthodox Freudian school considers this hoarding a characteristic of the anal stage of libidinal development.

As we shall see in subsequent chapters, paleologic cognition is superseded by higher forms and is relegated to unconscious microgenetic stages, which are followed by more mature and conscious stages. Only in dreams, in periods of greatly diminished attention, in pathologic conditions (such as schizophrenia, aphasias and some forms of psychoneuroses), and in some facets of collective behavior, is conscious thinking arrested at a paleologic level.

8 ° *THE CONCEPT*

After having gone through the intricate stages described in the preceding chapters, cognition reaches the level of the concept. Here, finally, the secondary process prevails.

The word *concept* has two principal meanings. In the first, it signifies a general notion or a highly schematized idea, which embraces all the attributes common to the individual members that make a (secondary) class. For instance, the concept "table" is a notion which applies to all tables. In its second meaning a concept is a symbol for the represented thing. For instance, the word *table* is a symbol for the object *table*.

The concept has been studied much more by philosophers than by psychologists. The most important ideas about it originated in the classic period of Greek philosophy. Aristotle (*Metaphysics*, XIII, 4) and Xenophon (*Mem.*, IV, 6) attribute to Socrates the discovery of the definition of the universal —that is, of the concept of concept. For Plato, ideas or concepts become the ultimate reality. Thomas Aquinas believed that a knowledge is perfect to the extent to which there is a similarity between the concept (or essence) and the thing which is conceived (*Summa contra gentiles,* IV, 11). Many philosophers—in particular, Husserl—refuse to see the concept as a psychological formation. For Husserl, psychological forms are representations or visions of things, whereas the concept is an immutable essence. Traditionally in philosophy, a concept is "the perfect definition," which reveals the immutable essence of the thing.

I shall consider the concept only from a psychological point of view; that is, as a cognitive form and not as the ultimate description of reality. We can in fact differentiate several conceptual substages of unequal value. At times the demarcation between a preconceptual and a conceptual form is not sharp: a concept which appears definitive at a certain stage of development is considered a preconcept later. If it is found that concept does not include all the essential attributes of what it wants to define, it may be recognized as a paleologic or faulty construct.

Concept formation has been studied by many psychologists with different methods. In Hull's classic study, the subjects were requested to discriminate the characteristic common to a certain group of constellations of stimuli and associate with it a specific vocal reaction (1920). In Piaget's early studies, children's conceptualizations were divided into realism, animism, and artificialism (1929, 1930), which correspond to our preconceptual levels. Piaget's later studies of more mature forms of conceptualization are more complicated, but his key conceptions concern grouping and classifying (1957). Bruner and his associates have devised interesting ways of studying the "strategies" by which a concept is attained (1956). A description of all these methods is not given here. Following is a brief summary of the ways in which concepts are formed in natural conditions, not in experimental setups.

In the first method of concept formation, the subject collects data and then recognizes an enduring association between these data. The association is often based on temporal or physical contiguity. All the attributes which need to be together form a concept. For instance, the following attributes—(1) being a figure, (2) formed by three straight lines, (3) which intersect by twos in three points, (4) and form angles—make up the concept of triangle.

People continuously form new concepts from old ones by discovering or adding new attributes. For instance, if we add an additional attribute (that two of the lines be perpendicular) to the attributes of a triangle, we have the concept of a right triangle. Similarly, we may discover that some of the objects included in the class of animals have a vertebral column. We form thus the class "vertebrate," which is a subclass of the class "animal." We may discover that some vertebrates nourish their young with milk, and we form the class "mammal," and so on.

New concepts originate unexpectedly when apparently unrelated objects can be put into a new class by the discovery of a previously hidden attribute or predicate. For instance, the brain and the skin of an organism may seem to be different and unrelated parts until we discover that they have the common quality of originating from the ectoderm. Then we have the concept and class of ectodermic tissue.

New concepts may be developed by a second method which is the opposite of the one just described: The subject realizes that certain attributes can be omitted and that a different class containing only some essential attributes can be formed. For instance, primitive people have names for different types of birds, but not one which designates just bird. More civilized people drop all the attributes which are characteristic only of certain groups of birds and form the concept "bird," which refers to all birds because it includes only the following attributes: (1) vertebrate, (2) warm-blooded, (3) covered by feathers.

The production of a new concept is a difficult process. Concepts represent acquisitions of the human race attained through the ages, collectively adopted and transmitted from generation to generation. Social life imparts a large number of concepts. Formal education in schools expands our conceptual life even more. Learning complex skills consists of learning concepts pertaining to that particular skill in addition to learning specific exocepts.

Concepts have many functions. The main one is related to

what was described in Chapter 4. There we saw that the variety of biological reactions is much more limited than the variety of stimuli. Thus it is necessary to respond to groups of stimuli in the same way. The stimuli which elicit the same response become equivalent. Responses are generalized, and eventually, at the paleologic level, primary classes are formed. The same procedure occurs at the level of concepts. As Mach (1883) wrote, concepts are in a certain way symbols and indicators of the possible reactions of the human organism in front of facts. In other words, man does not necessarily respond to things or facts but to concepts. A concept is a parsimonious device, inasmuch as it permits man to respond in similar ways to various facts which are under the same group. A concept is also a parsimonious measure because with it we do not need to know all the facts in a situation in order to respond. For instance, if we know that Socrates is a man, we also know that he will eventually die, although we may not actually witness his death. If a physician knows that a patient has diabetes, he also knows that if the patient eats more than a small quantity of carbohydrates, his glucose rate will increase in his urine and blood. In addition, the doctor can deduce that there is something wrong with the pancreas of the patient, and he may prescribe insulin.

In summary, the concept is a parsimonious device because (1) it offers us a more or less complete description, (2) it permits us to organize, since the different attributes or parts appear logically interconnected, (3) it permits us to predict, because we can deduce what is going to happen to any member of the class covered by the concept. With time concepts become more and more organized into higher mental constructs. The enormous importance of concepts in human life will be discussed in the last section of this chapter.

The concept as a symbol

The development of concepts is more or less parallel to the development of language. At a conceptual level, a word does not stand only for the external object but for the concept of the object. It seems almost as if meanings become more detached from their corresponding external objects and almost fused with the words which represent the objects. For instance, the word *mother* does not represent only my mother or my children's mother but the concept of mother—of the female parent.

Words and concepts have been divided into many categories. Recently Werner and Kaplan have accurately and painstakingly illustrated symbol formation from the early to the latest developmental stages (1963).

What follows is this writer's classification of different conceptual stages. As far as the early stages are concerned, I have been partially influenced by Werner. This classification does not represent a necessary sequence of steps or stages in the developmental history of individual concepts, but it does reflect what occurs in the majority of cases. Some concepts skip some stages; others remain indefinitely at one stage; finally, some return to a less advanced stage. In numerous instances several stages overlap.

If the word transcends the denotative stage and tends to recapture endoceptual qualities (which now can be expressed orally), we have the level that Werner has called holophrastic. Such a word represents a somewhat fuzzy, foggy, motor-affective syncretic experience. I call this stage of conceptual development the holophrastic stage, and as a mnemonic device, I call the words belonging to it type F words.

At a slightly more advanced level is what Werner called the expressive stage (type E). At this stage the concept is anthropomorphized. The emphasis is no longer on the motor-affective experience, but on the fact that the object, enriched or animated by the concept, stirs the knower. In this type of conceptualization the projection is obvious. Some authors refer to this stage as animistic. It is important to remember that even in modern languages many words have remained at the holophrastic and the expressive levels. They are words that represent feelings or subjective states in general.

Next, the word may reach a stage of conceptual development which has a predominantly descriptive character (type D). The word is a symbol for those attributes which, by being together, constitute the referent. For instance, the word *cave* describes a hollow place inside the earth.

At the following stage (type C), a word does not merely describe the characteristics of a thing but also indicates a certain relation either between it and other concepts, or between the different parts of the referent itself. For instance, the word *uncle* does not just denote a person. It refers to a relation; uncle is the brother of one of the parents. There is thus little possibility of error about the meaning of the word. In the definition of *triangle* given in the previous section, the attributes must be in a certain relation: the three straight lines must intersect by twos at three points.

Needless to say, scientists would like to use only type C words—relational words. They convey the ideas that Descartes called clear and distinct. It is only with type C words that the concept acquires a distinct form which makes us recognize a definite relation between whole and part. In medical practice, we evolve from type D to type C when an illness is no longer seen merely as a collection of symptoms, but as a logical relation of facts.

Let us remember, however, that even type C words, such as *mother* and *uncle,* carry an extra connotational load. Not only a specific mother, but the word *mother* in general stands for more than the woman who gives birth to a child. As a rule she is the woman who loves the child, nurses the child, and takes care of him. These attributes do not enter into the definition because they are not necessary ingredients; but they are generally present, and if I think of a mother, I think of them. For instance, I may even find out that the mother of a friend of mine is not his biological mother but only an adoptive mother. Although she does not possess the necessary ingredients of the definition *mother,* she is still his mother for me—and, what is more important, for my friend too. This extra load of meaning at times confers a remnant of holophrastic or even endoceptual qualities to type C words. It can lead to confusion and mistakes even in the use of these generally clear-cut words.

In scientific terminologies, it is advantageous to eliminate accessory meanings from the words used. Do words exist that are completely free of additional connotations? Yes—numbers, for instance, and mathematical concepts and symbols in general.[1] I shall classify these as type A words. Numbers as symbols carry only their numerical attributes, which are all implied or grounded in the definition of each number. The connotational import of type A words, however, is not so simple and clear as it would seem at first. Although seemingly naked of accessory meaning, on closer examination these words imply other properties which are not apparent in the original meaning. As a matter of fact, the aim of mathematics and geometry is the discovery of these properties which are grounded but not apparent in the original definition. For instance, we may define 3 as the successor of 2. Such a definition does not tell us, although it implies, that 3 is a divisor of 2,151. In the definition of a triangle, it is not apparent that the sum of the angles of any triangle is 180 degrees. It is often impossible to determine which hidden attributes can eventually be discovered in some of these A concepts.

In this description of word types we have jumped from C to A because of a certain continuity between the C and A types of symbolism. Actually there is another large group of symbols which may be included under type B: basal. They are mostly abstract words, but not abstract in the same manner as those of type A. They generally connote a concept which, although conceived at a high level of development, may expand into many directions in search of a clearer and more definite meaning (of the A type or even the C type). Such words as love, sympathy, personality, character, popularity, justice, and surprise belong to this group. Many of these words have connections with endocepts, primary aggregations, or holophrastic words. Their connotation is vague and diffused. They signify a global or large appreciation of experiences which are related to great segments of the external world and of our inner selves.

If a type B word is connected with endoceptual precursors, it is rich in affective content. If it derives from a primary aggregation, it oscillates between a vague and general

[1] Of course, special accessory meanings can be given to numbers too by magical, obsessive-compulsive, and ritualistic practices. These special cases are not considered here.

meaning and a fragment of this meaning. In religion, philosophy, and art there is often a confusion between a holophrastic and a basal concept. At times the undefinable concept is reduced to a concrete essence of type D; for instance to a personalized god or a piece of sculpture. At other times some B words eventually reach the level of type A, or turn all the way back to types E and F. B words, however, require a power of abstraction which is not possessed by endocepts, holophrastic words, or even D words. They do not possess a potentially infinite implication, as the words of type A do, but have what might be thought of as an open end, with possibilities of ramification in many ways. On the other hand, most times (though not all) these words cannot be operationally verified. That is why many people—semanticists, scientists, and some philosophers—are vehement against the B type.

I myself do not share this antagonism toward B words. Although they do have many disadvantages and may be used to deceive people or to encourage unwarranted mysticism, I feel that they have an important role at a certain stage of cultural development. Often men are not ready for a type A definition. Something has to be used at least as a temporary way to convey the unclear meaning. Furthermore, some of these concepts, although remaining slightly indefinite, undergo a gradual clarification. There is a certain progress, for instance, from the concept of soul to the concept of psyche.

The danger which type B words present is actually that of *reification*—of inducing people to believe in the existence of things as concrete entities, when what we have are only words attached to vague concepts. Reification would not be an evil if we were always aware that the concept exists in man's inner reality. The danger exists when these entities of inner reality are confused with external things or relations, in a form of sophisticated, or high-level, dualism (see Chapter 5). Type B words which are susceptible to reification are common in psychology, especially in psychiatry and psychoanalysis. Examples are personality, character, relatedness, sentiment, etc. These are words which, as Bertrand Russell would say, we know by acquaintanceship rather than by accurate definition.

Different groups of people, by practice, occupation, or psychological inclination, prefer the use of different types of words. Mathematicians generally favor types C and A; philosophers, B and A; artists, B, E, and F; practical men, C and D. Artists, especially writers, often use type D—to which, however, they attribute a B, E, or F meaning. This use will be more clearly explained in Chapter 21.

Mnemonic Table of the Types of Conceptualization

Type	Characteristics	Meaning
F	Fuzzy, foggy	Close to the endocept; holophrastic
E	Expressive	Anthropomorphic, physiognomic, animistic
D	Descriptive, distinct	Constellation of main or essential attributes or predicates
C	Clear	Connoting a relation of parts
B	Basal, branching	Diffuse, abstract meaning branching in many directions
A	Abstract, arithmetic, algebraic	Connoting a relation devoid of accessory parts, but with many hidden, eventually definable implications

High-level thought processes

We shall take into consideration now some special thought processes that belong to the conceptual level: induction, deduction, deterministic causality, and the conception of the future and the possible. An additional type, arithmetical thinking, will be examined separately in Chapter 10. Although all these topics can be discussed from a purely philosophical or logical point of view, the presentation here will be restricted as much as possible to a psychological frame of reference.

INDUCTION

As conceived by Mill, induction is that type of inference by which we attempt to reach a conclusion concerning all the members of a class from observation of only some of them. "What is true of part is true of the whole class, or what is true at certain times will be true in similar circumstances at all times." In brief, induction consists of the following steps: (1) Facts are experienced as being together or in succession, and some associations are made between them. For instance, night is associated with sunset. (2) A general proposition is derived from propositions about single facts. For instance, to repeat the example given, a person has seen in his lifetime a relatively small number of nights following sunset, and yet he is willing to conclude that night will always follow sunset. He has made comparatively few observations, but he nevertheless jumps from repetition to generalization; he is willing to extend to a hypothetically unlimited series what he has observed from a part of that series. This process is what Reichenbach called induction by enumeration (1951).

It is this apparently unjustifiable generalization that has worried philosophers since Hume. In their view, the observation that B follows A a certain number of times does not warrant the inference that B will always follow A. But although they may be right in an absolute sense, life can exist only on such presuppositions. In the case of the conditioned reflex, for example, if the sight of food is preceded by the ringing of a bell, the ringing bell (A) after a few exposures will make the experimental dog secrete gastric juice (B). This reflex of the dog follows *induction*. The only difference between us, conscious beings, and the dog, is that in us induction is accompanied by awareness, whereas in the dog it is an automatic process.

Thus although it is not logically sound to assume that just because B has followed A several times, B should always follow A, without such an assumption life mechanisms cannot be understood. When we say "assumption" we actually anthropomorphize, since by assumption we mean expectation. Although expectation is a human faculty, perhaps it can be conceived of as a property of life—a certain type of memory and preparation for similar events, which may exist in every protoplasm.

Of course, B may not follow A. In that case life may be extinguished. As an illustration, here is a modified version of one used by Mower (1960a, b): A turkey raiser taught his birds to come and be fed when he made a certain signal. Every day he called them with that signal and they went toward him in a state of readiness for being nourished. One day close to Thanksgiving, however, the farmer repeated the same signal: the turkeys went to him expecting to be fed, but instead he grabbed them, killed them, and took their bodies to market. In this case C, not B, followed the signal A. C brought death, not prolongation of life; the interruption of the A-B association just one time was enough to extinguish the group. This anecdote has to be taken metaphorically for many reasons, the main one being that the will of the farmer and not a biological law was involved. However, in general it illustrates the inductive procedures of life mechanisms.

Although induction may be based on something which cannot be proved philosophically, life depends on it. Only the organism that can perform inductively and transmit this inductive functioning genetically can survive. Not every association to which living forms were exposed became an unconscious induction in phylogeny, but only the small number with high survival value. This fact of selection again shows that the validity of induction, if any exists, is in reference to survival and not to a philosophical absolute. It also implies that some kind of regularity or uniformity of nature exists. The physiology of organisms can be seen as an incorporation of regularities of nature, which has occurred through evolution and as the result of the transmission of survival mechanisms.

Induction as a cognitive process is only the conscious adoption of a mechanism which automatically and unconsciously had already been adopted by the organism. When the individual becomes conscious of what phylogeny had unconsciously introjected, he projects the process back to the external world. This is to say that inductive reasoning reflects at least a partial order, a relative regularity, existing in the universe even prior to the appearance of life. This relative regularity, once incorporated, is the very foundation of our knowledge. Some previous authors, especially Reichenbach (1951), have implied the biological origin of knowledge, but have not individualized the basic mechanisms, such as the emergence in consciousness of the organism's inductive mechanisms.

However, when we say that through induction the organism has incorporated some order of the universe, we do not mean that it reflects the whole order, nor an absolute reality. The organism is equipped to live in what, following Čapek (1957), we can call the mesocosm. The organism may reflect only the laws of the mesocosm and therefore becomes adjusted only to mesocosmic reality. The mesocosm is the world of the Euclidian-Newtonian-Kantian tradition: it does not include the macrocosm of Einstein, or the microcosm of Heisenberg. We shall return to this important topic in Chapter 11.

DEDUCTION

The deductive method, on which a great deal of our secondary-process thinking depends, is more difficult to understand than the inductive. In deduction we proceed from the general to the particular: If it is true that all men are mortal, then Socrates, being a man, is mortal.

In order to conclude that Socrates is mortal, the individual must accept two premises: (1) that all men are mortal; (2) that Socrates is a man. That Socrates is a man he can easily verify. That all men are mortal he will never be able to verify, but he assumes that the premise is true because he has accepted an *inductive inference* as true. He has seen several men die and has heard or read that previous men, who lived in the past, died. A human being cannot see all men dying in all ages, but he accepts as a truth the ineluctability of human death. That is, particular experiences, direct or indirect, are inductively applied to the whole series of man. Then what is true of the whole series is in turn applied to the particular case of each man; for instance, Socrates.

In traditional logic, the two propositions above are graphically illustrated with the Euler method: a big circle (big premise) contains a small circle (small premise).

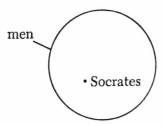

Since the big circle contains all mortals, it will contain Socrates too. This method is useful in the frame of reference of traditional logic. However, the psychological process which leads to logical deduction is of a different nature and cannot be represented by such a drawing.

Let us examine again the sentence, All men are mortal. "All men" is actually a symbol, like an algebraic symbol, standing for a number. Like an algebraic symbol, it may stand for any number (a small number when man first appeared on earth, a large number now); but it must be the number which includes all men. Inasmuch as we use the words "all men" as an algebraic symbol, the deduction is already grounded in the symbol. However, at first we do not conceive the expression "all men" as an algebraic symbol, but as a symbol standing for all the subjects involved in an inductive series. If with the symbol $M{\rightarrow}D$ we mean an observation that a man (M) eventually reached death (D), then we may represent an inductive series in the following way:

$$M \longrightarrow D$$
$$M^1 \longrightarrow D^1$$
$$M^2 \longrightarrow D^2$$
$$M^3 \longrightarrow D^3$$
$$- \ - \ - \ -$$
$$- \ - \ - \ -$$
$$- \ - \ - \ -$$
$$M^s \longrightarrow D^s$$

The symbol M^s stands for the man Socrates, and D^s stands for the death of Socrates. $M^s{\rightarrow}D^s$ is another instance of the inductive series.

Thus we have actually followed the inductive method again. However, it seems to us as if a new method has emerged, because we have partially replaced the inductive series with the symbol "all men." The symbol "all men" assumes that an *indefinite* number, actually *impossible to verify*, is really *definite* and *known*, at least in some aspects. This is the same unjustifiable generalization which philosophers object to in inductive reasoning. The subject of the first premise is a symbol or an algebraic sign for a whole class. Any concept is in a certain way an algebraic symbol of a class, because it includes the whole class, irrespective of the actual number of the members of the class. The concept *table* includes *all tables,* whether there are only a few or millions.

Within the limitations of the world known to us, the inductive assumption is pragmatically valid. We can repeat here what we have said about induction and state that a deductive procedure is followed unconsciously by the functioning organism. Only organisms which can operate in this way can survive. For instance, all bacteria coli produce an antibody reaction in the human organism. In a given case a particular strain of bacteria coli invades the organism: the organism will then produce antibody defenses and will survive. Immunity is based on the capacity of the organism to incorporate a deductive procedure. The difference between the organism and the psyche is that the psyche is able to subjectivize; that is, to become aware of the mechanism. Actually, the organism has incorporated only the inductive method, which implies a certain regularity of nature. But for an organism not provided with consciousness there is no difference between induction and deduction.

In other words, there is no difference between (1) behaving or functioning as if a series will unfold regularly as in the past, and (2) assuming that the whole series is already there, at least in a state of potentiality, and that each case is a present example of it. The difference between (1) and (2) becomes significant only when man reaches the level of conceptual cognition. If d^1 is a member of the class D, it will "behave" as is implied in the concept D. There is really no difference between concept formation and deduction. Both are the results of preliminary inductive methods. Deduction is a new unfolding of the inductive premise. Both induction and deduction require concept formation. In deduction, however, the concept is at a more advanced stage of evolution: it includes the potentialities of the whole class, as an established fact, and then applies to the single member what is true of the class.

DETERMINISTIC CAUSALITY

Deterministic causality, or the search for and finding of an antecedent cause of an effect, is another important secondary-process mechanism. It should not be confused with induction or deduction. Philosophers rightly point out that to associate A and B does not necessarily imply that A is the cause of B or that B is the effect of A. The concept of causality requires not only the implication that there is an association between A and B, but also the institution by A of a mechanism which brings B about. For instance, the phenomenon on whose account night (B) follows sunset (A) is not merely an association of temporal contiguity. The sunset implies a change in the position of the earth with respect to the sun, so that the rays of the sun soon will not reach a given part of the earth, which will then be in a state of darkness.

Such reasoning would not satisfy some philosophers, who with some justification would say that with this explanation we have enlarged the number of associations, not explained causality. However, for our purpose here I shall state at this point that the concept of causality implies that A not only associates with B, but does something to bring B about. Notice that in using the expression "does something," I have anthropomorphized A.

We saw in Chapter 7 that causality, as a psychological notion, originates as teleologic causality; that is, as a personification or interpretation of acts of will as causes of events. For instance, I drink *because* I want to quench my thirst. The "because" of teleologic causality means "for the purpose of." It refers to an action brought about by a wish or a will. The river runs because it wants to satisfy its wish or tendency to run.

At the conceptual level the phenomena which, by a generalization of early interpersonal experiences, had been anthropomorphized, are depersonalized again. Wish and will are disconnected from causality. The "because" of deterministic causality means "on account of." For instance, the water became ice because (on account of the fact that) the temperature was below 32 degrees. It is surprising how seldom, even in such high cultures as those of the Hebrews, Greeks, and Romans, deterministic causality has been recognized. Undoubtedly some individual persons were able to see causal deterministic connections, but the culture as a whole was not permeated by such a concept. Just as the two causalities overlap in some stages of child development, first with a preponderance of teleologic causality and then of deterministic causality, so in some period of history we find a preponderance of teleologic thinking gradually changing into a preponderance of deterministic thinking. It is only at the time of the Renaissance, after Bacon, Kepler, and especially Galileo, that deterministic causality became dominant.

Thus deterministic causality, which seems so evident as to have been classified by Kant as one of the a priori categories, has only recently been recognized as a concept. People undoubtedly lived as if they knew of its existence, but they did not have a clear and distinct idea of it. Even in Aristotle's philosophy, deterministic causality played a dubious role.[2] It is often said that although the mainstream of science developed much later than the Greeks, they laid its foundations. This statement is correct, but mainly because of Greek discoveries in the fields of logic and mathematics, particularly geometry. Geometry is based on deduction, not on deterministic causation.

How is the transformation from teleologic to deterministic causality possible phylogenetically? Probably in a gradual process which took thousands of years man became aware that inanimate objects have a group of distinct characteristics to which the notion of volition, and consequently of responsibility, is hardly applicable. He recognized that objects

[2] Although Aristotle divided causation into four parts, (1) the material cause, (2) the formal cause, (3) the efficient cause, and (4) the end or final cause, the end (*entelechia*) was the predominant part.

are things which are moved, rather than being movers. In man's conception, the last things in the physical world which lost will and responsibility were moving things—rivers, brooks, seas, winds, lakes, storms, etc. At the levels of endocepts and holophrastic and expressionistic concepts, things retain their teleologic qualities, at least partially. They are at least things-of-action and disturbers of the organism. Eventually the object is transformed into an *it*. Such a process of "itification" may become exaggerated—as, for instance, in some neurotics who go to the extent of dehumanizing persons (Arieti, 1957a). Some scientists too believe that the concept of free will and consequently of responsibility is not applicable to human actions.

If we recognize A as an it, we will eventually understand that it is not A's *intention* to bring about B. This understanding will remove teleologic causality from our thinking, but might bring about a return to that form of understanding which is based on naïve precausal association. This form of interpretation was typical of the phantasmic world (Chapter 5). A return to naïve associationism has been contemplated by philosophers as a desirable possibility. Hume and Kant, for example, have tried to determine with philosophical arguments whether we are really justified in seeing more than precausal association in causality.

It is beyond the purpose of this chapter to discuss the validity of the concept of deterministic causality in a philosophical sense. When we study the evolution of deterministic causality as a psychological mechanism, we find that after teleologic concepts are removed from the A-B association there is no going back to a naïve associationism. What takes place between A and B will be interpreted as a special relation: B is associated with A because it is intrinsic in the nature of A to bring about B. Perhaps we could say that deterministic causality is at first conceived as teleologic causality, minus the concepts of volition and responsibility.

Determinism reached full expression in Leibniz's law: Each effect has a cause. In traditional logic this law, which was formulated twenty-three centuries after Aristotle differentiated the three laws of thought, is often referred to as the fourth law of thought.

THE FUTURE AND THE POSSIBLE

The development of language at a conceptual level enables the individual to form concepts not only of things, but also of relations. It is true that relations are also experienced at a level of mentation as low as that of simple perceptions, but the abstract interpretation of these relations is much more distinct at a conceptual level.

We have seen that at a paleologic level the individual is able to anticipate the future. However, this mental anticipation is not well systematized and is connected with practical needs: survival and adjustment. It is only at a conceptual level that man can give a clear mental structure to future times. At this level man's greater concern with causality, especially with deterministic causality, also leads him to an understanding of the unidirectional aspect of time. If A is the cause of B, B follows A. But the reverse is not true; a temporal dimension cannot be retrieved, as a spatial one can.

Another development related to future anticipation and to the creation of symbols without objective referents is the emergence of the possible as a concept. The mind now conceives not only what *is* but also what *is possible*. In his *Critique of Judgment* Kant states that the basic faculty of the human intellect is the ability to distinguish between the reality and the possibility of things. The possibility of things is represented by concepts, which man can formulate without corresponding objects. He thus becomes able to assume, to presume, to make hypotheses, to construct ideals, and to conceive the potential, the metaphorical, the probable and the improbable, the possible and the impossible. Even the impossible becomes a possibility, at least as an assumption.

The world of concepts

The conceptual level can be examined from two perspectives, both very important. From the first, this stage of development consists of a set of functions which enables man to create, learn, use, and integrate concepts. From the second, the important fact is that most concepts are learned from others, either individual persons or social and cultural institutions. The second view, which follows the Lockean tradition, has recently been set forth in the Whorf-Sapir theory of cognition (Whorf, 1956). Culture, with its systems of knowledge, languages, beliefs, and values, bestows upon each person a patrimony of concepts which becomes part of the individual himself.

At the conceptual level, the last known stage of psychological development, concepts become the most important part of man's inner reality. In thinking, feeling, and even in acting, man becomes more concerned with concepts than with things.

At this point we should try to clarify a matter which leads to frequent misunderstanding. Some existentialist writers (for instance, Friedman, 1964) give great value to the particular and to concrete, and seem to belittle the abstract and the conceptual. Psychologists of the self-realization and self-actualization group also minimize the role of concepts. Even Maslow, who deserves great credit for having opposed the main currents of our time in stressing the importance of the highest levels of the psyche, apparently does not have a high regard for concepts (1948, 1954). According to him, concepts "rubricize" our experiences; they prevent us from making contact with the unique qualities of things.

More properly, Maslow should disparage not the faculty of conceptualizing, but a common *wrong* use of concepts. For instance, if I see a policeman coming toward me and I don't know why, I might imagine that he is going to arrest me or fine me for a traffic violation. Thus I respond not to him but to the class "policeman": his uniform makes me automatically put him into the class of policemen and removes him from other classes. Actually he might be a neighbor of mine who wants to ask my opinion about a neighborhood matter. However, although I am wrong in reacting to the category of policeman rather than to him as an individual or to the category of man, this does not mean that I would be better off if I did not know what a policeman is and what his function should be. Possibly I made a wrong use of the concept "policeman" because of some problems of mine; say, because of my paleologic need to see people as threatening figures. This example shows how psychodynamic factors may predispose us both to become aware of certain classes rather than others, and to see concepts as static stereotypes.[3]

The person who uses concepts is not necessarily like a museum curator who labels specimens and puts them in the proper departments to lie there forever. If a comparison is to be made, conceptual man should be likened to a physician who—having observed that a patient has lost weight, often feels hungry and thirsty, and has glucose in the urine and a large concentration of glucose in the blood—"rubricizes" this patient as a diabetic. The knowledge that the patient is a diabetic will help the physician to select the treatment; and no longer will it be trial and error treatment (that is, error most of the time), but effective insulin therapy. The fact that he already knows many things about the patient because he has put him in the category of diabetics also enables the physician to concentrate on the special nondiabetic features of the patient's illness; that is, on what is dissimilar between him and other diabetics, on what requires special care.

Some anticonceptual philosophers have enjoyed great popularity in the anti-intellectual movements of the nineteenth and twentieth centuries. One of them is Bergson, who advocated abandoning conceptual thinking and reverting to intuitional forms of knowledge that correspond to our paleologic and even endoceptual levels of cognition (1912). Although these forms of cognition, if properly used, are useful in some areas, they fail us miserably in other aspects of life. As a matter of fact, in order to evaluate the validity of our thinking, we often have to determine whether or not our apparent concepts are disguised paleologic preconcepts.

It seems to me that anti-conceptual writers are afraid of two possibilities. The first is the reduction of man to the status of a computer. The main target and scapegoat of these anti-intellectual people is Descartes, who with his *cogito* formulation is said to have seen man as a thinking machine rather than as a whole person endowed with feelings and the capacity to make choices. The second undesirable possibility which these anti-intellectual writers fear is that conceptual

[3] Wrong uses of concepts are frequent in preschizophrenic states (see Chapter 16).

man can become a prisoner of reality or a captive of society's conventions. We have seen that this does happen to some people, not because they use concepts, but because of the wrong use they make of them.

Although concepts enable man to deal more adequately with some aspects of life, they transcend the empirical world. They help us see what is beyond facts. Science, for instance, does not stop at empirical data but is concerned with the implications of these data. Following is a brief review of the ways in which concepts go beyond their immediate and apparent content.

First of all, not only the highly creative person, but any normal human being uses and associates concepts in innumerable complex ways: in clusters and inventive derivations that are eventually transmitted to others in interpersonal relations. By using concepts in multiple, often unpredictable ways, man reacquires that originality which he temporarily lost when he assimilated the concepts conveyed by others.

Second and equally important is the fact that clusters of concepts become the repositories of intangible feelings and values. Not only does every concept have an emotional counterpart, but concepts are necessary for high emotions. Faith, loyalty, patriotism, aesthetic rapture, love in the agapic or fullest sense, and anything usually referred to as pertaining to the spirit—none of these would be possible without concepts. Such conceptual emotions are more differentiated but not necessarily less intense than primitive emotions. I have mentioned only positive emotions, but others which we may regard as negative are also common; for instance, feelings of vanity, pride, hate, etc.

In the course of reaching adulthood, a person's emotional and conceptual processes become more and more intimately interconnected. It is impossible to separate the two; they form a circular process. The emotional accompaniment of a cognitive process becomes the propelling drive not only toward action but also toward further cognition. Only emotions can stimulate man to overcome the hardship of some cognitive processes and can lead to complicated symbolic, interpersonal, and abstract operations. On the other hand, only cognitive processes can extend the realm of emotions indefinitely.

If man studies complex mathematical problems, looks at the stars, or thinks of things which occurred in the remote past or are expected to occur in the distant future, he not only attempts to mirror events regardless of space and time, and not only searches for a coherent relationship among the apparently unrelated parts of the universe. In addition, his inner self, his inner status, his highest-level homeostasis are altered as a result of these endeavors. Every cognitive process becomes an inner experience. The spectator of all times and of all existences is "touched inside" by all the times and by all the existences. Whatever is conceived touches the core of man.

Unless we recognize this reciprocity between cognition and the highest experiences of inner status, we may make the mistake of focusing on one or the other. The experience of the inner world is a vehicle for understanding the external world; the experience of the external world is a vehicle for understanding the inner world. Every emotion has a secret logic behind it; every logical thought rests on a secret emotion.

The third way in which concepts transcend their immediate content is in the process of creativity. This topic will not be discussed here because it is treated in Part III.

Fourth, concepts about the possible make us envision worlds better than the one we live in, and motivate us to get closer to such ideals through our own efforts. It is at this conceptual level that the greatest psychological growth occurs. Concepts of concepts and symbols of symbols can continually be formed by creative people and used by the community of men.

The conceptual level thus enables man to create, or to be exposed to, an unending organization of cognition, an unending variety of emotions, and as we shall see in Chapter 12 the possibility of moral choice. The endlessness of man can now be recognized. This conception of man was expressed by Vico: *Posse, nosse, velle, finitum quod tendit ad infinitum.* (A finite center of possibility, of knowing, and of willing, that tends to the infinite.)[4] Man is a self-conscious finitude that

[4] The meaning of the word *posse* is somewhat ambiguous, but in this context it seems to refer more to possibility than to power (Caponigri, 1953).

challenges itself (1) by transcending empirical facts and building an ever-increasing number of concepts and symbols, and (2) by transcending the determinism of nature, thus creating the possibility of moral choice and of systems of values. Because of this challenging and transcending, man is a product not simply of nature, but also of his own making; he belongs not only to the physical cosmos but to history. He is no longer satisfied with the possible and the conditional; he now conceives the impossible, the unconditional, the infinite, the absolute, the whole, and nothingness—concepts that he includes in his religion and philosophy.

Here we must make a distinction between those inner objects which, although they seem impossible to realize, are incentives toward progress and are therefore constructive, and the impossible mental constructs which become possible only as paleologic or phantasmic entities. In the first case, the impossible motivates creativity but remains a potentiality unless it can use lower forms for its realization (see Chapters 19 and 24). In the second case, the "impossible" becomes actualized in dreams, superstitions, prejudices, decadent modes of living, and psychopathologic conditions, unless it is rescued by higher levels of integration, as in myth, religion, creativity, etc. Utopias, ideals, or anything which cannot be actualized or easily actualized tend to remain inner objects. Thus they are different from the pleasant phantasmic objects which seek transformation into sensori-motor behavior (see Chapter 5).

There is a fifth way in which concepts go beyond their immediate content. Actually it is the most important from a psychiatric point of view, but is the last to be examined because it presupposes the other four. Concepts enter into and to a large extent constitute the image of the self. Man at the conceptual level no longer sees himself as a physical entity or as a name, but as a repository of concepts which refer to his own person. Concepts like inner worth, personal significance, mental outlook, knowledge, ideals, aspirations, ability, and capacity to receive and give love—all are integral parts of the self and of the self-image, together with the emotions which accompany these concepts. The discrepancy between the way we think we are and the way we feel we should be (or the way we feel parents, society, God expect us to be) may create a sense of guilt which is based on pure conceptual ground. Needless to say, a conceptual image of the self does not necessarily eliminate previous ones. Some pre-conceptual self-images may be repressed; others may coexist, at least partially, with the conceptual one.

9 ⊛ HIGH LEVELS OF MOTIVATION, CONSCIOUS AND UNCONSCIOUS

Reality adjustment

As discussed earlier, the two categories of motivation (search for pleasure and avoidance of unpleasure) existing at the sensorimotor level are directly connected with the physical needs of the organism. Starting with the phantasmic level, pleasure is not merely attained with simple motor responses; it is also imagined and wished for. At a paleologic level, wished-for pleasure and feared unpleasure are maintained by verbal proxy and may bring about primary-process transformations.

At these low levels, the survival of the individual and the preservation of the species are dependent on the chance that what is pleasant, and therefore sought, is useful to life and reproduction. Selective evolution transforms this chance into a statistically favorable coincidence by eliminating the possibility of reproduction of the organisms in which there is no correspondence between experience of pleasure and enhancement of survival.

This correspondence is no longer crucially important when

man acquires a sense of himself as an entity transcending the here and now, for then he understands that future survival does not depend on present pleasure. Survival probably became a major concern at the phantasmic-imaginal stage, remained later as an endoceptual construct, and was much more clearly cognized later in speech-endowed human beings.

With the advent of conceptual levels of cognition, the need for survival becomes much better understood by the individual, but it is not so strongly or so frequently experienced as a motivational force as is generally assumed. Although life is almost constantly threatened by external dangers, most of the time the individual is not overwhelmingly concerned with the possibility of his annihilation. He feels this possibility when it is most immediate, as in epidemics, wars, drought, famine, isolation, cases of accidents, violent attack, illness, and similar circumstances. When man becomes aware of danger, he tries to overcome it in different ways, from primitive magic to science. No matter what he does, however, his efforts to remove his chance of survival from the whim of external forces are doomed to fail eventually. Even if he succeeds in controlling the noxious external factors, he will never be able to arrest the tendency of living matter to rejoin the rest of the entropic, deterministic physico-chemical universe. It is part of reality-oriented cognition to deal with the notion of one's death.

At an early conceptual level, other motivations exist which have been produced by the expansions of interpersonal relations and of the functions of language, symbol making in general, and several categories of concepts. The primary physiological needs decrease in importance as motivational factors, although they continue to exist and may resume a predominant role at any level of development.

All the motivational factors which emerge at an early conceptual stage may be considered as belonging to the *reality-adjustment level*. Unfortunately, neither *reality* nor *adjustment* is a satisfactory word to describe this level. Many thinkers altogether exclude the possibility of achieving any knowledge of "reality." "Adjustment" too, as a condition requiring acceptance of the environment as it is, is a self-contradictory term, as we shall see later in the chapter. However, until a more appropriate designation has been found, I shall continue to use the phrase reality-adjustment level.

Many authors—for instance, Maslow, Rogers, and Fromm —have stressed that when the personality goes beyond the earliest levels of integration, it becomes structured more by cultural-social factors than by biological ones. This emphasis is a useful correction of those Freudian theories which dealt almost exclusively with physiological needs and drives. I should like to point out, however, that even the authors who have stressed the motivational role of society and culture have not dealt adequately with the topic of expanding cognition, which is a prerequisite to the great role played by society and culture.

Although it is true, as discussed in Chapter 8, that many concepts could not originate without complicated exchanges with others, it is also true that complicated interpersonal relations could not occur without the intermediary role of concepts. Circular mechanisms are constantly formed at a reality-adjustment level and at subsequent stages of development.

The person who lives at a reality-adjustment level is able (1) to remove major states of disharmony in his intrapsychic functions; (2) to deal satisfactorily with the people of his group—first with the members of his family or clan, later with the members of larger groups; (3) to distinguish the objects of inner reality from external objects; (4) to inhibit behavior aiming at lower levels of motivation—for instance, behavior directed toward immediate satisfaction.

Life at a reality-adjustment level demands constant alertness and necessitates prompt changes within the self, as the numerous stimuli coming from the internal and external worlds require diverging types of responses. At this level the individual is already aware that he is affected by different types of motivation. He feels that he can *choose* between the attainment of satisfaction or of reality adjustment. Often the conflict is between what the individual wishes and what society requires. A high order of motivation thus seems to imply an active renunciation of a lower motivation. The lower motive is not inhibited by an involuntary or automatic physiological process (as a lower function is inhibited in many neurological mechanisms), but is restrained by an act of choice or by habit. The individual must choose, or must be trained, or must train himself, to give up archaic or more immediate objects of gratification. He comes to feel a sense of responsibility for his actions.

Can attainment of reality adjustment be interpreted as a special form of satisfaction—a pleasure-seeking maneuver not too dissimilar from those of lower levels? In other words, can the aim of this level be a form of calculated or long-delayed hedonism? It depends on how we define hedonism. If we simply use the word to indicate a state of pleasantness, then the answer is yes. However, the concept of hedonism as used in some psychological schools implies that any form of pleasure is a derivative of primitive instinctual pleasures, and that its origin is more important than its outcome or ultimate expression. In this case we cannot use the word hedonism.

Although motivations of the reality-adjustment type are in many respects necessary and beneficial, they have their own serious shortcomings. The person becomes too concerned with the problems of adaptation and cannot expand his own individuality or the parts of himself which transcend adaptation. In an effort to find a correspondence between his inner reality and the external world—that is, between internal and external objects—he succeeds in almost eliminating magic and wish-fulfilling practices. In doing so, however, he tends to become overfactual and to discard enriching endoceptual experiences and the basal types of conceptualization (Chapter 8, pages 133–134). Halos of meanings and the possibility of unforeseen ramifications are eliminated. What remains is adaptation and, at best, efficiency at a "reality" level.

Self-expansion

Until not too long ago, reality adjustment was considered the goal of mental health. Reestablishment of adjustment, when it was lost because of psychopathological conditions, was deemed to be the aim of psychiatry. But although adjustment to reality is important, it cannot be considered man's highest aspiration. Some authors, especially Horney, Fromm, and Maslow, see man's highest goal in what they call self-realization or self-actualization.

Horney, who has dealt at length with the concept of self-realization, gave what is perhaps the best description of it in the introductory sentences of her last book:

> Whatever the conditions under which a child grows up, he will, if not mentally defective, learn to cope with others in one way or another and he will probably acquire some skills. But there are also forces in him which he cannot acquire or even develop by learning. You need not, and in fact cannot, teach an acorn to grow into an oak tree, but when given a chance, an intrinsic potentiality will develop. Similarly, the human individual given a chance tends to develop his particular human potentialities. He will develop then the unique alive forces of his real self: the clarity and depth of his own feelings, thoughts, wishes, interests; the ability to tap his own resources, the strength of his willpower; the special capacities or gifts he may have; the faculty of expressing himself or to relate himself to others with his spontaneous feelings. All this will in time enable him to find his set of values, his aims in life. In short, he will grow, substantially undiverted, *toward self-realization.* (Horney, 1950)

Self-realization is conceived as the fulfillment of one's potentialities; but in the complexity of human existence the individual seldom succeeds in making use of all or the greater part of his capacities. A neurophysiologist might prefer to say that the billions of neurons or the infinite combinations of neurons, especially in the associational areas of the human cerebral cortex, are not fully used. A sociologist might be more inclined to assert that although society helps the individual in many ways and makes his growth possible, it hinders him in other ways and makes him accept a life where adjustment and adaptation are of paramount importance.

I agree that man should not accept reality adjustment as his highest goal. If man's inclination is to grow further, he cannot adjust at any definite level. This adjustment, unless understood in a relative sense, is a self-contradictory concept. I am inclined to feel critical also, however, of the concept of self-realization. The implication seems to be that our actions are predetermined by our native endowment. According to Horney, if we were not hindered by neuroses or other adversities, we would be able to live according to our "potentialities," just as an acorn can become an oak.

My objection to this concept of self-realization is that the example of the acorn, first found in Aristotle's writings, cannot appropriately be applied to man. The course of man's psychological development is unpredictable and not necessarily inherent in a "potentiality." Even with knowledge of its inherent mechanisms and of environmental circumstances, no one can predict the outcome of the human psyche. Inasmuch as the human symbolic functions are capable of infinite combinations and expansion, man is an unending product (Chapter 8, pages 147–149). This is not to say that man is infinite; he is indeed finite, but in his own finitude he is always unfinished.[1] Biological growth stops at a certain stage of development, but psychological growth may continue as long as life does. By psychological growth we mean the expansion of feelings, understandings, and possibilities of choices and actions with agreeable and often unforeseeable effects.

Man thus cannot aim at self-realization but at an unknown, undetermined, and undeterminable self-expansion. The quality and extent of the expansion will depend on what he can make of his inner experiences, conceptual life, interpersonal relations, work, and actions.

Self-expansion acquires a particular aspect in a relatively small number of creative people. Although every human being is to a certain extent creative, we shall reserve this term for those persons who make new contributions which are later shared by their fellow men. Several questions about the creative person's development have been debated intensively. Is his motivation similar to the need for self-expansion of the average healthy human being? Is he moved by a desire to enrich the lives of his fellow men, by a wish for self-expansion, or by the urge to placate a neurotic demand? In addi-

[1] Lapassade, a contemporary French philosopher, has recently expressed similar views. He describes man as *unachevé* (1963).

tion to a special talent, does he have a special need? We shall examine these problems in Chapter 19.

Ethical motivation

In addition to those already discussed, man has other motivations: to avoid what he feels is evil and to actualize what he feels is good. "Good" generally means the common good, irrespective of how unpleasant or harmful this "good" is for the person who actualizes it. Even life may be sacrificed if the actualization of the common good requires it. By evil is generally meant what has unpleasant or harmful effects for the community, no matter how pleasant it may at first seem to the individual.

When man is motivated to avoid what he considers evil and to do what he considers good, he follows ethical motivation. There are two kinds of ethical behavior: one, the easier, consists of avoiding evil; the other, more difficult to attain, consists of actualizing good.

Ethical motivation is generally made up of internalizations, conscious or unconscious, of societal demands. It does not necessarily reflect demands overtly stated by parents or other representatives of society; it can also be created by tacit generalizations of these demands and by unverbalized assumptions. We do not yet know whether there is an autonomous moral sense independent of sociocultural factors. The internalizations which together form ethical motivation are usually projected to forces greater than the human being or even greater than the human community, such as God, religion, the fatherland, etc. Lower motivations, even when they may bring about evil, are also occasionally projected or personalized (in such forms as the Devil, the alluring goddess, the flesh) or are conceptualized in psychoanalytic terminology as the id.

Since ethical motivation has to be studied in a social context, this book will not discuss it further except to point out that, at the ethical level, the purpose of man's actions is not merely that of protecting his vital cycle or satisfying his own wishes, but of preserving or bringing about something which he considers more valuable than his own life and his own pleasure. Self-expansion and ethically motivated behavior are not necessarily in conflict. They are not necessarily in agreement, either; their relation is contingent upon the outcome of the action in question.

Conflicts of motivation

The various levels of motivation (satisfaction, wish fulfillment, reality adjustment, self-expansion, ethics) coexist in every person. Their coexistence complicates life and brings about conflicts. These levels, of course, are only abstractions; what exists are rather vaguely defined groupings of motivations. Even within a given level there may be conflicts: for instance, between responding to fear or to appetite; to anxiety or to wish.

Conflicts generally originate externally and then become internalized. Society participates in the production of conflicts, usually, but not always, because it favors what is regarded as a higher-level motivation. When society favors a lower-level motivation, the individual may submit to persecution and martyrdom in order to assert his higher aims. Often no agreement is possible between what is seen as higher and lower. When the conflict over different motivations ends with the selection of what is regarded as a higher motivation, people often speak of "redemption" or "salvation." Actually, because of man's never-ending symbolic development (Chapter 8), what seems the highest form of motivation and the road to salvation at a given historical time may not seem so in a different era. One can thus speak of redemption and salvation only relative to particular ethics. Perhaps it would be more nearly correct to speak of self-expansion and of progress than of salvation.

Until solved, conflicts increase a person's anxiety, insecurity, depression, and guilt feelings. They decrease his efficiency, undermine his self-esteem, block his actions, and sometimes bring about psychiatric disorders. A psychodynamic study of a mental disorder is often the study of the origin, development, and later vicissitudes of conflicts. We should not forget, however, that conflicts may also stimulate the emergence of new outcomes, new points of view, and unforeseen syntheses.

In concluding this section on the high types of conscious motivation, let me stress again that conceptual thinking as a motivational force has been underestimated in psychology, psychiatry, and psychoanalysis. The emphasis has been on the importance of bodily needs, instinctual behavior, and primitive emotions, all of which can exist without a cognitive counterpart or with a very limited one. In the second half of the twentieth century, fewer men than ever before starve for food or sex, and yet psychological malaise and mental illness have increased, not decreased. It seems to this author that among the powerful emotional forces which motivate or disturb men are many which are sustained or actually engendered by complicated symbolic processes. The individual's concept-feelings of personal significance, of self-identity, of his role in life, of self-esteem, could not exist without these complex cognitive constructs. According to the Freudian school, such concept-feelings are only displacements, detours, or rationalizations which cover instinctual drives or more primitive constructs. Although this is true in several cases, to think that it is so in all or most of them is a reductionistic point of view.

Changes in motivation are explained by the Freudian school with such concepts as drive transformation, drive fusion, drive neutralization, absorption of cathexis, displacement of psychic energy, etc. It is my belief that these hypotheses are unnecessary and their content should be used only in a metaphorical sense. Except in the earliest phases of development, the individual's state of cognition determines most of the changes which occur in his psychodynamic life. It is his state of cognition that re-elaborates past and present experience and, to a large extent, alters their emotional associations. There is a constant attempt in Freudian theory to minimize the role of the idea as an emotional force and to see it in a physical sense, as a quantity of energy.

Historically this point of view was an outcome of the tendency to equate sexual life with the whole of psychological life. And yet psychiatric and psychoanalytic practice reveals that the concept of the self which the individual acquires in relation to his sexual life is even more important than sexual life in its physical manifestation. If he sees in himself the image of a sexually inadequate person, a homosexual, an undesirable sexual partner, or a person who lacks sexual self-control or has no definite sexual identity, he may develop a devastating self-concept. This concept may be more traumatic than a physical obstacle to normal sexual relations.

Another factor which has caused psychiatry and psychoanalysis to underestimate conceptual thinking in motivation is that they have put so much emphasis on the effects of past life as a motivational force. Indeed there should be no misunderstanding on this crucial point: past life, especially childhood, is extremely important, and it is one of Freud's greatest achievements that he demonstrated this. However, we must also recognize that in human beings the future too has a considerable effect on the *present* state of psychological health and pathology. It is when we *conceptualize* our anxieties and hopes and the significance of our lives in a temporal dimension, involving the segment of the future which will be the rest of our life span, that our strongest emotions are stirred. This is particularly true in the period of life that begins with the onset of puberty and extends through involutional age. No motivation toward reality adjustment, self-evolvement, and ethics is possible without some conceptions of the future. As discussed in earlier chapters, our discovering and understanding of the future is based not on simple perceptions and protoemotions, but on high conceptual processes.

Even Rapaport, although he reaffirmed the importance of thought in psychoanalysis and emphasized that drive dynamics are translated into behavior through thought processes (1953), had an incomplete grasp of the problem. He did not see the other side of the coin; namely, that cognitive processes themselves create emotional situations and thus become major dynamic forces.

In the most benevolent circumstances, concepts which are in conflict lead to what Festinger called "cognitive dissonance," that is, to lack of mental consistency (1957). Conflicts may give rise to much more serious conditions. In my opinion such illnesses as severe anxiety, psychoneuroses, schizophrenia, and paranoid states have very little to do with hunger, thirst, or sex per se, but very much to do with conflicts arising from the individual's conceptual world, after his early interpersonal relations have prepared the ground for such conflicts. As we shall see in Part II of this book, in some of these conditions the disintegration of the conceptual world brings about a reversal to a preconceptual level of cognition and re-establishes the supremacy of the phantasmic and paleologic worlds of inner reality.

Unconscious motivation

Motivation grows much more complicated when it becomes totally or partially unconscious. The discovery of the importance of unconscious motivation is almost universally considered one of Freud's two major contributions.[2]

Some aspects of man's behavior seem unmotivated. At times their goal-directedness is retrieved with special techniques. At other times an apparent motivation hides another one whose existence is unknown to the individual himself. Following is a brief review of the various states of unconsciousness which we have already considered in this book.

A subhuman animal, organized at a level no higher than that of sensorimotor behavior and protoemotions, as a rule does not undergo removal of experiences from consciousness, except through the mechanism of automatization (Chapter 3). Loss of awareness of simple sensations and some protoemotions may occur in human beings who have developed beyond the sensorimotor level. In addition to some neurological conditions, this loss of awareness is found in some abnormal states, such as hysteria, hypnosis, and schizophrenia.[3]

After the phantasmic-imaginal level, it seems as if repression occurs when the individual transforms an image into an endocept. Actually, however, the mechanism at this point is not regressive but developmental (Chapter 4).

---

[2] The other is the discovery of the primary process (Chapter 1, page 10).

[3] Cases of children with congenital lack of pain perception have been reported. Present evidence points more to a congenital defect than to repression in these cases.

At the paleologic level, transformation or displacement occurs rather than repression (Chapter 7). In thinking processes a cognitive dissociation is found when, because of some abnormal condition like epilepsy, a person is capable of a certain understanding, but this understanding is not accompanied by awareness (Chapter 7).

According to Freud, repression (that is, loss of the quality of being accessible to consciousness) occurs when the individual wishes to forget or not to be aware of certain mental representations. The additional motivation to repress supersedes the original motivation, which remains in a state of unconsciousness. At first Freud thought that only the unpleasant events of childhood are repressed by means of a form of amnesia. The memory of these events, however, is not really lost and can be recaptured with special procedures. Later Freud believed that repression also occurs in the case of wishes which the individual does not want to admit to himself or to others because, directly or indirectly, they concern a satisfaction of infantile strivings that is opposed by the superego. The motivations (or the wishes) are said to be unconscious in two cases: (1) when the person who has carried out an apparently motivated act then claims that he was not aware of the act, or at least of its purpose; (2) when the person gives unconvincing reasons for his apparently goal-directed behavior.

According to the Freudian school, the wishes that are denied access to consciousness are the most primitive wishes experienced by humans. They generally involve sexual or oral needs that are forbidden by society or by the superego. It is this writer's feeling, however, that what an individual wants to deny does not concern only his most primitive wishes and infantile strivings. Derivatives of the higher levels may also be denied complete or partial access to consciousness through repression or distortion. Cognitive constructs may be very unpleasant, and therefore subject to repression, when they involve such things as the self-image, the images of people whom the individual loves or hates, his likes or dislikes, his interpersonal relations, philosophy of life, vision of the world, family or group allegiances, etc. Emotions which one cannot rationally justify—such as some specific loves or enmities, or a need for hostility, approval, self-effacement, cowardice, power and glory, etc.—tend also to be denied or minimized. At times the lack of gratification of a primitive wish gives rise to a group of conceptual constructs which is more traumatic than the original deprivation, and therefore is more likely to be repressed. For instance, sexual deprivation may be unpleasant, but the image that the sexually deprived person may form of himself as a sexual object can be much more traumatic: Is he sexually adequate? Is he sexually desirable? etc.

According to some authors, for instance, Robbins (1955), there is no such phenomenon as unconscious motivation, but only faulty or different ways of comprehending reality. Robbins quotes a patient who had formed an agreement with his wife that they could continue to love each other and yet have extramarital relations. The patient thought at first that this decision was reached out of understanding, maturity, and reciprocal admiration. Soon, however, therapy disclosed that it was motivated by the patient's hostility toward his wife—a feeling which was more appropriate to the actual decision. According to Robbins, the hostility was not unconscious before the patient experienced it. Rather, it did not exist, because the patient's way of interpreting reality was making him reach different conclusions and consequently have different feelings.

Robbins does not seem to give much value to a major tenet of psychoanalytic theory: that the way a person interprets reality is determined not only by his more or less direct thinking, but also by his underlying emotions, of which he is not always aware. These emotions may come from primitive sources, as Freud stressed, or from other complicated cognitive constructs. For instance, in the example reported by Robbins, the patient might not have been able to stand the image of himself as that of a husband who hates his wife. Thus circular mechanisms, consisting of both emotions and high cognitive processes, are continuously being created and are involved in conscious and unconscious motivation.

We have seen that man is subjected simultaneously to several levels of motivation. At first society, but then his own self-image, real or idealized, requires that he live in accordance with the highest types of motivation. The types that are lower, or those that are not regarded as low but for some reason are less congruous with what he considers a consistent image of himself, are repressed and continue to affect him in ways difficult to discern. Often it is a complex procedure to sort out the different levels of motivation. Although this topic is better understood in an interpersonal context, the following example concerns intrapsychic processes.

A patient, a married man in his middle thirties, is on the verge of divorce. Hostility and lack of tenderness characterize the relationship with his wife. Nevertheless, as he comes home from work one evening, he finds himself acting warmly and considerately toward her. He does not understand why: the reason seems unknown to him, or at least unexplainable in words. Shortly afterward, he becomes aware that his behavior possibly has a motivation which embarrasses him: he feels a sexual desire for his wife. Only if he prepared the ground could he have sexual relations. He concludes then that his desire, which he had been unaware of up to that moment, has motivated him to change his attitude toward her. If we accepted this explanation we could add that a subliminal or unattended inner status of this patient's organism has directed or motivated his behavior.

Another consideration in this case is the fact that recently the patient has had no sexual desire for his wife and has abstained from sexual relations. Since he possesses a certain degree of psychoanalytic sophistication, he tends at first to believe that the mere abstinence is a tension-producing factor strong enough to change his attitude. Quite correctly, he does not dismiss this possibility as too superficial; but he becomes aware of a second motivation, for he experiences what up to then has been an unconscious wish for a reconciliation with his wife. This wish was in its turn the outcome of many other psychological constructs: a feeling of guilt toward his wife, fear of loneliness, love for the children, etc. At any rate, the wish for a reconciliation makes the patient experience a feeling of being attracted erotically to his wife. Now, his wish to bring about a reconciliation is a much more elaborated motive than the mere sexual desire. Nevertheless, for a long while it has remained unconscious, presumably because other parts of the man's psyche have not permitted him to admit it. Whatever the basis for the wish is, it cannot be considered just an expression of an instinct or of an intellectual idea. An emotional component acts as an underlying unconscious motivation.

If such a thing as unconscious motivation exists, both the idea and the affect must be unconscious. If only the idea were unconscious, how could it become a driving force, without an emotional charge? Orthodox psychoanalysis is ambiguous concerning this question. Freud dealt with it in his paper, "The Unconscious" (1915b). He wrote that although in psychoanalytic practice we are accustomed to speak of unconscious emotions (like love, hate, etc.), and although for practical purposes we may continue to do so, actually there are no unconscious affects. Affects may be displaced, or suppressed altogether; but if they exist, they exist in a state of consciousness. In *The Ego and the Id* (1927), Freud writes, "Certainly the qualities of feeling come into being only by being felt." Fenichel (1945) and most orthodox psychoanalysts follow Freud. In some cases, however, the problem is not clearly expressed. Some orthodox analysts, for instance, Nunberg (1955), seem to think that affects too may be unconscious.

Freud's reluctance to accept unconscious affects is understandable if we grant the fundamental premise of traditional psychology that emotion is a felt experience. But then how do we explain unconscious motivation? Do we mean that only the cognitive part of motivation is unconscious, or that motivation is only a cognitive process? These positions cannot be upheld. Although motivation undoubtedly has a very important cognitive element, it is also loaded with affect. Indeed, we have seen that it is the experience of inner status (either a feeling in general or an emotion) which constitutes the motive as motive, as a drive toward a goal. As just mentioned, this difficulty cannot be overcome if we maintain the premise that emotion is only a felt experience.

The reader will remember, however, that Chapter 2 demonstrated at length the neurophysiological point that "sensation" is not necessarily accompanied by consciousness. It is in the nature of *physiological* sensation not to be felt. Later chapters showed how emotions and sensations belong to the same category of psychological functions. There is thus no logical reason for assuming that unconscious emotions are not possible, i.e., that in some cases not only the cognitive element but also the emotional element of the apperception is unconscious. In other words, in feelings, whether they are sensations, physiostates, or emotions, we distinguish two parts: (1) the pathopoietic, which produces the feeling; (2) the pathopathetic, which permits the feeling to be experienced. Now it could be that feelings become unconscious when they are deprived of the pathopathetic mechanism, but retain the pathopoietic. Feelings deprived of the pathopathetic mechanisms would be similar to the servomechanisms of computing machines: they would elicit responses without being experienced.[4]

Freud thought that only ideas can become repressed. If the idea is repressed, the accompanying affect cannot develop and therefore is not felt. At times the idea becomes conscious, or isolated, but the affect is inhibited and therefore not felt. Freud thus generally speaks of inhibited rather than repressed affect. It is difficult, however, to conceive a distinction between this type of inhibition and repression.

If emotions have remained in evolution because of their utilitarian effect, why do they become unconscious? Is not this against the evolutionary trend which takes advantage of the state of awareness of the emotion? Emotions undergo repression when they constitute too heavy a burden to the individual. This generally occurs when the cognitive ramifications are too many, too conflicting, and too difficult to repress. Pleasant affects, too, are repressed at times. As already mentioned, they may be repressed when their gratification would eventually bring about unpleasant consequences. For instance, a forbidden love may elicit anxiety about punishment.

---

[4] Thoughts and feelings deprived of awareness are still in a borderland between biology and psychology. They represent bridges between natural and experiential man.

The mechanism of repression

Discussions of the actual mechanism of repression are conjectural, since our present knowledge of neurophysiology is inadequate to explain the phenomenon. Freud envisioned an ingenious mechanism; he thought that at a preconscious level the unconscious motivation is, so to say, examined by a sort of censor. If the censor allows the material to come to consciousness, the ego takes over its management. If the material is objectionable to the censor, it will not be allowed to pass the threshold of consciousness. Not much is explained with this mechanism. The censor is anthropomorphized as a type of homunculus residing in the preconscious and endowed with properties not granted to the conscious self.

It is not the unconsciousness of the process that is questionable in Freud's conception, but the way the censor is supposed to function. If emotions are not felt in the preconscious, how is the censor to "decide" that some material is objectionable? The censor would have to have some kind of intellectual understanding superior to that of a conscious mind. One quick but inadequate explanation would be this: If an idea, in the state of consciousness, has been associated with an unpleasant emotion, then some kind of negative conditioned reflex will be set up which will automatically make the subject keep the idea in a state of repression. It is difficult to imagine how this is possible, however, because ideas are continuously created by unforeseeable mixtures of previous ones, and we do not know what kind of emotion will accompany them. Thus no conditioning in a Pavlovian sense is possible. Again we face the same problem: if motivation is unconscious, the emotional component of the motivation must be unconscious too.

Freud is not at all clear when he speaks of wishes. What is a wish? Is it just an image or an idea, without an emotional counterpart? In this writer's opinion it is an emotion which accompanies a cognitive process. That a wish can be unconscious, even when the accompanying ideas are at least partially conscious, is common experience. Let us consider a simple example in which A and B have a political discussion.

Let us say that A belongs to the Democratic and B to the Republican party. In most instances it will be possible to recognize that A's arguments are directed by an underlying wish to show that the Democratic party is right. Similarly B's thoughts reflect the underlying wish to demonstrate that the Republican party is right.

Now, it may happen that A and B are conscious of what they are doing; however, most of us have witnessed honest debaters who sincerely believed that they were following their reasoning and not their emotions. They experienced emotions only at the end of the debate, over winning or losing, but not before. I have taken this example from politics, but the same observations could be made about honest debaters in other fields, including science. It would seem that emotions too may be preconscious and unconscious.

Chapter 1 mentioned that mental processes go through a microgenetic unfolding. Our knowledge of the microgenetic development of feelings in general and emotions in particular is much more limited than that of thought processes. However, we may distinguish at least two stages: first an unconscious stage which consists only of the pathopoietic mechanism; second a conscious one which consists of the pathopoietic and pathopathetic mechanisms.

At this point we must reconsider thinking in relation to emotion. Many people, starting with the early German experimentalists of the Würzburg group, have demonstrated that thinking is goal-directed, i.e., tends toward a certain task or goal (*Aufgabe*) which is motivationally chosen. Sells (1936) reported that in making syllogistic conclusions, "the atmosphere affect" is very important. Janis and Frick (1943) also found in their experiments that a subject's previously held attitude of acceptance or rejection of the offered conclusions was very important. It predisposed him toward acceptance or rejection of these conclusions when he judged the logical validity of the syllogisms.

How is this possible? It would seem almost as if the conclusion which the person has not yet reached and the accompanying affect, which cannot yet have been experienced, have already influenced the preceding steps leading to that conclusion. Ach stated, "The activity of the determining tendencies is brought to fulfillment in the unconscious. The determination . . . is affective without conscious memory of the task" (1935, quoted by Humphrey, 1951). Messer, too, wrote long ago about an unconscious machinery underlying the conscious process of thought (1906).

We could advance the following hypotheses: Thinking processes advance by stages, each of them accompanied by some emotions. In each stage there is an initial period of unconsciousness; the process may remain unconscious, or may finally reach consciousness. It is mostly the accompanying unconscious or physiological emotion which will determine whether the stage becomes conscious or not. These unconscious emotions operate like extremely complicated servo-mechanisms of cybernetic systems. Only gross motivational trends, conscious or unconscious, can be discerned. We may recognize that in order to avoid certain emotions, the psychological process becomes arrested, or is directed toward lower or higher goals, or takes detours apparently unrelated to the original aims.

We must stress that it is not the mere unpleasantness of the emotional component that determines the consciousness or unconsciousness of a particular mental construct. The most important factor is whether the person is capable of coping with that unpleasantness. But what kind of complicated mechanism "decides" outside the realm of consciousness whether the person is or is not capable? At this stage of our knowledge, the question is impossible to answer. In many cases, too, the emotion becomes fully conscious even though it is unpleasant and the subject is unable to cope with it. In this eventuality the emotion has been too strong to escape the pathopathetic mechanism.

Unconscious phenomena of cultural origin

Another large and important group of unconscious phenomena clearly are not primitive at all. They originate in the cultural milieu but become intrapsychic constructs. Only brief reference can be made to them here.

Many ways of thinking are automatically imposed upon us

by the structure and vocabulary of the language we use and are unconsciously followed by us. In a nutshell this is the content of the Whorfian theory (Whorf, 1956). Earlier than Whorf, Durkheim (1950) studied how culture impinges upon the individual. Although Durkheim could not use this recent formulation, his approach might be summarized by saying that culture imprints its patterns, mores, standards, etc., on the person in a very effective way. Durkheim spoke of "collective consciousness," but actually this imprinting, or its effects, becomes unconscious. According to Durkheim, the social fact acts as a force which makes the individual behave according to given patterns. He may have the illusion of freedom; actually he unconsciously follows the patterns of his culture. Sapir, who has also illustrated this point clearly (1949), was one of the first to realize that Jung's "collective unconscious" is not a necessary concept. What seems an archetype, deposited in our primordial unconscious, is actually a collective pattern transmitted by the culture in which we live.

Leslie A. White (1949) has described the cultural constructs existing in the psyche in this way:

> The unconscious also is a concept that may be defined culturologically as well as psychologically. Considered from a psychological point of view, "the unconscious" is the name given to a class of determinants of behavior inherent in the organism, or at least, having their locus in the organism as a consequence of the experiences it has undergone, of which the person is not aware or whose significance he does not appreciate. But there is also another class of determinants of human behavior of which the ordinary individual may be and usually is unaware, or at least has little or no appreciation of their significance. These are extrasomatic cultural determinants. In a general and broad sense, the whole realm of culture constitutes "an unconscious" for most laymen and for many social scientists as well. The concept of culture and an appreciation of its significance in the life of man lie beyond the ken of all but the most scientifically sophisticated.

10 ⊛ *THE PSYCHOLOGICAL BASIS OF ARITHMETIC*[1]

Problem solving and mathematical thinking are two important cognitive processes which need psychological interpretation. Because the subject of problem solving has received much more attention from psychologists, I shall confine this chapter to the mathematical topic of arithmetic.

Mathematical symbols have been invented at different times in different cultures, to make up a body of knowledge so vast and complicated that no single person can master it in its entirety. Although arithmetical symbolism is probably of much more recent origin than ordinary language, in trying to retrieve its beginning we encounter difficulties similar to those we met in studying the origin of language. The origin of positive integer numbers is lost in prehistoric times.

The most primitive people have relatively complicated languages with many words and definite grammars, but very

---

[1] This chapter and the next one deal with two aspects of cognition which are not directly related to clinical problems. The clinically oriented reader can turn to Chapter 12 without losing continuity.

rudimentary numerical concepts. According to Dantzig (1954), many primitive people "have not reached the stage of finger counting." Such is the case among numerous tribes in Australia, the South Sea Islands, South America, and Africa. Curr, quoted by Dantzig, made an extensive study of primitives in Australia and found that just a few were able to conceive the number 4. Dantzig reports that the Bushmen of South Africa have no number-words beyond 1, 2, and many. Even problems which seem obvious to us, such as the addition of $2 + 2 = 4$, are not evident to some human beings, such as the Australian aborigines. However, all human beings seem to have the concepts "one" and "two." Were we to understand the origin of these concepts, we could eventually attempt the study of the psychological basis of more complicated mathematical conceptualizations.[2]

I shall follow an approach which is in disagreement with that of the well-known mathematician Frege, who wrote, "It would be strange if the most exact of all sciences (that is, mathematics) had to seek support from psychology, which is still feeling its way none too surely" (1953). Frege's assumption is similar to that made by many capable thinkers, who forget that the exactness and rigor of a major discipline are generally later outcomes, refinements of original approximations.

Toward the concept of unity

A definition of numbers in common use tells us that every number *is to be defined in terms of its predecessor.* For instance, 2 is defined as 1 and 1; 3 is defined as 2 and 1. But how is 1 defined? Since even the most primitive people know number 1, should we consider this number an a priori universal concept, on which the whole science of mathematics is based? There is no doubt that the concept "one" is of basic importance; but we cannot dismiss the problem of its origin by calling it a priori or intuitional.

[2] Brower (quoted by Black, 1933) wrote, "This intuition of two-oneness, the basal intuition of mathematics, creates not only the numbers one and two, but also all finite ordinal numbers inasmuch as one of the elements of the two-oneness may be thought as a new two-oneness, which process may be repeated indefinitely."

Baumann (1868), quoted by Frege, rejects the view that numbers are concepts extracted from external things. How can we decide what is *one?* A tree may seem one to us, but it contains thousands of leaves. A deck of cards is one, but the cards are many. There is no *one* thing, in our sensible world, which cannot be divided into *many*. Leibniz said that "By *one* is meant whatever we grasp in one act of understanding"; but this, Frege remarks, "is to define *one* in terms of itself." Baumann gives the following definition, "That is one which we apprehend as one." Frege adds, "How can it make sense to ascribe the property *one* to any object whatever, when every object, according as to how we look at it, can be either *one* or not *one?* How can a science (mathematics) which bases its claims to fame precisely on being as definite and accurate as possible repose on a concept as hazy as this is?"

Baumann, however, refers to certain criteria for being *one:* the qualities of "being undivided and being isolated." Frege comments that if this point of view were correct, then we should have to expect that animals also are capable of some ideas of unity, because they distinguish objects individually. Frege adds, "I infer, therefore, that the notion of unity is not, as Locke holds, 'suggested to the understanding by every object without us, and every idea within,' but becomes known to us through the exercise of those higher intellectual powers which distinguish men from brutes. Consequently, such properties of things as being undivided or being isolated, which animals perceive quite as well as we do, cannot be what is essential in our concept." Frege is correct at this point, although he contradicts one of his previous statements. If the concept "one" becomes known to us through the exercise of those higher intellectual qualities which distinguish men from brutes, it is obvious that psychology is involved. For what are these high intellectual powers but psychological functions?

In my opinion, before we can study the origin of the concept "one" we must distinguish it from the concept of unity. The two are related, but they are not identical and should not be confused. A unity is something which is apprehended as separate and distinct from the rest of the universe. One is a numerical quality; namely, a specific quantity. The discussion of causality and biology in Chapter 2 may be of help at this point. We saw there how the most primitive organism V reacts to C, an environmental substance. It is grounded in the biochemical or biological nature of V to react to C, that is, to separate C from the rest of the universe. The rest of the universe remains indefinite, but C, the substance needed in order to live and reproduce, becomes differentiated and finite. Actually, what becomes finite is the effect that C has on V. Thus it is not that C has to be distinguished in order to be reacted to, but that it will be distinguished because it is reacted to.

We human beings may recognize C as a complicated entity. For instance, if it is a glucose solution, we may know that it consists of several atoms of different elements. In its effect on V, however, it is simply something which detaches itself from the rest of the universe. V is not endowed with sensation and therefore is not *aware* of C's effect as something detached from the rest of the universe. However, when the first organism in the phyletic scale becomes endowed with sensation, it will feel C as different from non-C. What appears to us as a unity, at least as a primitive unity, will then be formed as a psychological construct. It will not be unity C (the formation of this unity will require a much more elaborate process of projection which will not occur until later), but rather the unity of R (that is, of the response that C elicits in the organism V).

This description implies that certain changes in V and in its environment do not occur continuously or by infinitesimal steps, indistinguishable among themselves, but by *discrete steps*. Undoubtedly some changes, like breathing, growing, and metabolic processes, occur as continuous changes. However, if all changes were perceived in this way, men would in this respect be like vegetables and would never have attained mathematical concepts. Fortunately, even before the animal organism could think, it was functioning by means of separate or discrete reactions. In summary, the human ability to conceive unities probably had its primordial origin in the ability of V to separate its reaction to C from the rest of its previous state, or from the rest of the organism, or from the rest of the environment. However, between V's primitive reaction and the human conscious conception of unity there is a huge quantity of intermediary steps.

As described in Chapter 4, primitive perception consists of an alteration or disturbance in the perceiving organism. It is not yet the apprehension of a perceived object as a separate entity in the external world. The organism will not perceive an external object as something which exists independently in the environment until it reaches a stage of evolution which permits projection of the inner disturbance to the external world. At this stage, the external elements which, by being together, produce an effect in the organism are perceived by the organism as being together—as separated or distinguishable from the rest of the universe. In being separate from the rest of the universe, and in being together, they form what is perceived as a unity. This ability to separate is the beginning of what eventually will become the concept of unity. Unity, as man later conceives it, is based on the reaction to a contiguous group of stimuli. It is the *finite* reaction of the organism (for instance, a reflex) to an aggregation of entities. As we shall see later, to be *finite* implies to be *one,* but only man becomes aware of this implication. In a universe that is otherwise continuous, indefinite, and infinite, aggregations are differentiated which become finite.

A critic could suggest, however, that we see the concept of unity grounded in the primitive organism because *we,* at our present stage of evolution, have such a concept. We are projecting it, or anthropomorphizing primitive organisms. It is difficult to answer this type of criticism. We can only state that some of our concepts seem to be derivatives of subjectivizations (or acquired awareness) of biological phenomena taking place in animal organisms.

Does a low-species animal separate things from the rest of the universe? As already mentioned, no such separation occurs in those vital functions which occur by infinitesimal or continuous changes. In the animal organism, however, some reactions are not continuous in type. When the animal becomes equipped with muscular and nervous tissues, some functions are regulated by the law of "all or none" (Walsh, 1957). The neuron is subject to a discontinuous, not continuous, stimulation. The stimulus is either capable or not capable of eliciting a response. "The propagated disturbance set up in a single nerve fiber cannot be graded by grading the intensity or duration of the stimulus—the nerve fiber gives a maximal response or none at all" (Best and Taylor, 1939). When some nervous activity becomes endowed with awareness, this discontinuity, which had already existed in a state of unconsciousness in lower animal forms, becomes the basis for the appreciation of finite entities: first finite reactions, then finite objects.

How does the psyche evolve from the perception of separate things to the human concept of unity and then to that of number one? Frege is right in stating that infrahuman animals do not have such concepts, even though they do perceive things as separate objects.[3] Frege felt that the abstraction of unity or the perception of unity cannot be considered as the foundation of mathematics because our ways of deciding what a unity is are too arbitrary. To me, this arbitrariness of our unity formation seems to be a result of our degree of evolution, both biological and cultural, which offers us many concepts and many points of view. But at an earlier stage of evolution, such arbitrariness was not possible. The limited amount of responses which were available gave a more definite entity status to the responses (and later, by projection, to the stimuli producing the responses). The response appeared isolated, undivided, and incapable of segmentation, although later each unity proved to be divisible.

But from the unity of response (an inner status) to unity of perception there is a big difference. As discussed in Chapter 4, there is no difference when the animal responds not to the whole but only to releasing elements, for then the releasing element is the unity. When the organism eventually reacts at once to many contiguous parts, however, it reacts to higher unities. We saw in Chapter 4 that the ability to respond to wholes rather than to parts is one of the most difficult functions for the psyche to acquire. Eventually responses occur to what appear to us as wholes, because

[3] It is assumed by some that birds are able to "count" the eggs in their nests, and that some wasps are able to "count" caterpillars on which they feed their young, because they react to a difference in number of eggs and caterpillars. However, it is doubtful that "counting" is involved here. Probably a more elementary instinctual reaction takes place.

evolution has selected holistic patterns which have more survival value. What is a whole is thus, at a certain stage of
evolution, determined (not defined) by its survival value. A
very narrow and parochial appreciation indeed—but it is the
only one on which later logical distinctions of parts and
wholes are founded! As Chapter 4 described, whole appreciation and distinction between figure and ground become
introjected and transmitted genetically.

The concept of unity is complete when the person reacts to
an *a*. The word *a* abstracts something from what we react to,
and becomes close to the concept *one*. It is no surprise that
in several languages (for instance, French and Italian) the
same word means *a* and *one*. *Une pomme* (or *una mela*)
means an apple as well as one apple. In English, too, the indefinite articles *an* and *a* derive from the Anglo-Saxon *an*, the
same word as the numerical *one*. If I say "an apple," I imply
that I know what apples in general are, and that I am referring to an object which I consider a member of the class
"apple." "An apple" means any (and not a specific) member
of the class of objects which we call apples. When a word is
used with the indefinite article, it stands for a concept and
for an embodiment of the concept. "Any" falls between *a* (or
an) and *one*, but is not yet *one*. The numerical significance is
not yet clear.

One, two, three, and many

In order to evolve from the psychological construct of
unity as the recognition of something being separate and distinct, to the idea of *one* as a numerical concept, the concept
two is needed. Spinoza in a certain way was right when he
wrote in *Epistolae doctorum quorundam virorum*:

> A man who holds in his hand a sesterce and a dollar will
> not think of the number *two* unless he can cover his sesterce
> and his dollar with one and the same name, viz., piece of sil-
> ver, or coin; then he can affirm that he has two pieces of sil-
> ver, or two coins; since he designates by the name *piece of
> silver* or *coin* not only the sesterce but also the dollar . . .

From this it is clear, therefore, that nothing is called *one* or *single* except when some other thing has first been conceived which, as has been said, matches it. (Quoted by Frege, 1953.)

Spinoza discloses a crucial point: there cannot be *one* without the concept *two*. He understands that although there can be an idea of unity, no true concept of *one* can appear without the concept of *two*.

How is this possible? Isn't this point of view against the opinion of many mathematicians who believe that the theory of numbers is based on number one? Is it not also a common-sense view that number two presupposes number one? Although I am not a mathematician, I do agree that arithmetic may be based on the concept of number one; but this does not prove that the concept *one* was the first to be discovered. Although one logically precedes two, it did not necessarily precede it historically. The history of numbers, like that of many scientific fields, does not follow a logical order, nor an order of importance. For instance, Galileo's law about falling bodies was discovered before Newton's law of inertia, and yet Galileo's is based on Newton's more fundamental law. Moreover, Galileo's discoveries undoubtedly helped Newton to make his.

If an individual responds mentally to unity B (let us say a bird) as he responded to A (another bird), and knows that B is not A, he has discovered number two. He recognizes that he reacts to B as he did to A, and yet that B is not A: they belong to the same class, but are not the same object. At the same time that he identifies, he distinguishes. In other words, the concept of two implies the simultaneous recognition of difference and sameness. The two objects, although separate, must be apprehended in a physical or logical togetherness. Of course, similarity may be recognized in any number exceeding two. At first, however, similar objects in quantities exceeding two are not numbers, but just collections of similar objects. The primitive concern over stabilizing identities induces the individual to collect and hoard, as we have seen on page 125, but not yet to calculate. Undoubtedly the process that mathematicians call one-to-one correspondence, though based on the ability to collect, also implies comparing quantities, or the cardinal aspect of numbers, which requires more than the concept two. However, the recognition of similarity must have been particularly important for the concept two. After all, it must have been easy for primitive man to recognize that his fellow humans had eyes, ears, hands, legs, arms, and nostrils, and that these were situated on each side of the body. As soon as he saw one eye or arm of another person, he would also see the other eye and arm: the two organs would be apprehended in a state of separateness and togetherness. The double symmetry of the body, together with the concept of similarities, must have thus facilitated the abstraction of that collection of similars which came to be called *two*.[4] A plurality of two is a special plurality, occupying a special role in some languages. For instance, Greek grammar possesses not only the singular and the plural numbers, but also the dual.

From the concept two it is possible to go to the concept one. One is what remains of two when the symmetrical status is lost; that is, when the two parts undergo separation, in the sense that each is considered separately. In other words, in order to have knowledge of one, the individual has to know that there is more than one.

We can at this point summarize the tortuous path of the cognitive processes which finally led to the concepts of numbers one and two. If the person could have isolated and reflected upon the singularity of a perception, or the finitude of an experiential status, then he could have leapt relatively easily from a perception to the concept "one." But the processes did not follow this simple course. As a matter of fact, with the development of imagery and then of the endocept, the isolation of finitudes became more difficult. The concept of finitude, implied in the "all or none" law, was lost and had to be reacquired. Although unities were experienced throughout many levels of cognitive evolution, unity was not perceived as a numerical quality until the human being could conceive the smallest aggregation of distinguishable

---

[4] This double symmetry also gives rise to the concept of right-left orientation. The two sides are first recognized as similar, then as two; then one is called right, the other left. As we shall see later, in the pathologic condition called Gerstmann's syndrome, counting and right-left orientation are both impaired (see pages 181–182).

identities: number two. When the parts forming two could be separated, the concept "one" could be conceived.

With the concept of numbers one and two, any number can theoretically be built up. The first new number, of course, is number three, which in many languages and cultures is still the symbol of multitude. The Latin *ter* and the English *thrice* generally mean three times, but occasionally they are also used to mean many times or a loose multitude of times. Perhaps there is a connection between the Latin *tres*, three, and *trans*, beyond (three going beyond the easy number two). In French there may be an etymologic connection between *très*, very, and *trois*, three.

By repeatedly adding the first two numbers we have an infinite series of numbers. What we understand about the first three numbers can be repeated and can stand for the rest of the system of positive real integer numbers. This is not to suggest that once the concept "three" is grasped, any other number is simultaneously conceived. On the contrary, probably the first few following numbers, like four, five, six, etc., were gradually added as the need for them arose. However, we may assume that once the first three numbers were devised, it was relatively easy to proceed to larger numbers. For very large numbers, of course, more complicated symbolic devices had to be invented, and with these the series of numbers may be protracted to infinite possibilities. Thus with "simple" concepts of integers, like those of one, two, and three, man can eventually transform the infinite into an infinite number of finitudes. Later on, the finite state of two successive numbers can be reopened with the concepts of fraction and of infinitesimal. Between two successive finitudes, an infinite number of infinitesimal numbers can be conceived. The unity is broken again, and the indefinite re-emerges.

Ordinal numbers

At this point the objection could be raised that our hypotheses may be pertinent for cardinal numbers, but not for ordinal. In other words, if numbers originated as we have postulated, they would represent quantities of similar things, not a progressive numerical sequence. And yet we know that a number, as it is generally conceived, indicates a place in a natural sequence at the same time that it represents a quantity. For instance, *three* does not represent only that special quantity which is three, but also a quantity located between quantity two and quantity four. Quantity three is the *third* in the numerical series.

The idea of the ordinal system may have occurred to primitive people from observation of their fingers. The very fact that finger occupies a certain position in a group of fingers may have evoked the insight of natural succession. In many primitive languages, words for numbers up to four are identical with the names given to the four fingers (Dantzig, 1954). In some languages, number five is expressed by the word for hand, number ten by *two hands*, or sometimes by *man*. In Latin, numbers 1, 2, 3 are represented by the symbols I, II, III, which look like fingers. Number five is represented by the symbol V, which may also be derived from the shape of the hand, and number ten by X, which may indicate two hands. *Digitum* means both finger and figure in Latin. The propensity to use a decimal system seems to most students of this subject to originate from the fact that we have ten fingers. Were we endowed with a different number, probably we would have devised a different system. Aristotle himself asked the same question: "Why do all men, both foreign and Greek, count in tens, and not in any other numbers? . . . Is it because all men have ten fingers?" (Problem XV).[5]

Neurological support for this idea may be drawn from a syndrome first reported by Gerstmann in 1924 and named for him. Since then Gerstmann and other authors have reported additional cases (see Critchley, 1953). The syndrome is characterized by the following symptoms: (1) Finger agnosia. The patient is unable to recognize the fingers, so that if he is asked to move a certain finger, he is unable to find it. (2) Right-left disorientation. The patient does not

[5] Actually some people, like the Maya, counted in twenties. Their "vigesimal system" was probably the result of adding toes to fingers. It seems that an old vigesimal system existed among Celtic peoples, from which such French expressions as *quatre-vingt*, *quatre-vingt-dix* may indirectly derive. The Sumerian system (Babylonian) was based on the number 60.

know which is the right or left organ or part of his body. (3) Agraphia (or inability to write). However, the patient is able to copy, thus disclosing that there is nothing wrong with his motor function. (4) Dyscalculia. The patient is unable to make even simple calculations or to enumerate the odd or even numbers in series. (5) The hand is demoted from its status of a highly evolved tool to become a mere prehensile implement for putting food into the mouth (R. Klein, quoted by Critchley).

Gerstmann's syndrome is the result of lesions in the left parietal lobe. It discloses an anatomical and functional relation between the phenomena of finger recognition, right-left orientation, and ability to calculate.

The concept of zero

The concept of zero is a very important one in the theory of numbers. In Peano's classic formulation of arithmetic, the three fundamental concepts are zero, number, and successor. Peano named five points as the bases of arithmetic, and the concept zero appears in all of them. In his examination and elaboration of Peano's theories, Russell too (1919) attributed great importance to zero. Zero as a numerical concept, however, is an advanced achievement. Although of fundamental importance, it was absent not only from primitive systems of arithmetic but even from relatively advanced ones. People as culturally developed as the Chinese, the Egyptians, the Jews, the Greeks, the Romans, and all Europeans up to the early Renaissance did not have anything resembling zero.

The anthropologist Kroeber (1948) wrote that zero as a symbol was independently invented first by the Babylonians, then by the Maya of Guatemala and Yucatán perhaps as far back as in the fourth or third century B.C., and then by the Hindus in the sixth century A.D. The Arabs learned the concept from the Hindus and transmitted it to the Italians, and consequently to Western civilization, at the very beginning of the thirteenth century (possibly in the year 1202, through Leonardo Fibonacci, at times called Leonardo da Pisa or Leonardo Pisano). What Kroeber does not mention, however, is that the concept zero, as transmitted to us by the Hindus via the Arabs, has two different meanings. It is a curiosity of our mathematical system that these two meanings may coexist and not interfere with each other. (1) Zero may indicate a decimal position. For instance, if we add one zero to 1, we have 10. Number 1 acquires the meaning of 10 because its position has been changed by the zero. If we add two, three, etc., zeros, we have 100, 1,000, etc. With this ostensibly simple device, "positional numeration" is created. Even very large numbers can be written in a relatively simple manner. (2) Zero also may indicate nothingness, or void (the Indian idea of nullity, called *sunya*).

These two abstract concepts are not necessarily related, and not necessarily represented by the same symbol. Zero as the indicator of a decimal position is not a discovery but rather a great invention, the result of a high level of civilization. It permits the writing in simple forms of an infinite number of finitudes in the framework of the decimal system. Zero as an indicator of nullity or void is a symbolic representation of the abstract concept of nothingness. It required great creative power to transform nothingness into a figure: *zero* or 0. The infinity of nothingness becomes, so to say, finite in its abstracted numerical quality. We do not know how zero as a numerical symbol of nothingness came to be.

11° *TOWARD A UNIFYING THEORY OF COGNITION*

Can general principles be found which apply to such different levels as perception, recognition, memory, learning,
simple ideation, language, conceptual thinking, arithmetic,
etc.? If such principles are found, will they be so generic that
nothing will be added to our common knowledge?

My belief is that such an inquiry is worth being pursued,
first, because what appears simple may imply much more;
second, because principles found at a certain order of generality do not exclude the fact that each subsumed level has an
organization of its own. For instance, thinking may have some
properties which are not inherent in learning, and learning
may have some characteristics which are not inherent in perception.

In other words, following the method of Von Bertalanffy
(1956), I shall pursue a "general system theory," although
one which can be applied only to cognition, not to the whole
universe. However, since cognition plays such an important
role in the understanding of the universe, any presentation of

this kind has implications that transcend cognition itself.

This inquiry cannot follow a neurophysiological approach because we do not yet have the necessary knowledge for it, although great progress has been made (for instance, in the work of Eccles [1953, 1957]) and daring working hypotheses have been advanced (for instance, by Hebb [1949]). The author will adhere to a psychological approach. In what follows, a few new ideas will be presented and a considerable number of old ones will be examined in a new and larger context. Actually what I am going to adopt is the inductive method: from several instances, occurring at different levels of cognition, I shall infer general rules.

Sensory organization and perception

Sensory-perceptual data undergo some kind of organization as soon as they are experienced. We shall take into consideration here those sense perceptions which do not remain predominantly experiences of the inner status of the organism, but become parts of the field of cognition. These psychological phenomena seem to me to follow three types or modes of organization.

The first mode of organization is *contiguity*. Sense data experienced together tend to be re-experienced together, if they produced *one* effect in the organism by the fact of contiguity. The effect in its turn strengthens the connection between the sense data.

Figure 11–1

Let us assume that the four components of Figure 11–1 produce an effect E in the perceiving organism. The effect E binds the four components together. Obviously the qualities which the components must have in order to produce E vary with each case, but what is important is that they must be experienced together. Only those elements will be perceived together which are retained together by the feed mechanism of the effect. In stating that the elements should be experienced together, I do not mean it in an absolute sense. I mean that the perception of them is simultaneous, or overlapping, or contiguous in time or space. The organismic effect, which is important in segregating perceptual wholes from the infinity and indefiniteness of the universe, varies with the level of organization and evolution. At first it may be a not-felt chemical change; later a not-conscious nervous change; still later a felt change, etc. With the evolution of cognition, however, the immediate effect loses importance, and what counts increasingly is the externalization of the perception, more or less independently of the effect. In Figure 11–1 the four elements by being contiguous constitute a form reminiscent of a human face. However, sensory data may be experienced together even when they do not form a definite whole or a definite gestalt, but just a group. In Figure 11–2, for example, the nonsensical lines are seen as forming one "group" of lines.

Figure 11–2

The mode of operation by contiguity, which at first seems so simple, actually requires the solution, through evolutionary mechanisms, of a difficult problem which has been discussed throughout this book: response to a part versus response to a whole. In normal conditions, whole perception wins out, and the mode of perceptual organization by contiguity generally applies to the contiguity of the various parts which form differentiated wholes.

The second mode of organization is the mode of *similarity*. Figure 11–3, for example, contains dots of different shapes and colors, and the dots which are alike tend to form a separate group, or to be perceived together. Here similarity and contiguity reinforce each other. Similar or identical elements are readily associated.[1] The mode of operation by similarity applies to both part perception and whole perception.

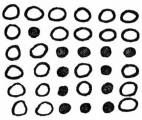

Figure 11–3

The third mode of operation is *pars pro toto:* the perception of a part has upon the organism an effect which is equivalent to that of the perception of the whole.[2] If we look at Figure 11–4, for example, we see a triangle, in spite of the fact that there are three gaps in the picture, which technically therefore is not a triangle.

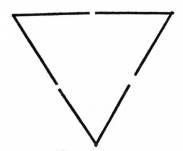

Figure 11–4

The followers of the gestalt school call this way of perceiving "closure." According to them, the closure, as a principle of organization, permits the perception of the whole; the small gaps are filled in. They consider this tendency to close a gap the expression of a fundamental principle of brain functioning. Tension is supposed to be built up on both sides

[1] Operators of newsstands often display the cover of the same magazine many times. The increase-effect is not merely due to the repetition of the advertisement, but to the fact that when similar elements are together, they reinforce one another.
[2] This mode of operation is related to what the early behaviorists, after Hollingworth, called the principle of redintegration.

of the gap until it is closed, in the same way that an electric current will jump a small gap in the electric circuit.

Let us give another look at Figure 11–4, however. Actually, the gaps are never closed. We continue to see the interruptions; but in spite of the gaps we perceive a triangle. The triangle of Figure 11–4 is not a whole triangle, but it *stands for* one. The gestaltists speak of closure because they have devised special experimental stimuli with small gaps. In fact, however, very little in nature is perceived totally. More often than it seems at first impression, we perceive parts which stand for wholes. I see only a crescent in the sky and I know I see the moon; I see only a side of the table and I know I see the table; I see only the façade of the cathedral and I know I see the cathedral. This phenomenon is not the gestaltists' simple phenomenon of closure but a general faculty of the psyche, which permits a part to stand for the whole. As will be discussed later, it is on this third mode of organization that the entire phenomenon of symbolism is based. Let us remember, however, that except for a few optical illusions purposely arranged, the whole is not experienced at a sensory level. The whole is filled in by our responses (when we react as if to wholes), or by our memories (of parts being generally associated with their respective wholes), or by symbolic processes.

Previous chapters have discussed how important the biological struggle is between part and whole, and in other writings I have shown how pathological or antievolutionary it is for the organism to confuse the part with the whole (Arieti, 1962a, 1963, 1965). Now, on the contrary, we come to the realization that the third mode of operation on which (as we shall see later) the highest levels of our cognition are based, actually consists of the ability of a part to stand for the whole. The whole seems again broken up, and a part or a few parts together seem to reassume importance. Often what is perceived is a *clue* or a *sign*, which stands for a whole. It could be that this psychic faculty which permits a part to stand for the whole is somehow based on that ancient property of the organism of responding to parts rather than to wholes (Chapter 4).

Learning

Examination of a different level of cognition, learning, shows that it also is related to the three modes of operation outlined in the previous section. By learning is generally meant a change in behavior as a result of individual experience.

Unquestionably, there is a strong relation between the mode of *contiguity*, or first mode of operation, and learning. Some learning theories, like those of Thorndike, Guthrie, and Pavlov, regard contiguity as the most important factor in learning. According to these theories, an association (that is, a relationship based on temporal or spatial contiguity) occurs between stimulus and response. For instance, in conditioning, the dog learns to salivate in response to the ringing of a bell. During the learning period, the bell is rung shortly before or at the same time that food is seen. There is thus a temporal contiguity between food (unconditioned stimulus) and ringing of the bell (conditioned stimulus). In this type of learning, a congenital response is extended to a stimulus which ordinarily would not elicit the response. Such learning is relatively simple: nothing new is added to the repertory of the dog's responses. The animal learns only to extend to a different context what it was already capable of doing.

This chapter will not discuss the many ways in which the mode of contiguity operates in learning, because numerous psychological books on learning deal with the subject. Also, it is beyond our purpose here to explore why, out of all possible associations, only some actually occur. This would require a study of the law of effect, the topic of reinforcement, etc., which were briefly reviewed in Chapter 4.

Although the mode of contiguity plays a tremendous role in learning, and is probably the mode on which the other two are founded, it is difficult to subsume all types of learning under this mechanism. What psychologists call "transfer" may be viewed as an application at the level of learning of the second mode of operation, or mode of *similarity*. An acquired response is extended to similar situations. For instance, if I have learned to avoid certain insects—say, wasps

—I may extend my avoidance reaction to similar insects, like bees. Learning by transfer is based on the fact that similar situations have identical elements (Chapter 4). Thus learning by the mode of similarity requires a power of abstraction, just as perceptual organization by the mode of similarity does. Although generally useful, learning by similarity may lead to errors when the identity of a few elements in two situations does not warrant the same response in both.

The third mode, *pars pro toto*, operates in all types of learning, even the simplest. For instance, in conditioning, when the dog secretes gastric juice in response to the buzzing of the bell, the buzzing may be seen as a part which stands for a whole (buzzing of the bell plus sight of food). At a neurophysiological level too, the entire process of learning can be seen as an application of the third mode. The activation of certain neuronal elements through the stimulus brings about the arousal of the whole neuronal circuit or patterns involved in that learning situation (Bugelski, 1956). The phenomena which gestalt psychologists attribute to insight may be viewed as based on the concomitant application of the second and third modes of operation. Thus the "insight" is due to the fact that the organism responds as it would to a previous situation because of the presence of identical elements in the old and new situations. The *identical elements* stand for the total situations.

Since the three modes of operation are mixed together in learning, the possibility is that even these three may be synthesized into just one mode. For learning, we may be tempted to reduce the whole process to the fact that reactivation of a part leads to the reactivation of the whole. However, we have to assume that prior to this reactivation the modes of contiguity and similarity have already been in operation.

Memory

We shall take into consideration only two mechanisms of memory: recognition and recall; and shall look at them only in relation to the three modes of operation. Recognition is the simpler of the two mechanisms and exists, at a more or less elaborate degree, in most animals. It means that a perception A^1, occurring now, is compared automatically or unconsciously with a past experience A and is found to be eliciting the same response as A. A^1 is then considered similar or identical to A. The first mode of operation, *contiguity*, differentiates perception A from the manifold of experiences. A will remain as a differentiated memory trace. The first mode of operation will later differentiate A^1 too. The mnemonic trace of A and the perception of A^1 are connected by the second mode of operation, *similarity*.

How this is possible at a neurophysiological level must remain a subject for speculation. Perhaps the perception of A^1 sends several "echoes" throughout the nervous system, and the only echo which is absorbed is the one received by the engram of A. The engram A thus becomes associated with the perception of A^1, reinforces this perception, and also confers the feeling of recognition. The perception of A^1, however, brings about the reactivation not only of A, but also of many things formerly associated with A. Thus we again have a *pars pro toto* mechanism.

Recall is a much more complicated mechanism. It differs from recognition in that it is not brought about by an external perception, but by a voluntary effort to reproduce stored images. Once the images are recalled, however, they also organize according to our three modes of operation.

Simple ideation, or associations of ideas

It is difficult to isolate all the cognitive forms which enter into the process of thinking. Simple ideation is a form of thinking which is organized by the laws of association. Although simple ideation is possible through sensory images, it generally consists of verbal symbols. The discussion of language in relation to the three modes of operation will be found in the next section of this chapter; here we shall examine the process of association by itself.

The study of associations of ideas, which goes back to Aristotle, has been discredited in the past fifty years by people who point out that the laws of association are too simple and mechanical to explain the whole field of cognition. Of course, any attempt to explain the whole field of cognition by the laws of association is an extreme reductionistic approach. On the other hand, the phenomenon of association of ideas must be acknowledged and recognized as one of the foundations of high levels of cognition. To discredit association because it is insufficient to explain the whole human psyche is just as inappropriate as a reductionist approach.

The first law of associations of ideas, the law of contiguity, is another expression of the mode of *contiguity*. This law states that when two mental processes have been active simultaneously or in immediate succession, the recurrence of one of them tends to elicit the recurrence of the other. For instance, if I think of my grandmother, I may also think of the home where she lived when I visited her in my childhood. The mode of contiguity which existed even in low animal forms now acquires an evocative and representational status.

The second law (or law of *similarity*) is another expression of the second mode of operation. It states that if two mental representations resemble each other—that is, if they have one or more characteristics in common—the occurrence of one of them tends to elicit the occurrence of the other. For instance, I visualize the Eiffel Tower and I may think of the Empire State Building. I think of Beethoven and I may start to think of Brahms and Mozart.

A third law, mentioned in old books of psychology, is the law of contrast. For instance, the idea of white brings about the idea of black, its opposite. Actually, contrast plays a secondary role in normal mentation, and may be subsumed under the second law (for instance, black and white are both similar, inasmuch as they are both colors). In primitive and schizophrenic thinking, however, association of opposites plays an important part, for reasons discussed elsewhere (Chapters 8 and 16).

The third law of association which I wish to propose, although it is not mentioned in other psychology books, is actually inherent in the concept of association and corresponds to our third mode of operation: *pars pro toto*. The few ideas which are associated by contiguity and similarity stand for a constellation of ideas and tend to bring about the whole constellation. For instance, the idea of my grandmother may stand for my whole childhood and evoke many memories of my childhood. This is also, in a certain way, *thinking by cue.* A small cue may arouse a complex pattern. A fragment of a situation may evoke the total situation; a member of a series may evoke the whole series.

High levels of cognition

High levels of cognition cannot be easily distinguished from one another. Some functions which appear different are based on the same fundamental processes, as can be seen from the unavoidable repetition in this section.

In language, a sound (the word) becomes connected with an object or meaning by the mode of *contiguity.* It becomes applied to all the members of the class by the mode of *similarity,* and it may stand for the denotation or connotation of one or more members of the class, or for the whole class (*pars pro toto*). Approximately the same description applies to concept formation. The mode of *contiguity* is used to collect and connect the data which form the concept. By the mode of *similarity* the concept is extended to all the members of a class. Finally, by the mode of *pars pro toto,* the concept comes to stand for the whole class.

In induction, the mode of *contiguity* makes us associate A and B because we have observed that B has followed A many times. The mode of *similarity* makes us associate all A's with all B's. The mode of *pars pro toto* causes us to extend to the whole series of A's and B's what we have observed in a segment of that series (Chapter 8).

In deduction, the whole membership of the series is included in the big premise; for instance, all men are mortal. The big premise is made possible by the fact that the mode of *contiguity* (which connects "men" and "being mortal") is used together with the mode of *similarity,* which extends the concept to the whole series (all men). The third mode (*pars pro toto*) is also applied in the big premise, since the symbol "all men" stands for the whole class (all past, present, and future men). The second premise (Socrates is a man), by following the mode of *similarity*, makes us attribute to Socrates membership in the series of men. The inference which we shall be able to draw, again using the mode of similarity, will apply to Socrates the characteristics of the members of the class of men.

In deterministic causality, the process is more or less the same as that for induction: an association is made between B and A (mode of *contiguity*). The association is extended to all the sequences A → B. Inasmuch as this law will be applied to all similar data in the cosmos, it will follow the *pars pro toto* mode.

The three modes also apply, of course, to arithmetical thinking. Although all numbers imply the three modes, we could say that in number 1 the mode of contiguity predominates. In fact, by the contiguity of parts, a unity is formed which is separated from the rest of the world and will be later recognized as 1. In number 2 the mode of similarity predominates. In fact, unless objects are at the same time seen as distinct and similar, no concept of 2 or of any subsequent plurality is possible. The properties of 1 and 2 and of 1 and 2 together are then applied by *pars pro toto* to the whole series of positive integer numbers (Chapter 10).

Unifying hypotheses

At this point perhaps we can conclude that the three basic modes of operation determine and structure our knowledge of the world. The first mode determines *what is and what is not*. What *is* constitutes a unity. The second mode *identifies*, by revealing similarity, or identity, and permitting class formation. The third mode *infers* the not given from the given.

These three modes could really be considered three basic pre-experiential categories. We can, however, represent the general process of cognition by a different formulation and say that it is based on two fundamental characteristics: progressive abstraction and progressive symbolization. The first mode abstracts unities and groups from the manifold of the universe. The second mode abstracts the similarity between different unities. The third mode abstracts (that is, infers) the not-given from the given.

Abstraction, important as it is, however, does not comprehend the whole cognitive process. Symbolization has to be added. If we include both signs and symbols under the general process of symbolization, we can say that even a perception is a symbol, inasmuch as it stands for the perceived thing. Images, endocepts, paleosymbols, and verbal symbols, both preconceptual and conceptual, are different forms of progressive symbolization.

The ideal symbol is the symbol which, although different from the thing it represents, has the same properties as the represented thing. The symbol which comes closest to this ideal is not the onomatopoietic symbol or the iconic symbol, but the number. Although the number is not the thing that it represents, it has the numerical properties of the represented things. For instance, the symbol 15, although a symbol, has all the numerical properties of the group of 15 integer objects. Although 15 is an abstract symbol, it retains its concrete numerical qualities. At the same time it is independent of its concrete embodiments and other concrete qualities, so that it permits the best possible identification with any of its embodiments.[3]

We can therefore say that abstraction includes all the modes of operation, whereas symbolization is a different name for the third. Although there may be some merit in conceiving cognition in this way, the writer's preference is for retaining the formulation of the three modes of operation. It seems to come closer to a unifying theory of cognition.

The question may be asked whether these three modes of operation rule the other important areas of the psyche—for instance, the experiences of inner status (whether sensations or emotions). The answer is that if we separate feelings from their cognitive associations, it will be very difficult to apply the three basic modes to them. Unity of feeling as feeling is hazy at best. Moreover, if a feeling—like a pain, for *instance*

---

[3] We could make approximately the same statement about algebraic symbols; n is independent of any embodiment and yet retains all its algebraic qualities.

—is recognized as similar to a previous feeling, this act of recognition is a cognitive act. Feelings do not have the finiteness nor the potential symbolic infinity of acts of cognition, unless they are associated with acts of cognition. However, they do have the power to transform or determine cognitive processes.

The biological origin of knowledge and the mesocosmic reality

It would seem that the basic principles of cognitive organization are responsible for the way we interpret reality. Saying this is tantamount to advocating a biological origin of knowledge.

Let us re-examine briefly some of the basic concepts we have dealt with in this book. The ability to perceive wholes and parts eventually led man to distinguish subjects and predicates. The ability to recognize, or to respond in the same way to, similar or identical things led to the formation of classes and to the laws of Aristotelian logic. The excluded middle, or the third law of thought of Aristotle, represents the victory of identifying by wholes rather than by parts. Our process of induction is nothing else but the subjectivization of the inducting capacity of the animal organism.

We must add something to which we have not yet referred: space perception. Three-dimensional or Euclidian space is based not so much on our visual perceptions, as some people believe, but on our vestibular apparatus with its three semicircular canals. It is not owing to chance that we perceive space as we do: we have no choice.

Thus our whole interpretation of nature is imposed on us by the biological origin of our cognition. Moreover, it would seem that *the psyche brings to awareness what was already implied in the living matter.*

Does this mean that in our understanding of the world we use a priori categories? For instance, are the three basic modes of operation that I have described a priori categories? I think they are, but not in the Kantian sense; I believe that the animal organism, through evolutionary mechanisms, has assimilated them from the external world. They are a priori as far as the individual is concerned. However, they are a posteriori if we consider evolution as a whole. Evolution has to "learn" them from the external environment and transmit them from generation to generation.

These *biologicogenic categories* permit man to conceive the universe in a frame of reference which seems to reflect the Euclidian-Newtonian-Kantian approach. Thus, in a certain way, they seem antiquated in a world which is viewed today in Einsteinian-Heisenbergian terms. To give just two examples of fundamental importance: (1) We perceive space as three-dimensional, but modern non-Euclidian geometry considers it more appropriate to consider space non-three-dimensional. (2) We have seen how not only our cognition but life itself is based on the reliability of induction. And yet we know that according to Heisenberg's principle of indeterminacy, the ideas of exceptionless repetitions, induction, and strict causality have to be abandoned.

Reichenbach (1951) and Čapek (1957) made it clear that modern physics does not deny the validity of the Euclidian-Newtonian-Kantian world. It only restricts it to the mesocosm, a world of middle dimensions. For the microcosm (a world of subatomic dimensions) or the macrocosm (a world larger than solar systems), the Einsteinian-Heisenbergian physics applies.

But life exists in the mesocosm. In order to originate and evolve, it had to incorporate mesocosmic laws. Without such incorporation, life could not exist. On the other hand, the fact that life exists proves there is some order in the mesocosm. Perhaps it is an order which applies only to the mesocosm, but in its restricted dimensions it exists and has to be taken into account. If a man were deprived of his three semicircular canals and consequently of equilibrium and space perception, he could not survive for more than a few days unless helped by others. If the principle of induction did not apply to life, the living world would be transformed into chaos.

The order which we, as animal forms, have incorporated is then re-externalized or projected into the external world where it originated. What Euclid, Newton, and Kant did was to increase our awareness of mesocosmic categories and to enlarge our understanding of the mesocosmic reality of which we are the products. The categories represent what we have acquired from mesocosmic reality through a process of evolutionary adjustment. It would have been unnatural for Euclid to describe a non-three-dimensional space.

We often hear Freud criticized because he viewed the human psyche in restricted Euclidian-Newtonian-Kantian terms. Alas, this is not the error of Freud: The psyche itself —all of life as it is known to us—is based on the Euclidian-Newtonian-Kantian world. If some aspects of life do not follow mesocosmic categories, neither Freud nor anybody else could have demonstrated the fact at that stage of our knowledge. The error Freud made was to apply to the psyche, especially in relation to the libido theory, concepts which pertain only to physics and economics, thus bypassing general biology and neurophysiology. Einsteinian-Heisenbergian notions, which are usually derived from the physical world, would be equally inappropriate if transplanted in their original form to the study of the psyche. And modern economics is no more applicable to the inner world than the economics of Freud's day was.

We must add an important qualification, however, to the statement that the order of cognition derives from the order of the mesocosm. At least one aspect of psychological life does not seem to come from the mesocosmic environment: awareness, or subjectivity. As far as we know, only animal life is endowed with awareness. Automatic cognition can be seen as existing outside of the animal kingdom—and not exclusively in modern computers made by men, either. For instance, a solar system can be viewed as a machine which reflects a cosmic order—a machine which in spite of its immensity is not, as far as we know, aware of its existence. Cognition acquires a human flavor when it is accompanied by awareness and thus leads to the possibility of making choices and of *willing*.

Does the fact that our knowledge is mesocosmic in origin deny us access to the understanding of a macro- and microcosmic reality, or of an absolute or noumenal reality? Excursions into these other segments of reality are difficult because of the biological limitations of man. That is why they have occurred so late in history. Nevertheless they are possible, as modern physics shows. This author's belief (or, perhaps wish) is that our mesocosmic knowledge, particularly the *pars pro toto* mode of operation, will permit men to understand not only the microcosm and the macrocosm but realms of reality now unimaginable and unthinkable. In fact, the *pars pro toto* mode implies that if a small order exists, a large order also exists. But in believing this, I am making an unwarranted generalization—applying to the unknown the inductive method which I know may be valid only in the mesocosm. This belief, then, must remain a belief.

12 ⊚ CONATION

Movement

Before life appeared on earth, all movement was more or less directly related to physico-chemical phenomena, solar energy, and the force of gravity. With the advent of animal life, evolutionary mechanisms selected and preserved adaptive movements; that is, movements which enhance survival. When awareness emerged in animal species, some movements became purposeful, as they facilitated the seeking of pleasure and/or the avoidance of pain. During the evolution of cognitive faculties, movements became more and more directed by different motivations, until eventually they were controlled by man's various conceptualizations and will.

Conation in a broad sense means the ability of the conscious organism to *direct* movements. We must exclude from conation those body movements which, although adaptive, are not consciously directed. A broad classification of movements into conative and nonconative, although useful for didactic purposes, is not accurate, because in many instances movements which are beyond awareness or control become conscious or controllable. Often it is difficult to determine when the movement ceases to be automatic and unconscious. Also, some movements which are beyond control are nevertheless conscious and goal-directed, and therefore are included under conation.

The topic of conation is even more complicated because, at least theoretically, it implies a knowledge of what movement is. Many philosophers through the ages have tried to understand the phenomenon of movement. From the original meaning of change of position, this word came to mean any change (in Latin *mutatio* or *permutatio*). Anaximander saw movement as a quality which pertains to the cosmic totality. Aristotle saw in it the actualization of entelechy, Avicenna a volitional or psychic component.

Perhaps Bergson is the philosopher who has studied movement from a point of view closest to the psychological (1912). Bergson felt that when we analyze a movement we decompose it, and we find out that the moving body was at different positions. We may increase these positions indefinitely, but what we get then is an increasing number of "immobile views of its mobility." In other words, we become aware of the numerous positions of the object, but not of the movement itself, which will continue to elude our inquiry.

We could define movement as "a change of position," but this would be a circular definition, because the word *change* includes movement. We must reluctantly accept a certain naïveté and take for granted that we know what movement is, at least when it refers to a living organism.

Animal movement has been intensely studied. Even a cursory examination of books of neuroanatomy and neurophysiology discloses how much their content deals with movement and its control. Although directed movement is by no means completely understood, many more pages are devoted to this subject than, for instance, to affective and cognitive functions, which are even less understood in their anatomico-physiological nature.[1] Directed movement is one of the most efficient tools the organism possesses for adjusting to the ex-

---

[1] Movement is studied in the peripheral nervous system, at a spinal level, at suprasegmental levels, including the cerebellum, the hypothalamus, the thalamus, the nucleus lenticularis, and finally the motor and premotor cortex. A directed movement, to be carried out, requires at least the cooperation of the pyramidal, extrapyramidal, spinocerebellar, and vestibular systems.

The Evolving of the Self © 202

ternal environment. It extends the automatic and reflex mechanisms, which the organism has acquired genetically through a large number of favorable mutations.

In what follows we shall try to outline the main developmental stages of directed motor behavior, from primitive adaptive biological mechanisms to the appearance of various types of motivation and of human will. Our knowledge of this immense evolutionary process, which took billions of years to unfold, is at a rudimentary stage. We can only attempt to distinguish some of the major trends.

Preconation and primary conation

According to Schneirla, any organism's first types of movement are those of approaching a stimulus or withdrawing from it (1939, 1949, 1959). This is a fundamental activity to be found in all animal forms, from the most primitive to the most complicated. Schneirla, who calls his interpretation the theory of biphasic processes, has reported in detail the evidence from protozoan to man that he has accumulated in support of it. For him approach means the coming nearer to the source of the stimulus; withdrawal means increasing the distance from the source of stimulus. Schneirla correctly points out that withdrawal does not necessarily imply "avoiding," just as approach does not necessarily imply "seeking or searching for." Avoiding and seeking are higher functions which occur only in high phyletic forms. Both withdrawal and approach are adaptive, as they enhance survival.

According to Schneirla, we can make the following generalization for all organisms in early ontogenetic stages: Low intensities of stimulation tend to evoke approach reactions, high intensities withdrawal reactions. These are forced reaction types which permutate through the evolutionary scale "to provide the basis for psychologically advanced types, such as seeking or avoiding." For instance, "insects are superior to protozoans, and mammals to insects, in that ontogeny progressively frees processes of individual motivation from the basic formula. . . ." (Schneirla, 1959). That is, whereas early in phylogeny and ontogeny the two types of reaction are engendered by the low or high intensity of stimulation, in later stages of development the type of reaction is determined by the pleasantness or unpleasantness of the stimulus.

The withdrawal reaction will eventually unfold into the system of movements which follow the experiences of fear, threat, and anxiety. Withdrawal will become avoidance or flight. The approach reaction is determined by a hunger-thirst–reducing stimulus or by a sexual stimulus. At this level the feeling is what I have called appetite (Chapter 3). At a higher level, however, we find that approach may be motivated not only by appetite, but also by rage, or a combination of appetite and rage. This occurs when the animal does not flee from the adversary but fights it, either in order to chase it away or in order to consume its flesh.

Generally at an exoceptual level, conation consists of relatively simple and relatively fixed patterns of motor behavior, which occur in response to either physiostates or elementary emotions. In Chapter 3 we concluded that at an exoceptual level there is a coincidence between cognition and motivation. We can add that at that level all three dimensions of the psyche (cognition, motivation, and conation) overlap and seem to be only three different aspects of the same basic integrating process. However, greater and greater differentiation of these dimensions occurs at higher levels, when high emotions and high cognitive processes impose detours and postponement of gratifications.

In my view, Schneirla's theory of biphasic processes is a great step in the understanding of animal behavior, including man's behavior. For the evidence supporting this theory, the reader is referred to Schneirla's works. Here I shall only summarize his conclusions that the primitive biphasic processes continue in the biphasic organization of the autonomic nervous system of high species, where the parasympathetic concerns mainly the functions of approach and the sympathetic the functions of withdrawal. It is interesting to note that the parasympathetic nervous system controls the functions of ingestion and digestion. Thus approach can be reduced in many cases to oral contact with an ingestible stimulus. The sympathetic system mainly controls emergency types of behavior. Perhaps the processes of agonistic and antagonistic muscular functions which Sherrington illustrated (1948) are related to the biphasic processes.[2]

Protovolitional conation

Conation includes some phenomena which can be called *protovolitional*, because they can be considered immature forms of volitional activity. Although two types of protovolitional behavior can be encountered in subhuman animals, both are found with greater frequency and complexity in children. One consists of spontaneous and playful activity. A baby who grabs rattles or other objects toward the fifth or sixth month of age cannot be considered endowed with mature volition. His actions are directed by pleasure seeking and gratification. There seems to be no hesitation, conflict, or choice in these actions, which therefore cannot be considered willed. On the other hand, they do not seem compulsive or impulsive in the usual meaning of these terms. Using a different expression, we can say that at this stage there is no differentiation between pleasure seeking and will.

The other early form of protovolitional conation is imitation. By imitation we mean *the copying of an act for which there is no instinctive pattern*. Thorpe, briefly reviewing the subject of imitation in subhumans, concludes that up to primates there is very little of this behavior. Vaguely imitative actions which have been reported by several authors are just a local following of "pioneer animals" by other animals which happen to be nearby (1956). Yerkes (1943) and Hayes and Hayes (1951), however, have found scientific corroboration of the popular notion that apes have the habit of imitating.

[2] Recent neurological findings seem to corroborate Schneirla's theory. Apraxic disorders have been recently divided by Denny-Brown into two categories: (1) magnetic apraxia, where all the contactual reactions (approaching reactions) are perseverated; (2) repellent apraxia, in which all withdrawal responses are perseverated (Denny-Brown, 1950, 1958; Denny-Brown and Chambers, 1958).

He writes, "We believe that these two types of response represent two areas of normal organization, positive and negative, of the tropisms to the environment managed by the cerebral cortex. Damage to the mechanism of either one releases abnormal activity of the other" (1958).

There is no doubt that imitation occurs to a much greater extent in human beings than in primates. McDougall felt that emotional responses are also imitations of emotional expressions observed in others (1926). Although he is correct in some cases, most of the time imitation consists of a perceptual evaluation of behavior of other members of the same species and the learning of the same mechanisms of behavior. However, we must be careful not to confuse pseudoimitation with real imitation. Asch gives the following example of pseudoimitation: A 4-month-old baby often smiles in response to the smile of an adult (1952). This is not an act of imitation, because the baby's perception is visual, but his response is kinesthetic. He does not see himself smile and is not aware of the mechanisms which make him adopt the adult's facial expression.

Both in subhuman animals and in children, it is often difficult to determine whether we are dealing with simple acts of imitation or with pseudoimitation. Some of these copied actions take place almost unconsciously and would seem similar to the smiling response of the baby. However, they require learned voluntary movements and not congenital reactions. Often they seem to be based more on an "osmotic" relation to the environment than on a fully volitional determination to imitate. This type of osmotic imitation is not directly or forcibly imposed by the adults. It is welcomed by them, however, and their approval has the value of a reinforcement.

Observing is not sufficient for real imitation; an understanding of what is observed and an ability to produce an equivalent motor act are necessary. It is impossible at this stage of our knowledge to understand the mechanism by which the observation of an action leads to the unfolding of a chain of coordinated movements which reproduces the action.

A less immature type of protovolition consists of the ability to inhibit consciously. The individual experiences the possibility of a choice: He can either allow the discharge of primitive mechanisms into overt behavior (withdrawal or approach, reflex action, instinctual responses, "imprinted" behavior, protoemotions, exocepts, adventitious or immature movements, basic physiologic responses, etc.), or he can inhibit these mechanisms. The neurological mechanisms of inhibition are complex and will not be discussed here.[3]

Although the normal young child develops these inhibitory mechanisms, they are still difficult and unpleasant for him, and he would not use them if other human beings did not train him to do so. For instance, when his rectum is distended by feces, it would be easier for the baby to relieve himself and defecate, but during toilet training he learns not to do so because he understands that another person (generally the mother) does not want him to. Thus, in early childhood, behavior acquires a new dimension when it becomes connected with the anticipation of how other people will respond to that behavior. A behavioral unity ceases to be just a movement, a physiological function, or a pleasure-seeking activity on the part of the individual: it acquires a social dimension and thereby becomes *an action.* Thus, even in the primitive volitional acts which imply choices, a new dimension, the interpersonal, enters.

From a philosophical point of view it seems a contradiction in terms that the first acts of real or choice-requiring volition should be not real choices but acts of obedience, submission to the will of others, or at least approval-seeking devices. Yet it is a fact that the portentous tool of choice making that emerges in phylogeny with the human race cannot, in the earliest ontogenetic stages, be exercised independently of others and almost denies itself in the act of emerging from involuntary conation. At this time the child learns to will an increasingly large number of acts, which are wanted by his mother. In other words, he learns "to choose" as mother and the other adults around him would want him to choose.

The child is in a state of receptivity, imitation, and suggestibility, which permits him to understand and to introject forms of behavior from the surrounding adults. Without this stage of receptivity, his psychological development would not continue. But we must distinguish two forms of introjection: at times the child introjects by spontaneous imitation, as we have seen earlier in this chapter. At other times he

[3] For the importance of the mechanisms of inhibition at various levels of development, see the monograph by Diamond, Balvin, and Diamond (1963).

assimilates patterns of behavior that he feels the adults want him to reproduce. In the second case, there is a certain imperativeness in the attitude of the surrounding adults. The adult is experienced as giving a command, which the child has to obey in order not to displease or in order to please. This imperative other who imposes his will and, in an apparently paradoxical way, teaches the child to will on his own, is in some respects similar to the Freudian superego. In order not to feel guilty, the child obeys. If his guilt feeling and anxiety persist, he may develop obsessive-compulsive ritualistic symptoms.

In later years the child does not remember that these habits were impositions from others; he believes that he has willed them. All this is reminiscent of what occurs in hypnosis. Although the evidence is only analogic, we may postulate as a working hypothesis, which needs much more investigation, that hypnosis is an artificial reproduction (and perhaps exaggeration) of this stage of receptivity, imitation, and suggestibility which occurs spontaneously at an early stage of phylogenetic and ontogenetic development. The hypnotized person, like the child who is extremely receptive to the will of others, does not remember who gave the instructions or suggestions (Arieti, 1960; Spiegel, 1959). Meares has recently advanced his atavistic theory of hypnosis, which is similar to this one (1960).

The act of liberation from the influence or suggestion of others appears ontogenetically during the negativistic stage. During this stage children refuse to do what they are told, and by disobeying, practice their newly acquired ability to will. They want to assert themselves, but they do so by resisting the suggestions of the surrounding adults. Inhibition now no longer involves primitive functions, like the inhibition of reflex, automatic, or elementary physiologic behavior; it is inhibition of behavior willed by others. At times the child's refusal to do what the adult wants him to do is accompanied by an act which is the opposite of what the adult wishes. Here acting with approval is not only resisted, but replaced by the opposite act, a mechanism which perhaps again follows the archaic biphasic character of primitive conation. A period of negativism at a higher level occurs in some adolescents when they try to assert their individuality by resisting parental-societal influences.

The study of primitive man reveals phylogenetic equivalents of these early ontogenetic stages of volition. As discussed earlier, Diamond has advanced a plausible theory that the first words were used as verbs in the imperative tense (Chapter 7). In very primitive groups of men, the first imitative or "voluntary" actions possibly reproduced the two basic opposite movements which we consider elaborations of Schneirla's primitive approach and withdrawal. Chapter 7 referred to biphasic conation in relation to the formation of opposite meanings. It could be that in a social situation, the selection of one rather than the other of the two basic movements was determined either by imitation of others or by what was experienced as a command.

At a certain stage of societal organization, a deep sense of obedience seems necessary for acculturation and socialization. Uncritical acceptance of ideas from a strong person may have relieved the insecurity of primitive people, insecurity which was caused by the paleologic permutability of their thinking (Chapter 5). Individual primitive man, as an independent doer, tends to feel guilty very easily. To do is to be potentially guilty because, after all, you cannot know exactly what event will follow what you are doing. It might have an effect on the whole tribe; its repercussions might be enormous, such as an epidemic or a drought. Kelsen has illustrated this relation between *to do* and *to be guilty* in the primitive (1943). In order to diminish his feeling of guilt, primitive man refrains from acting freely; he performs only those acts which are accepted by the tribe. The tribe teaches the individual what act to perform for any desired effect. Ritualism and magic thus originate. By performing each act according to ritual, primitive man removes the anxiety that arises from the expectation of possible evil effects. The ritual ensures that the effect will be good.

In some respects, the development of civilization can be seen as a process of gradually acquiring freedom from reliance on leaders or on ritual. In some regressive forms of societal organizations, like the fascist, absolute reliance on the leader, blind obedience, quasi-hypnotic effects on crowds, guilt feelings for individual actions, and expansion of ceremonial practices again become important aspects of human life.

Volition

Mature volition requires (1) the ability to evaluate several alternatives, (2) the choice of one alternative, (3) the planning of the chosen alternative, (4) the will (or determination) to carry out the chosen and planned alternative, (5) the motor execution of the chosen alternative. The fifth step actually presupposes an additional one: (6) inhibition, since, in order to will, the individual must be able to inhibit the nonwilled forms of behavior.

These six steps are not easily differentiated. They overlap and blend into one another, and often one implies some of the others. Because the first three steps are actually cognitive processes, no mature volition is possible in the absence of high cognitive faculties. It is with step 4 that conation is added to cognition to permit willed behavior.

As Terzuolo and Adey write, our physiological knowledge of willed movement is "very meager" (1960). These authors add that none of the known neurophysiological data can account for the initiation and arrest of movement, nor for the purposive changes made in the course of a movement on the basis of previous experience. There is considerable proof that sudden starting or stopping of motor activities takes place through the pyramidal fibers in the primary motor area. However, information has already been integrated in other neural centers before executive orders are transmitted to the motor area. The neurophysiology of the inhibitory mechanisms which permit choice has been reviewed by Diamond, Balvin, and Diamond (1963).[4]

Volition is not a favorite topic in American psychology and psychiatry.[5] The concept is reputed to be in opposition to

[4] Of course, inhibition is also part of simpler functions of the nervous system. For instance, in the mechanism of a local reflex, all antagonistic or conflicting acts must be inhibited (Coghill, 1930; Herrick, 1948). According to Coghill, a reflex consists of two components, one excitatory and the other inhibitory.

[5] In Europe this topic has received some consideration, especially by Ach (1935) and Bostroem (1928).

the basic tenet of scientific determinism and therefore is relegated to philosophy. The indeterminacy principle of Heisenberg does not seem applicable to the psyche, which, as we have seen, appears to follow the laws of the Euclidian-Newtonian-Kantian cosmology (Chapter 11). *Undetermined* does not mean *willed*.

Actually volition, like awareness, is a characteristic which makes it impossible to approach man as if he were a complicated physico-chemical machine. A machine reacts to environmental forces according to the same laws which govern inorganic matter. Even the subhuman animal organism, which cannot refrain from responding to physiological needs, appetites, or wishes, can be seen as a reacting, not a choosing, entity.

There is no doubt that volition is a difficult subject, but to deny that it exists because it complicates our schemata, or because it does not fit with certain mechanistic theories that we hold, is to take a reductionistic attitude like that of people who for similar reasons refuse to recognize the phenomenon of consciousness.

This writer cannot presume to clarify the process of volition, but wishes to reaffirm that it is at least partially psychological and is mediated by the nervous system. I should also like to point out three errors commonly made in studying this phenomenon. The first error goes back to Socrates' teachings, as reported by Plato in the dialogue *Meno*. According to this viewpoint the individual chooses, and then puts into effect what he thinks is the best choice. To will is thus to know—namely, to know what is the best or the right choice.

Possibly Socrates and Plato meant that once the individual fully understands all the consequences of his acts and is able to consider them in terms of ethical theory (the intellectual search for what is universally good, beautiful, and true), he cannot help but do the right thing. If a man acts contrary to reason, it is because he does not have sufficient knowledge. Plato's concept is not accepted by any legal system. It seems rather naïve and contrary to the daily observation that people do not always choose what their reason tells them is the right or best alternative. Plato's viewpoint takes into consideration only the first three of the steps listed at the beginning of this section, and not all the six which are necessary for mature volition.

The second error, which is made frequently by the majority of modern psychological schools and especially by the Freudian school, is to confuse volition with motivation. This is the same error made by some philosophical schools, who equated will with what in Latin was called *appetitio*. According to this viewpoint, to will means to *wish*, or to choose the wished alternative. Actually, Freud stressed the point that to follow the wish is to live according to the pleasure principle and not according to the reality principle. The child learns that some wishes should not be actualized. If he actualizes them, some unpleasant effect will be brought about by environmental forces existing either in his family or in society at large. The child has the choice of either actualizing or inhibiting the forbidden wish. Furthermore, throughout his life the individual will find himself confronted with many contrasting wishes. He must choose among them. Chapter 9 has already examined this problem from the point of view of motivation.

At times the individual chooses a course of action not in accordance with the strongest of his wishes, but in contrast to it. For an act of will may consist of resisting a wish—or resisting the strongest wish. For instance, this occurs when a man, following the ethical principle, decides on a plan of action which will be beneficial not to him but to others, or to his ideals. Critics of this point of view believe that willing to resist the wish is also determined by a wish—namely, the wish to resist the wish. We must partially accept this point of view and state that to act ethically, and not for the exclusive benefit of oneself, is also motivated action. As discussed in Chapter 9, ethical motivation belongs to one of the different levels of motivation. We could say that it is a volitional function to choose the motivation, even the weakest, when the cognitive processes have permitted the visualization of the different choices and their effects.

The possibility of choosing among the motivations permits the entrance of an entire universe of values. No value exists for man as long as he cannot choose. When volition appears, evolution in its strictly biological aspect has run its course. The law of the jungle (or of the pleasure principle), which

Darwin illustrated and by which he explained selective evolution, is now in competition with values which permit even the weak, the defective, and the generally unfit to survive and to be respected in their human dignity. The entrance of choice creates the possibility of a revolution greater than the Copernican revolution and capable of repealing the principles of biological evolution and establishing principles of ethics.

Choice permits the attributing of value even to needs, experiences, or things which existed before the possibility of choice emerged. For instance, primitive pleasures become hedonistic values once man has the prerogative of accepting or rejecting them. Perhaps even more important than choice of action is commitment. With this word we mean the determination to pledge to a given purpose not only our present but also our future actions.

The third mistake commonly made in the study of volition is that of assuming extremist positions—for instance, denying will altogether and accepting only the existence of motivation as the psychological determinant of action. According to this point of view, shared by many psychoanalysts of Freudian as well as neo-Freudian orientation, every act is motivated, not freely chosen. Thus the will does not determine the choice, but the motivation (conscious or unconscious), or the strongest of the possible motivations. If motivation removes the possibility of free choice, then the only act of free will would be the one which is not motivated. But an act which is not motivated at all is not performed *voluntarily* by any human being: it is automatic. Some psychoanalysts believe that everything follows conscious or, most of the time, unconscious determinism and that we fool ourselves into believing that we choose. For instance, acting against wish A is an effect of wish B. But even wish B, which on the surface looks like a willful determination, rests on another unconscious wish C.

Some philosophers and legislators, who are concerned with individual legal responsibility, take the opposite stand that a completely free choice exists. To them the will is like a sphincter, and it is up to the individual to contract or relax the sphincter when certain potential actions exert pressure to pass through. "Partial" choice and "partial" volition would thus be inherent contradictions from this viewpoint. They appear as contradictions, however, only if we forget the tortuous courses the psyche has to go through before reaching certain positions. We may, for instance, remember that what at times have seemed to mankind to be logical and final truths actually originated from paleological errors. Although men may still be under the influence of a general universal determinism, our range of choices or relative freedom is always increasing. This increase is obvious when we compare different levels of development in the phylogenetic and ontogenetic scales. It is also a common experience that our possibilities for choosing our behavior expand in the state of mental health and tend to become more rigid, or reduced to fixed, more automatic, and less voluntary patterns, in mental illness. Moreover, human creativity increases the range of possible forms of experience and of behavior for all men. Creativity is not restricted to practical and immediate goals but expands the realm of our ideals and ethical concepts.

Should we abandon the concept of absolute freedom? Not necessarily, if we follow an example from the more advanced science of physics. According to Galileo's principle, each body will continue in its uniform motion until it is made to deviate by an outside force. As far as we can ascertain, this principle is true, at least for the mesocosm. The whole field of mechanics is based on it; and yet there is no body in the universe that is not subjected to outside forces—for instance, to the force of gravity. Undeviated motion thus does not exist in reality; it is only a concept, but a concept which contributes to an understanding of any motion of the mesocosm.

I hope I am not following a fallacious analogy by advancing the idea that undetermined or free will may exist in the same way that undeviated motion exists. The concept of free will may be retained as an ideal that accompanies man in his ethical journey. In following this ideal, we renew the endless effort to transcend our deterministic origin and to add a historical dimension to the physico-chemical and biological orders of the universe. We constantly revise our actions, our choices, our ideas, our feelings. We come to the conclusion that ultimately more important than how we feel and what we think is what we do.

PART II

The Psychopathological Transformation

13 ⊙ GENERAL ASPECTS OF PSYCHOPATHOLOGY

Vicissitudes of various kinds may alter the psychological process and bring about psychiatric conditions. In Part II we shall examine five important groups of psychopathological transformations. No attempt will be made to offer a classification of psychiatric syndromes. Such classifications, always difficult, become impossible when we do not take into consideration all the factors involved, such as the organic basis of some conditions and the social factors that engender or facilitate others.

This presentation will be divided in the following way:

1. Disorders involving the highest levels of integration: Syndromes characterized by feelings of unfulfillment and arrest of motivation (Chapter 14)
2. Disorders characterized by a reversal of conscious motivation: Psychopathic states (Chapter 15)
3. Disorders characterized by a psychologic transformation incompatible with reality: Psychoses (Chapter 16)

4. Disorders characterized by a dystonic transformation: Psychoneuroses (Chapter 17)
5. Disorders predominantly involving movement and action (Chapter 18)

Organic conditions, psychosomatic syndromes, and sexual deviations will not be included. This chapter presents a brief introductory description of the basic pathological mechanisms occurring in the various clinical pictures. Several of them were originally described in classic psychoanalysis, but will be re-examined here in the framework of this study. I shall then discuss psychopathology in general from the points of view of determinism, adaptation, purposefulness, and preservation of the self.

Basic psychopathological mechanisms

Arrest. This condition occurs when the psyche or some of its functions do not unfold beyond a certain level of maturation. The point of arrest determines the degree of immaturity relatively to the usual pattern of development.

The best-known forms of arrest occur in various types of mental deficiency. They are engendered by genetic abnormalities or by organic alterations occurring in the intrauterine life of the fetus or early in life, before the nervous system has reached complete maturation. However, arrest often occurs in functional disorders: the person remains in a state of psychological immaturity relative to his age. The arrest may be of a general type or confined to some areas of the psyche. It may be permanent or may be followed by resumption of development. In the latter case it is proper to speak of delay of development rather than arrest.

A condition of arrest is often difficult to recognize, and in some cases the arrest is so slight as to make the therapist question whether it should really be considered pathological. Some immature traits are present in most people. At times they even confer a touch of diversity that contrasts pleasurably with the rest of the personality.

It should not be thought that arrest always occurs early in

life, or that the arrest is at the most immature forms of development. As a matter of fact, some persons can develop as far as the level of adjustment, but not of self-expansion (Chapter 9).

Reversal of motivation. Reversal occurs when the patient behaves in accordance with low levels of motivation, although he is potentially capable of functioning at higher levels (see Chapter 9). At least episodically, he not only cannot reach the level of self-expansion, but cannot even actualize the level of adjustment. The arrow of motivation points backward, toward the level of quick gratification.

Reversed motivation is often unconscious and in contrast with conscious motivation. In these cases additional basic psychopathological mechanisms, to be considered later, are needed to render the reversed motivation unconscious. With one exception (Robbins, 1955), the unconscious state of reversed motivation has been stressed by all schools of psychoanalysis, Freudian and neo-Freudian.

The reversal of motivation remains conscious in psychopathic states, as we shall see in detail in Chapter 15.

Motivational viscosity. By this is meant a condition in which the patient cannot give up some aims. He is not capable of the psychological reorganization required for the act of renouncing. Generally, motivational viscosity refers to psychoneurotics who harbor a grandiose self-image and cannot relinquish great expectations for themselves. This mechanism is found also in schizophrenics, drug addicts, and other types of patients. In the stubborn fixation of aims, motivational viscosity may become similar to arrest.

Disintegration. In this state certain levels of the psyche become disorganized, so that their functions are grossly impaired, eliminated, or blocked. Disintegration is engendered by organic factors as well as by intense tension and extreme anxiety. In its turn, disintegration causes the patient additional tension and anxiety when he realizes that he cannot function properly. A vicious circle is thus established.

Most of the time disintegration is a transitory phenomenon, because the psyche attempts a reorganization with the use of other basic pathological mechanisms, especially regression, somatization, and repression.

Introjection and projection. Generally these are normal mechanisms, required in the process of object relation and in all mental processes from perception to language acquisition.

In abnormal introjection, the patient attributes to the self qualities, actions, and feelings which belong to others or to fantasized others. In abnormal projection, as first described by Freud in 1896, the patient attributes to others feelings, actions, intentions, and ideas which originate in the self. When these feelings, actions, ideas, intentions, or determinations are attributed to inanimate objects and nonhuman organisms, we have a particular type of projection called *animism.*

The most pronounced forms of pathological introjection are found in psychotic depression. The most pronounced forms of pathological projection are found in paranoia and the paranoid type of schizophrenia.

Regression.[1] Contrary to the classic psychoanalytic use of this word, I do not mean by regression literally that the individual as a whole has returned to an earlier stage of development, but that he uses some mechanisms which are more typical of earlier developmental stages.[2]

Regression may be arrested at a given level or may proceed toward more immature levels. As a mechanism of the central nervous system, it is related to what Hughlings Jackson called dissolution. Jackson demonstrated that when a high level (for instance, the cerebral cortex) is diseased, the functions of that level are absent (negative symptoms), and the functions of a lower level, which are usually inhibited, re-emerge (positive symptoms).

In Jackson's view, regression (or, as he called it, dissolution) is a completely mechanistic or deterministic process. The high level is eliminated by an organic disease, and the

[1] A word which some authors use as a synonym of regression is dedifferentiation.
[2] This concept of regression as the availability of unusual mechanisms has been stressed by Bieber (1958).

organism operates at the lower levels, which are left intact. We shall see in the next section of this chapter that his interpretation of regression is too simple.

Regression is predominantly a cognitive alteration, but it also involves drastic changes in the emotional, volitional spheres and in behavior in general. The mildest form of regression, which often occurs in normal people too, is rationalization. Rationalization is an attempt to provide a logical justification for actions or ideas that are directed by an emotional need. This attempt is made by resorting to explanations that are not too incorrect and appear plausible because they succeed in hiding the real motivation. For example, a patient was suffering from feelings of rivalry for his brother, who was a singer. The patient used to warn his brother in paternal and affectionate tones, "Don't sing so often at clubs and parties. You'll ruin your voice!" This was a correct recommendation; the singer had also received expert advice that he should not strain his voice. In repeating the advice, however, the patient was actually motivated by his jealousy. He wanted to prevent the attention and honor that the brother was receiving when he sang. Rationalization is regressive inasmuch as it restricts thinking to the use of only those *apparently* logical and plausible cognitive processes which lead to emotional gratification.

As we shall see more clearly in Chapters 16 and 17, regression in forms more severe than rationalization can be interpreted as a mechanism of *active concretization,* that is, as a substitution of concrete representations for more abstract ones. Reification, or the change of a person or idea into a tangible or an inanimate thing, is a special form of concretization. Regression should not be confused with reversal of motivation, which does not necessarily include cognitive alterations.

Fixation. According to Freud, fixation occurs when psychic energy remains attached to infantile psychic structures. In our frame of reference here, fixation is the retention of a primary process or microgenetic mechanism even though its original cause was removed and the rest of the psyche has proceeded in its development.

In some cases it is difficult to distinguish a fixation from a partial arrest. However, a fixation differs from an arrest in that it consists of mechanisms which have not reached the microgenetic maturity of the secondary process. In reality, fixation is only a limited regression. Fixations are the predominant characteristic of some psychoneuroses, and also of some developmental anomalies. For instance, *imprinting*, as described by Lorenz (1937, 1953), can be considered a special form of fixation (see Chapter 4).

Psychodysplasia. Dysplasia is a medical word used to indicate that some parts of the body have undergone an abnormal growth, to the detriment of a good balance of the respective functions. We can extend this notion to psychopathology, and call psychodysplasia a condition in which a normal faculty of the psyche has become so pervasive or so intense that it prevents the normal functioning of the others.

Perhaps the most typical occurrence of psychodysplasia is seen in manic-depressive psychosis. Here a feeling of elation and, much more frequently, of depression undergoes a dysplastic growth, with consequent decline of the other states of the psyche. Psychodysplasia also occurs in many other conditions. In character disorders, a normal function of the psyche (for instance, anger, compliance, withdrawal, motility, etc.) often becomes pronounced to an abnormal degree.

In some conditions psychodysplasia is secondary to arrest, fixation, or regression. For instance, a patient undergoes a regression which transforms his anxiety into a specific phobia. The phobia then expands in its field of applicability and becomes a psychodysplasia.

Somatization. The transformation of a psychologic difficulty or disorganization into a physiologic or organic one is somatization. This mechanism, which Freud referred to as "the mysterious leap from the psychological to the physical," occurs in disorders generally called psychosomatic. Typical examples are gastric ulcer, colitis, hypertension, and bronchial asthma.

Some authors consider psychosomatic disorders only those in which "the leap" occurs through the intervention of the autonomic nervous system. Others (for instance, Arieti, 1956b; and by implication, Jung, 1903) also consider disorders psychosomatic in which psychological factors engender changes directly in the central nervous system.

Deviation. Often called "perversion" and occasionally "aberration," deviation is an abnormal psychophysiological mechanism which replaces the usual one by necessity or preference. The term almost invariably refers to abnormal mechanisms occurring in sexual practices.

Repression. According to Freud, repression is the active process of banishing unacceptable ideas or impulses from consciousness. This mechanism has been discussed in detail in Chapter 9. It is not necessarily a pathological mechanism, although often it becomes one when it invades areas which usually remain within the domain of consciousness. *Denial, reaction, formation,* and *undoing* are special forms of repression. Since their full significance is more evident in an interpersonal context, they will not be discussed in this book.

Contrary to common belief, the rendering unconscious of what is generally conscious does not apply only to ideas and impulses (see Chapter 9). Experiences of inner status, ranging from simple sensations to the highest forms of emotion, may lose awareness totally or partially. We have then those states usually designated as hysterical anesthesia, hypoesthesia, apathy, dulling or blunting of affect, depersonalization, and alienation.

At times the individual experiences fear, anxiety, rage, depression, love, etc., some time after the factors that have provoked these feelings have disappeared. This is *postponement,* which may be interpreted as a temporary repression. Postponement is often a valuable mechanism, as it permits the subject to react more adequately when he has overcome the acute distress provoked by the emotion. At other times it is inappropriate and conducive to harmful responses.

Inhibition. Inhibition is not necessarily a pathological mechanism. In normal conditions, the restraining of a psychological or motor response often permits the elaboration of a response at higher level of integration. In pathological conditions, inhibition occurs when conflict or the possibility of conflict (as engendered by guilt, fear, anxiety, etc.) prevents a process from continuing. Contrary to arrest, inhibition refers to specific and limited functions.

Short-circuiting. To use a short-circuited mechanism is to resort to a quick or not adequately elaborated mental process, when the situation requires a better-integrated response. Difficulties are bypassed. The patient finds an easy way out. This mechanism is frequently found in organic conditions as well as in psychopathic states.

Detoured circuiting. In some ways, this is the opposite of short-circuiting. It is a way of avoiding reaching the goal, either in action or thinking, in order to escape some consequences. It is often referred to as evasiveness and is common in paranoia and paranoid conditions.

If we now review the mechanisms described above, we can easily recognize in most of them an immediate relevance to the concept of developmental order. A definite temporal quality is inherent in arrest, reversal of motivation, regression, fixation, postponement, inhibition, short-circuiting, and detoured circuiting. Other mechanisms, like disintegration, somatization, psychodysplasia, deviation, introjection, projection, and repression, are not *necessarily* connected with a developmental order. Thus, although developmental notions enter deeply into our psychopathological conceptions, they should by no means be considered the only interpretations of psychological alterations. In several conditions, such as some specific psychosomatic disorders and manic-depressive psychosis, they do not play a major role.

With a few exceptions (fixation, for instance) the basic mechanisms that we have described may occur when the psyche operates in accordance with the primary as well as with the secondary process.

Determinism and teleology in psychopathological conditions

In mechanistic interpretation, psychopathological phenomena are exclusively the results of injuries. Antecedent
factors (either organic ones, such as brain damage, or functional ones, such as anxiety) do not permit the psyche to
function at its highest levels. As we have seen, this is the
interpretation that Hughlings Jackson gave to neurological
disorders. According to this conception, adaptation, but no
purposefulness, is seen in the symptomatology (see Chapter
2).

In my view, only disintegration can be explained in such a
simple manner. Psychological injury is, as a rule, dealt with
through mechanisms that are more elaborate than disintegration. These mechanisms seem to bring about a repair, defense, or compromise that is wished by the patient.

Goldstein formulated an important law of behavior, conceived in an adaptational frame of reference: "A defective
organism achieves ordered behavior only by a shrinkage of
its environment in proportion to the defect" (1939, 1940).
According to Goldstein, the organism of brain-injured patients attempts to recapture a certain equilibrium and to
cope with the environment in spite of the loss of function.
The organism does so in order to avoid the disintegration of
the "catastrophic reaction."

Goldstein's law, originally proposed for organic conditions,
can be applied with some modifications to functional syndromes too. However, the functional patient often does
much more than contrive a shrinkage of his environment.
He attempts to transform complex patterns of behavior into
simpler ones with which he can live somewhat more adequately. For instance, he can transform and therefore restrict
his fear of making excursions in the complicated interpersonal world, into a fear of walking on streets and squares
(agoraphobia).

The mechanisms described in the first section of this chapter are predominantly attempts to avoid catastrophe or disintegration not simply by creating a shrinkage of the environment in a direct way, but by using simpler modes of

processing the input from the environment and from the inner world. Regression, perhaps the most typical of these mechanisms, can be illustrated by an allegorical example. If the engine of a ship goes out of order, an attempt will be made by the crew to proceed toward their destination by using the sails of the boat. The ship thus "regresses" to the level of a sailboat. If a storm then blows up and destroys the sails of the boat, the crew will have to resort to the use of oars and the boat will regress to the level of a rowboat.

There are two sets of factors in this example: (1) the deterministic causal factors that make first the engine and then the sails of the boat unsuitable for navigation; (2) the teleologic determination on the part of the crew to use the best method available to reach port. The loss of the use of more adequate forms of navigating is equivalent to disintegration. Resorting to less adequate forms of navigation is equivalent to regression.

This discussion points to the two aspects of many psychopathological mechanisms. One is the return to earlier phylogenetic-ontogenetic-microgenetic forms. The other is the defensive, and in some cases restitutional, aspect of the changes involved. A large part of Freud's innovations consisted of demonstrating the defensive-restitutional aspects of symptoms.

However, it is not easy to explain the mixture of deterministic and teleologic causalities implied in this conception. The fact that a patient cannot function at a high level can be interpreted deterministically, no matter whether the disturbance is organic or psychological in origin. The difficult fact to explain is how the psyche comes to use purposefully the mechanisms that are released and available again.

The usefulness or adaptational value of a pathological mechanism is recognizable not only in psychiatric conditions, but in the whole field of medicine, as was first illustrated by Claude Bernard. In infective diseases, for instance, fever occurs as a reaction to the invasion of foreign proteins. This reaction can be interpreted in accordance with deterministic causality. Fever, however, seems to have a purpose: to combat the invasion of foreign proteins. Here the organism seems to follow teleologic causality. Only organisms that are able to build up adequate defenses can survive and transmit such a possibility genetically. Actually in these cases we should speak of adaptational mechanisms, not of purposeful or teleologic ones (see Chapter 2). It is not the individual but the species with its phylogenetic history that makes available a repertory of adaptive mechanisms which are put into operation automatically.

The psychopathological process is more difficult to explain. In a given case, its mechanisms seem to fit so well with the patient's general psychological situation as to make one believe that he has *purposely selected them*—just as the crew of the ship in our fictitious example selected the various means to reach their destination. But in saying this, we endow a presumed automatic mechanism with the ability to have a purpose and to choose in accordance with the purpose.

An example from psychiatric practice will explain the theoretical problem. A man who has serious family difficulties suddenly undergoes a hysterical amnesia one day on his way home from work. He does not remember his name and address.

This amnesia can be interpreted in several ways. We may say that the unpleasant family life, fraught with anxiety and sorrow, as well as the patient's basic neurotic personality, has weakened him to such a point that he can no longer function properly. Disintegration has then occurred. But the temporary disintegration is followed by an acute hysterical syndrome. Hysterical amnesia was available among many other mechanisms in the potential pathological repertory of this man. It seems obvious, however, that there is a relation between the situation of the patient and the symptom he developed. Most psychodynamically oriented therapists would be inclined to believe that the patient *wished* to forget the address of his unhappy home. The illness seems to have *chosen* the most pertinent symptom.

If we are to interpret this man's condition deterministically—that is, as a result of previous events—how can we say that the symptom was chosen because of the effect it would have? This difficulty is at least partially understandable if we remember the discussion in Chapter 12. If the patient regresses to lower levels, his volitional system too undergoes changes. No longer his will but his wish determines the symptom. The wish is actualized automatically without the necessary support of the will.

This patient's condition thus can be interpreted:

1. *Deterministically,* because (*a*) the will level fails to work and (*b*) lower levels of cognition, motivation, and conation become available to him.
2. *Teleologically,* because at the level to which the patient has reversed he can experience the wish that brings about gratification.[3]

To experience a wish is a way of acquiring a purpose (Chapter 5). We have seen in Part I that the general adaptational property of all biological forms is, at a certain point in the phylogenetic history of animal forms, reinforced by motivational mechanisms: search for pleasure and avoidance of unpleasure (Chapter 2); gratification of appetite and obtainment of satisfaction (Chapter 3); gratification of wishes (Chapter 5), etc.

Thus our amnesic patient has reverted to the level of wishes and has gratified his wish by the mechanism of repression. The interpretation of this clinical example shows that psychopathology is no longer viewed exclusively as a result of injury, not even exclusively as a simple adaptational regenerative process of the organism; but is also seen as a process which allows a purpose to be experienced and gratified in an unusual way. The psychopathologic alteration becomes teleologic. The arrow of teleology, which in normal phylogenetic, ontogenetic, and microgenetic development points toward higher forms, now turns backward.

In schizophrenia I have described a particular type of this phenomenon as teleologic regression (Arieti, 1955). Regression, which is useful and purposeful in some normal condi-

---

[3] It is questionable, however, whether interpretation 1 is actually necessary. It could be that even when the highest levels of the psyche are not impaired, the psyche may "wish and select" to operate at a lower level, either because it follows the law of parsimony or in order to avoid more difficult challenges. If this point of view is proved to be right, we will have to recognize the psyche as being endowed with even more extensive teleologic qualities.

tions, like sleep, rest, and play, becomes purposeful in illness too. The teleologic aspect of regression can be studied relatively easily. We should not forget, however, that other psychopathological mechanisms also have a teleologic aspect.

At a different level of abstraction we can say that in the presence of psychological injury—be it fear, anxiety, conflict, an attack on self-esteem, or other adverse factors—defenses are mobilized which aim at the preservation of the self. In almost all cases, these defenses succeed. Only in advanced schizophrenia does the patient lose the sense of his own self as an entity, a person, a center of consciousness, to which he can attribute some sensitive, cognitive, and conative functions. Our present understanding of the adaptational and teleologic mechanisms of the psyche permits only a partial clarification of how this overall aim or purpose is attained. We know the results; and they are very costly at times, for they imply a curtailment or a transformation of the whole personality, or at least of some important functions.

An additional consideration is that in spite of their restitutional or defensive role, most psychopathological mechanisms retain definite disturbing characteristics. They are *dystonic*. On the other hand, other mechanisms, called *syntonic*, seem regularly woven into the fabric of the patient's personality—or at least they seem to blend smoothly into his main ordinary ways of living. At times they may be so well integrated as to predispose him to a socially acceptable philosophy of life or world view. At other times they may be recognized as determining the overall quality of the patient's character. For instance, an original excessive experience of fear or anxiety may affect him in a general way, so that his personality will appear permeated by cautiousness and timidity. Or an original excessive experiencing of anger may mold a person into a hostile individual who relates to the world with suspiciousness and hate.

14 ⊚ DISORDERS CHARACTERIZED BY FEELINGS OF UNFULFILLMENT AND ARREST OF MOTIVATION

Psychological disorders which involve only the highest levels of integration are difficult to define and differentiate. Since relatively few persons function at the highest possible levels, it is questionable whether we can call pathological some of the conditions illustrated in this chapter. The discussion will be limited to a few common examples. Some may be considered just as normal alternatives among the possible ways of living; some others as outcomes of "free choice" and not of pathology, although this possibility seems rather doubtful.

Neurotic feelings of unfulfillment

As we have seen in Chapter 9, conceptual man cannot actualize his encounter with the infinite; nor can he come close to most of his ideals. A feeling of unfulfillment, which does not lead to despair but to a renewal of one's strivings, is thus a normal experience. Different, however, is the neurotic feeling of unfulfillment—the feeling of not being able to live up to an ideal which, because of neurotic reasons, one has envisioned for himself. Alfred Adler and Karen Horney have studied this neurotic experience, for which they have used the names *feeling of inferiority* and *idealized image*.

In departing from Freud, Adler and Horney have given more importance to the high nonbiological levels of the psyche. It is therefore not a surprise that these two authors should be concerned with feelings of unfulfillment. In spite of their original and significant contributions, however, they have neglected some important aspects of this problem.

THE GRANDIOSE AIM

Psychotherapists are often consulted by patients who complain that they feel unfulfilled. In many cases these patients attempt to give external evidence of how their lives are being "wasted," and often they succeed in doing so. Sometimes they are women who do not find fulfillment, as they put it, in being housewives, mothers, or secretaries. Many patients of both sexes have recently adopted a more refined expression for their predicament: they do not want adjustment but self-realization. They feel "maladjusted" in a society whose aim is adjustment. In the course of psychotherapy, it is easy to recognize that these people nourish grandiose aims. They have built what Horney called an idealized image of themselves.

In their youth many of these patients entertained the idea of being creative in art or science; and a considerable number of them do have moderate talent in one field or another. Possibly their talent would sooner or later have found adequate outlets if they had properly cultivated it, but the grandiose image did not permit them to. For instance, some may explain that they did not go to school to learn the basic techniques because "Teachers stunt creativity: they are concerned with technique, with the skeleton, not with the flesh. They teach you to do only what they want or the public wants. Sooner or later you will have to prostitute yourself to the crowds." Although there is some truth in these words, most of the great masters did have teachers. Technique, learning, discipline should not be confused with conformism.

These patients would be able to recognize their error if their grandiose self-image did not distort their views.

Other such patients attribute to themselves the quality of being excellent businessmen, executives, politicians, etc. Whatever their particular self-image, these people all live in the fantasized glory of tomorrow and accomplish nothing today. Often they make real sacrifices for the sake of their grandiose aim; and what is worse, they impose sacrifices on other people, especially their families. For instance, although there are small children to be taken care of, they insist that their wives go to work. They will be able thus to spend the day not working but waiting for the moment of inspiration to come. As they come to realize that their accomplishments are small in comparison with their expectations, these people grow increasingly discontented. The mechanism of "motivational viscosity" from which they are suffering makes it difficult for them to re-evaluate the significance of their lives (see Chapter 13). Sooner or later they find rationalizations for their difficulties: in some cases they blame their families; in others they feel that it is society which does not permit their self-actualization. They offer bits of political, sociological, or psychological evidence which allegedly show how people cannot be their "real selves." Or they may become involved in utopian or outlandish philosophical systems, and may argue that their problems would be solved if these systems were accepted by "stubborn society." As their lack of accomplishment makes their position increasingly untenable, they may be forced to accept jobs which their contemporaries have already outgrown; and again they feel resentful and discontented. Their grandiose aim has thus led to the opposite of what they wished: to a feeling of inadequacy and a neurotic feeling of unfulfillment.

Horney rightly pointed out that this idealized image, which leads to a search for glory, is a substitute for a self-confidence which is lacking (Horney, 1950). She also showed how this unrealistic image confers a neurotic but gratifying feeling of being superior to others. Horney vaguely formulated the concept that the idealized image is derived from the "basic anxiety" of childhood, but she made no clearer reference to its origin. She was more interested in its outcome, which is in a feeling of inadequacy. Thus to Horney, a feeling of inferiority is both cause and effect of the idealized image, in a sort of feedback mechanism.

It seems to me that although the idealized image is genetically connected with the basic anxiety of childhood, additional and more specific causal factors must be pointed out. The child who develops a grandiose image of himself is a child who thinks that he must live up to expectations congruous with this self-image, in order to deserve and obtain parental love.

Generally the mother, and many times the father too, has, often unwittingly, transmitted the idea to the child that he will be a worthwhile individual only if he lives up to their great expectations. Of course, as will be discussed in the next section, many parents believe that their child will prove to be a great person. Their transmission of this belief, almost always inaccurate, is generally not only untraumatic but actually helpful to him if it is an *expression of love and hope*. In other words, the normal mother is often inclined to believe that her child will be a great person because she loves him, and not because she expects greatness in exchange for love. The actualization of the parents' expectations becomes a neurotic aim only when it is interpreted by the child as a *requirement* for obtaining approval and love. In these circumstances the child's dormant feelings of omnipotence, which had been declining from the exoceptual-protoemotional and phantasmic levels, may well be reactivated (see Chapters 3 and 5). The request for greatness can bring about a return of these archaic feelings, and they may be additionally reinforced by the normal exalted aspirations of the high levels of the psyche.

Because of the unending realm of his symbolic processes, it is characteristic of man to visualize higher and higher goals for himself. It is thus not necessarily neurotic for a mother or for the growing child to have aspirations which later will be recognized as grandiose. On the contrary, to have high aspirations is a stimulus toward progress. The fact that, say, only one in 100,000 persons will live up to his own expectations does not make such high goals automatically neurotic in 99,999 persons. Educational systems long ago realized that grandiose aims are useful for inspiring young people. Teachers often portray the heroes of the past in an idealistic light to elicit in the child the desire to emulate those heroes.

In summary, specific conditions of various levels of the psyche can coincide to produce a self which is characterized by the grandiose aim it nourishes. Although a grandiose aim is not necessarily neurotic, it becomes so when the individual feels he needs it in order to attain the approval and love which are due him anyhow; when he perpetuates it by inappropriate claims (for instance, a desire for vengeance); and when it renders him unable to gradually accept his limitations.

Nonneurotic man eventually realizes that he may grow even if he is not creative or great. He comes to understand that the effort he was expending to actualize his grandiose aim or his archaic feeling of omnipotence or his supposed self-realization must instead be devoted toward the growth of the self.

THE FEELING OF INFERIORITY

Another condition which interferes with living at high levels of integration is the so-called feeling of inferiority, first described and interpreted by Alfred Adler. Adler took the superiority feeling into consideration also, but he thought of it only as a form of compensation for the feeling of inferiority and did not give it much importance. According to Adler, the feeling of inferiority originates generally from organic inferiority. Bodily malformation, weakness, or disease would give the child a feeling of inferiority very early in life.

However, Adler correctly realized that organic inferiority, although it is important, is only one factor in the inferiority feeling (1927). Children also feel inferior because they are treated as inferiors by adults, and because they feel that they cannot face the difficulties of the world without the help of adults. They feel small, weak, and helpless, unable to cope with the challenges of existence. This feeling of inferiority may become the "driving force, the starting point from which every striving originates," or may eventually become the crippling feeling of inferiority with which many adults are afflicted.

We must agree with Adler that the feeling of inferiority is very common and important. Probably in prevalence of effects it is second only to a more general or less definite feeling of anxiety. Psychiatric practice enables therapists to reach the conclusion that the feeling of inferiority is universal or almost so—that it affects men and women equally, and prominent people as well as average. Since I have observed it also in non-Western persons brought up in their native countries, I am inclined to believe that a specific culture is not the determining factor. However, it could be that some cultures, such as the Western, increase their intensity by placing an especially high premium upon competition.

This conclusion about the occurrence of the feeling of inferiority has not so far been contradicted, except in those cases where greater psychopathology replaced such a feeling. For instance, the exalted, fanatic paranoiac and paranoid, the maniac, the extreme narcissist, and the detached psychopath may not, at least at a conscious level, experience an inferiority feeling, unfortunately for them and for the people who have to live with them.

The inferiority feeling may be very pronounced, as in some psychiatric patients, or of moderate intensity, as in most people. Although practically universal, it is not among the most primitive feelings. Tension, some states of conflict, and some short-circuited feelings of anxiety may be more primitive and more general, and may occur in the young child when he is not yet ready for the cognitive processes needed to mediate the feeling of inferiority.

In the author's opinion, although the inferiority feeling becomes manifest as a feeling of helplessness in the child, it is actually grounded on the intrinsic properties of the human psyche. As in the case of the feeling of unfulfillment and the grandiose aim, a moderate feeling of inferiority is normal, and although unpleasant, is unavoidable. It is based on the fact that a discrepancy exists between the way man sees himself and the way his symbolic processes make him visualize that he could be (see Chapter 9). Man is always short of what he can conjecture; he can always conceive a situation better than the one he is in. This discrepancy is caused by the power of his symbolic processes. It is based on an a priori or pre-experiential condition, which becomes activated in the child somewhere around the age of 3 through his contact with adults.

Specific events in the life of an individual may make him misconstrue the unfinished state of man into a cause for a deeper than normally felt sense of inferiority. Organic inadequacy, as described by Adler, and early interpersonal difficulties are concrete situations which lead the child to magnify the inherent human discrepancy and develop a strong feeling of inferiority. As an adult this person may still think, in a vaguely verbalized or only endoceptual way: "How can Mother love me if I do not live up to what she expects of me? How can people approve of me if I have not achieved my goal? As a child I was small and weak, but I have not changed since I have grown." In severe cases this feeling of inferiority may affect the whole self.

Is it possible to decrease the disposition toward a feeling of inferiority and to prevent its reaching pathological proportions? The author believes that the best prevention for an abnormally strong feeling of inferiority is the mother's love. It is quite a common occurrence to see mothers lavishing on their young children what appears to bystanders as excessive love. These mothers seem to be in a state of worship. A little smile, an unexpected act of the baby are seized upon as signs of genius to come, of extreme sweetness and adorability. A critical observer may wonder if such an attitude is fostering narcissistic tendencies in the child. Actually this extreme fondness, this unconditional primal love, is a benign influence. The human baby requires a greater supply of love than the young of other species in order to overcome the greater difficulties that his symbolic faculties will bestow upon him.

This unconditional love must be followed by basic trust: a complex interpersonal feeling which consists of the child's expectation that the mother will be there to give and to love, and of the mother's calm assumption that the child will grow up to be a normal and worthy and loving person. (Erikson, 1953; Arieti, 1957b, 1959c.) The mother's basic trust will also be introjected by the child, who will then trust himself. Only the security, the feeling of being worthwhile and accepted, which comes from the mother first in the form of unconditional love and later in the form of basic trust, can prepare the child to overcome either the acute shock, or, more often, the painful slow realization of the discrepancy between the way he is and the way he used to envision himself. While he is growing, he must increasingly accept his limitations. His basic trust in himself will overcome "motivational viscosity" and will encourage him to continue his striving toward growth and self-expansion.

The adjustment syndrome

The adjustment syndrome, although less common than the previous conditions, is encountered frequently and deserves careful attention. It invades the whole personality and can be designated more accurately as a character neurosis than a psychoneurosis. The patient with this condition, although able to move toward self-evolvement, curtails himself and seems to concentrate all his efforts on one goal: adjustment.

People affected by this condition are generally very conservative in their views. They cannot be daring; they cautiously travel along beaten paths. Although restricted in their outlook, they are not necessarily unsuccessful in their dealings with society. On the contrary, in many instances they give the impression of being "well adjusted" and successful in every respect. Inasmuch as they tend to adhere strictly to conventional habits, they become stereotypes to a somewhat comical degree and are often portrayed as humorous stock characters in plays, movies, and novels. Since this type of personality has received little attention in the psychiatric literature, I shall report a case.

Mr. Q, a businessman in his late forties, had been successful in all his undertakings. Although he inherited his firm from his father, he was able to expand it considerably. All its departments worked at top efficiency, and the economic returns were very good. Mr. Q also managed a subsidiary firm, also successful, so that with the profits from the second firm

he could pay federal and state taxes on the income of the
first.

His home life was also regulated according to what is considered the best schedule. Every member of the family had
been trained to do the proper thing at the proper time. In
spite of this mechanical alertness and busy-busy atmosphere,
one detected a certain detachment in him, although it was
not too conspicuous. He showed a tepid warmth now and
then.

The patient returned home every day at a certain hour. As
he came in, he kissed his wife on the cheek and said a few
nice words to the children and the maid. During the treatment he repeatedly stated that people adored him: he made
an excellent impression. He had two lovely children, two
boys, a pleasant home with comfortable furniture, a nice,
honest, undemanding wife. What more should he want?

For many months during the first stage of therapy, he en-
ergetically insisted that he was happy and satisfied, except
for some physical complaints which will be mentioned later.
When the therapist remarked that it seemed as if rules and
regulations were controlling his life, he replied that there
was no contrast between his wishes and these "self-imposed
rules." Although there were some indications of compulsive-
ness in his actions, it was either masked by or channeled into
ostensibly admirable efficiency. When the therapist pointed
out to him that he was speaking rather unromantically about
his wife and other women, he launched into a tirade against
people who are unfaithful to their spouses. He added that at
a certain age romanticism is lost; that at any rate happiness
has no room for romanticism even at a young age. But fortunately, when people occasionally have the romantic itch it
can be easily satisfied. With a good stereo set one can play
romantic music and create a love atmosphere. Occasionally
reading a special novel will add to the feeling.

When the therapist pointed out to him that he never spoke
about intimacies with his wife, he replied, "Doctor, my wife
is not too young; beautiful or attractive she has never been. I
have learned to do what other men of my age do. I buy those
magazines with pictures of naked women that you see on
newsstands. Those pictures make you ardent, so that when

you go home your wife will do!" He went to great lengths to explain that, contrary to what women believe, these magazines are not bought by sex-hungry adolescents; adolescents could not afford them. They are bought mostly by well-intentioned middle-aged men who want to remain faithful to their wives. His observation of the men of his age working in his firm had convinced him that it was so. He boasted that when he was having intercourse with his wife he never thought about other women, as some men do. This he considered a form of secret unfaithfulness or, as he had read in a book, a form of "masturbatory intercourse." He had "said goodbye" to masturbation at the end of adolescence. He announced emphatically, "When you are with your wife, you must really be with her." On the other hand he did not object to using pornographic magazines, because "they made things easier" for him and his wife. He felt that these magazines have saved many marriages.

Another interesting aspect of his life was his reluctance to go on vacation. He belonged to a country club which had everything: pool, golf, tennis, gardens, nice people. Why go away, when it was so much easier to enjoy the country close to the city, where you had both the comfort of your home and the advantages of a country vacation? At the club people were friendly, liked him, and had elected him an officer.

It is unnecessary to go further; the reader can see an intelligent man who has no higher aim in life than adjustment. He has been able to replace spontaneity and creativity with efficiency, and a certain form of success has come to him. But why has Mr. Q diverted his energies from higher aims?

Although the answer to this question is very important for a psychodynamic understanding of Mr. Q's condition, I shall be rather brief on this point, because it is not the main topic of the chapter. Childhood interpersonal relations had convinced Mr. Q that he had to be successful in life in order to obtain the praise and love from his mother which his father and his siblings were obtaining spontaneously. He had to be even more successful than his father; he had to be the brains of the family. But the way to avoid the anxiety of dying without having achieved success was to increase his efficiency and to work along the usual paths, without venturing into new ones. Also to avoid this anxiety, he must disregard all inner voices and feelings unless they would surely receive social sanction.

What is particularly relevant to this chapter is that the patient's anxiety did not cripple him at the low levels of integration, but at the highest. To a superficial observer, Mr. Q could have appeared not only a normal person, but a very productive one. Certainly this was the way he appeared to himself and to the circle of his friends. At this point the question which comes to mind is: Why did he come for treatment, if he thought that everything with him and his life was good and normal? Not everything was good and normal, however: he had several psychosomatic symptoms, which he attributed to poor blood circulation. But what scared him most of all was the presence of areas of complete anesthesia on his skin. In some parts of his back and legs he could prick himself with a pin without experiencing pain. Repeated physical, neurological, and serological examinations were all negative. A few psychiatrists who had examined him felt that his repressed anxiety was converted into hysterical, hypochondriacal, and psychosomatic symptoms.

There is some truth in these statements but, of course, they do not clarify the picture beyond reference to the conversion mechanisms. Obviously Mr. Q could not reduce his whole life—his genuine existence and his potentially rich personality—to the level of adjustment. Only his unconscious anxiety required that aim. In order to adjust to the level of adjustment (and this is not a play on words), he had to give up a great deal; he had to transform his whole personality, so that in some aspects he became a caricature of what he could have been. The reshaping of his self required not only compulsive activity but also a form of alienation, or depersonalization, so that he could not even experience the unpleasant aspects of this transformation. The hysterical anesthesias were in a certain way a concrete representation of his depersonalization. The skin anesthesias of which he was fully aware replaced another kind of anesthesia, which existed at a higher level and of which he was not at all aware: the repression of that part of living which aims at spontaneity and creativity.

Incidentally, I wish to stress that I have found anesthesias and hypoesthesias in several cases of depersonalization and alienation. In my opinion it is an inadequate therapeutic procedure in these cases to focus on the hysterical or psychosomatic symptoms and to ignore the high levels of the personality. The somatic symptoms offer the patient secondary gains and may divert the patient's and the therapist's attention from the basic pathology. In the case of Mr. Q, for instance, they confirmed his belief that everything in life could be adjusted, controlled, and remedied except physical health. Whatever pertained to his will, he felt he could work out successfully; but whatever transcended his will—that is, what concerned his physical nature—could not be controlled. And it was his physical being, nothing else, that he thought was the cause of his troubles. He used these secondary gains to preserve an acceptable self-image and perhaps to get attention from the external world.

Although they were an important characteristic of the clinical picture, we should also not overemphasize Mr. Q's compulsive traits. They were actually the methods by which he diverted his higher aims into hard work, which would win success and recognition for him. More than anything else, we must consider that this very capable man was too insecure to adventure into the unknown, or to be in contact with his real feelings; he had to fit the image which he felt he was expected to fit. He gave up self-expansion for the sake of adjustment. Poor, poor Mr. Q! It is true that his disturbance did not interfere with his activities but, on the contrary, enhanced his success. It is true that by all generally accepted standards his disorder is considered far less serious than the other syndromes which will be discussed in this book. And yet how much more pathetic is the comic aspect of his condition! Not only did he pretend to be happy, successful, and well adjusted, but the world viewed him in that way.

Treatment was necessarily a harsh procedure for him, as it had to unveil what appeared to him defeat and pretension, and to deprive him of the pillars that had protected him from conscious despair.

15 ⊛ REVERSAL OF CONSCIOUS MOTIVATION: PSYCHOPATHIC STATES

A conscious reversal to low levels of motivation occurs in patients who are usually designated as psychopaths, sociopaths, or psychopathic personalities. There is much confusion in the psychiatric literature about the concept of psychopathic personality. The confusion is increased by the fact that it is often difficult to distinguish psychopathic features which appear as secondary manifestations in many psychiatric conditions from the syndromes in which they constitute the basic pathology.

The term *psychopath* generally designates a person of at least average and often superior intelligence who actualizes his drives and wishes by using antisocial behavior. The psychopath seems to lack anxiety or guilt over his past or future actions. He appears irresponsible and unable to learn from experience that his antisocial behavior is self-defeating even in his own limited terms.

Thus the antisocial character of his actions appears at first as the psychopath's most salient feature. A Robinson Crusoe could not be a psychopath; that is, a psychopathic condition manifests itself only in a societal environment. This statement does not imply, however, that societal or interpersonal factors are the only ones involved in such a condition. Although, as we shall see later, interpersonal factors are very important in both originating the psychogenetic patterns of living and shaping or evolving the overt symptomatology, they are not the only ones. Two other important factors, specific to the psychopath, must be taken into consideration. The first concerns the formal mental mechanisms which direct him toward low levels of motivation; the second concerns a particular way of experiencing some important aspects of inner and outer reality.

A low motivation based on the immediate gratification of drives and wishes is not found only in psychopaths, but also in people commonly called immature, infantile, or suffering from infantilization (Levy, 1939). These immature patients present a clinical picture of arrest rather than of reversal of motivation (Chapter 13). Their whole psychopathologic condition is simpler than that of the psychopath and generally does not include an antisocial aspect.

Although there are many mixed or transitional or unclassifiable cases, clinical experience and the study of the literature have led this writer to adopt the following classification of psychopathic personalities: (a) pseudopsychopaths (or symptomatic psychopaths) and (b) true psychopaths (or idiopathic psychopaths). A similar grouping has been made by other authors (for instance, Karpman, 1941). The main part of the classification presented here, however, concerns the true or idiopathic psychopath, of which I shall distinguish the following types: (1) the simple, (2) the complex, (3) the dyssocial, (4) the paranoiac.

The pseudopsychopath (symptomatic psychopath)

The topic of pseudopsychopathy will receive only cursory treatment in this chapter, for the main purpose here is to discuss some points of view concerning the true or idiopathic psychopath. The pseudopsychopath is a person who only symptomatically manifests psychopathic traits or tendencies, but whose main psychiatric difficulties have to be interpreted as part of other clinical entities.

A large group of pseudopsychopathic patients, when accurately examined, will be recognized as suffering from psychoneuroses or character neuroses. Many of them have manifested psychopathic behavior since childhood or adolescence. In the majority it is possible to recognize that what goes on is still a rebellion against the parents or symbolic parents. A pattern of behavior perpetuates itself, presenting antisocial features which at times seem impulsive, at other times compulsive. The patient reveals a hostile character structure which impels him to defy or to hurt others, especially when these others stand for parental authority.

Although the actions of these patients seem consciously motivated, it is the unconscious motivation (generally defiance of parents) which directs their behavior. To complicate the picture, however, often a conscious motivation (for instance, desire to possess stolen objects) becomes superimposed on and reinforces the original and more important unconscious motivation, so that it is difficult to distinguish the two. At times, especially if the patient is endowed with unusual intelligence, he may find support for his behavior in strange philosophies and ideologies. In some of these cases it is no longer the parents but society as a whole, or perhaps the highest authority of the land, which becomes the target of his hostile actions. Occasionally the patient may even become a leader of social movements whose aim is to defy or combat the prevailing norms of society.

In my opinion, the group of pseudopsychopaths also includes more complicated conditions which occur in children and whose dynamisms have been lucidly illustrated by Adelaide Johnson (1959) and by Szurek (1942). These two authors, however, consider such patients as real psychopaths and not as pseudopsychopathic neurotics. According to Johnson and Szurek, the delinquent child is an individual whose delinquency has been unconsciously sanctioned by the parents, especially the mother. The child's acting out offers the parents a vicarious gratification of their poorly integrated forbidden impulses. In other words, the child's antisocial behavior is the expression not of his conscious motivation, but of his parents' unconscious motivation, which he has introjected.

If I understand their writings correctly, Szurek and Johnson seem to believe that this mechanism is involved in all psychopathic children who do not belong to the "sociologic group." For Szurek the psychopathic person is a delinquent child grown older. I recognize that the contributions of Szurek and Johnson have been very important, and I believe that in many cases of juvenile delinquency the mechanism they have illustrated is certainly playing a decisive role. However, my clinical experiences have not led me to conclude that *all* delinquents or psychopaths except the "sociological" belong to this group.

The group of pseudopsychopaths also includes postpsychotic patients who recover from their psychotic, generally schizophrenic episodes, but reintegrate only at what seems a psychopathic level. Such a patient has lost the overt psychotic symptomatology, but now indulges in socially unacceptable behavior. Generally these are persons who before becoming ill had strong wishes which they did not dare to satisfy or act upon. After the psychotic episode they cannot control the wishes. An example is a married woman who had a paranoid schizophrenic attack with delusions, hallucinations, and ideas of reference. Later she lost all her symptoms and made an apparent recovery: her personality seemed to have made a good reintegration and to have expanded far beyond her prepsychotic level of adjustment. There was one important exception, however: she began to indulge in shockingly promiscuous sexual behavior and continued to do so until therapy had reached an advanced stage. In these postpsychotic cases, the pseudopsychopathic symptomatology has to be interpreted as a defense against psychosis. Acting at a mature level would be so anxiety-provoking as to cause a return of the psychosis.

Some organic patients who are given to antisocial behavior must also be included in the group of pseudopsychopaths. Relatively numerous among them are postencephalitics and patients with lesions of the prefrontal lobes.

The idiopathic psychopath

Idiopathic psychopaths are easily recognized as such by every psychiatrist, but the basic mechanisms underlying their symptomatology are difficult to interpret. We are dealing here with something beyond a fight against ethical principles or against the superego, and something beyond an acting out in accordance with the unconscious sanction of the parents. It is well known that psychoanalytic or dynamically oriented therapies are seldom successful with idiopathic psychopaths.

In the following section we shall examine in detail the intrapsychic and then the psychodynamic mechanisms of the simple psychopath. The psychodynamic mechanisms are interpersonal in origin, but they are so tightly integrated with the intrapsychic that it is impossible to understand one without making detailed reference to the others. In the subsequent sections we shall consider the other types only in the characteristics which differ from those of the simple psychopath.

1. The simple psychopath

INTRAPSYCHIC MECHANISMS

The simple psychopath is an individual in whom periodically a strong need or wish arises which urges him toward immediate gratification, even when this gratification is not sanctioned by other people. In some cases the need for prompt gratification is particularly felt by the patient when he has failed to live a normal life. The immediate gratification is thus a substitute for something else which he cannot achieve or get. In many cases of simple psychopathy, however, the individual experiences the need for immediate gratification even when his life in general would not be considered unrewarding by normal persons. As we shall see later in more detail, the gratification of these needs and wishes requires actions which are not compatible with the structure of the society in which the patient lives.

Moreover, this gratification involves a type of object relationship in which no delay is possible. The desired object is not an object of contemplation, but has to be possessed immediately. Even when it is not present and is represented only by an inner image, it tends to elicit a type of behavior which is identical or similar to the sensorimotor and exoceptual (Chapter 3).

The nongratification of the need builds up tension which is experienced by the patient as an unbearable discomfort. Whereas the psychotic realizes his wishes by changing his thinking processes, the psychopath realizes his wishes by putting into effect actions which lead to a quick gratification, no matter how primitive they are or how much in contrast with the norms of society. He resorts to a short-circuited mechanism which promptly leads to a feeling of satisfaction (see Chapter 13).

In many instances, the psychopath could satisfy his wishes in a more or less distant future, if he resorted to complicated series of actions which are necessary for a mature and sociably acceptable attainment of goals. But he cannot wait. When he acts psychopathically, not only does he experience primitive wishes, but his whole psyche seems to revert to a type of organization which needs quick responses. Future satisfaction of needs is something that he cannot understand very well and which has no emotional impact on him. He lives emotionally in the present and completely disregards tomorrow.

Intellectually, of course, the psychopath knows that the future exists and that he could obtain his aims in ways which are acceptable to society. But this knowledge has for him only a theoretical reality, and he experiences it only in a vague, faint way. Although the patient's development has reached high levels of motivation and cognition, he cannot adequately sustain the functions of these levels. For reasons that will be considered later in this section, when he is under the pressure of the wish he reverts to levels of integration which permit quick gratification with short-circuited actions. At times the patient is able to visualize all the steps which he would have to go through were he to satisfy his needs in socially acceptable ways. These steps, however, remain vague; they have a flavor of unreality, so that he cannot even indulge in thinking about them. On the other hand, he continues to experience the needs which urge him toward immediate gratification.

Psychoneurotic anxiety is predominantly long-circuited. It is not a fear of an immediate danger, but is connected with the expectation of danger; that is, with something dangerous which may or may not occur in a near or distant future. The psychopath does not experience this type of anxiety. He experiences the discomfort of what we have called tension or short-circuited anxiety (Chapter 3). Consequently he cannot even be too anxious about future punishment. He knows theoretically that he may be caught in the antisocial act and be punished. But again, this punishment is a possibility concerning the future, and therefore he does not experience the idea of it with enough emotional strength to change the course of his present actions.

We may thus conceive the simple psychopath as a person who is motivated by protoemotions (tension or short-circuited anxiety, fear, rage, and appetite) and who cannot postpone satisfaction (see Chapter 3). When he acts in a psychopathic way he lives in accordance with the pleasure principle. It is easier and quicker to steal or forge checks than to work, to rape than to find a willing sexual partner, to falsify a diploma than to complete long studies in school. Lying is a slightly more sophisticated way of obtaining satisfaction. The lie leads to immediate gratification, enabling him to enjoy, for instance, an undeserved reputation. Also, by professing to be something that he is not, the patient may immediately obtain an important position, money, assignments, etc.

In some psychopaths the need seems to consist of a primitive urge to discharge hostility through actions, without any apparent gain other than the pleasure of inflicting injury on others. In these cases the patient not only is more hostile than the average person, but, contrary to the usual neurotic, is unable to change, repress, postpone, or neutralize his need for hostility. His feeling actually cannot be differentiated from rage. Whether such an increased need for hostility is based on constitutional factors or on early environmental experiences is impossible to determine at this stage of research.

Most psychopathic needs are very primitive; in a large percentage of them sexual gratification plays a relatively unimportant role. There are, however, a considerable number of psychopaths who act out in the sexual areas—by raping or by seduction, by resorting to unfulfilled promises of marriage, etc. In women psychopaths sexual behavior is often manifested by promiscuity and prostitution.

True psychopaths are said to have no loyalties for any person, group, or code. They are also said to be unable to identify with others or to take the role of the other person. These statements are correct, but they refer only to the by-products of the basic formal short-circuited mechanism. The urge to gratify the need is so impelling that the patient cannot respect any loyalty or identify at all with other people—that is, cannot visualize the bad effects that his actions will have on others. As already mentioned, the patient may intellectually visualize these future bad effects, but his visualizations are not accompanied by deterring emotions.

The short-circuited mechanism by which the psychopath operates is self-defeating and leads inevitably to complications, even though it aims at the avoidance of all complications.[1] For instance, a psychopath may just want to rape a girl, and he carries out his wish; but then the sudden fear comes to him that the girl may report him to the police. So the quickest way to avoid this complication is to kill the girl; but sooner or later, the killing will produce more serious complications.

In attempting to avoid complications or ramifications which have to do with future happenings, the psychopath repeatedly places himself in a web of new dangers. This series of imbroglios is clearly illustrated in the following summary of a short story that a patient wrote. The story does not excel in literary value, but it portrays the predicament of the simple psychopath. Although the patient never acted in such a striking manner as the protagonist, obviously he identified with him.

---

[1] The simple psychopath is in some way reminiscent of the simple schizophrenic who tries to simplify life by avoiding abstract operations (Arieti, 1955). They both fail because the life of socialized man cannot be reduced so drastically.

A young man, during a boring afternoon at his job, has the urge to step out of the office for a coffee break. While he is out he sees a beautiful new car parked on the other side of the street. He goes up to it and sees that the ignition key has been left in the keyhole. The idea comes to him that it would be pleasant to interrupt working and go for a brief ride in the country in that beautiful afternoon of spring. He starts the car and drives into the country, and the riding is so beautiful that he keeps going until it becomes dark. Unexpectedly a girl crosses the street. The man hits the girl, but does not stop. He is afraid that if he does and the police come, they will believe that he has stolen the car. He drives farther and farther, and an hour later he hears on the car's radio that a girl, struck by a hit-and-run driver, has just died. The man does not know what to do. He must run away, but he has no money. In order to get money he holds up a jewelry shop. The owner resists, so the man has to kill him.

The story continues in that vein. What has started as an innocent coffee break ends in multiple murders. It describes a sequence of events similar to ones occurring in the lives of psychopaths. By writing this story the patient revealed once more that psychopaths have intellectual insight, which is not helpful. After a short period of therapy, the patient interrupted the treatment—and, of course, never paid the bill.

Another important characteristic of the majority of psychopaths is that new plans for actions leading to gratification or release from the state of stress can occur as a sudden insight. The patient, thinking of ways to solve his problem as quickly as possible, suddenly experiences some kind of "enlightenment" on "how to do it." This quick *psychopathic insight* may appear an act of creativity. In a certain way it is. Actually it consists chiefly of mechanisms by which it is possible to disregard some factors which for a normal person would have an inhibiting influence. Furthermore, the patient tends to resort to the same "solution" all over again, so that after the initial act, it can no longer be thought of as psychopathic creativity. Eventually it can even be discussed in terms of stereotyped responses.

PSYCHODYNAMICS

Why is the psychopathic patient affected so strongly by a primitive wish that he cannot delay, transform, or inhibit it? Is he physically able to live according to higher levels of motivation? Does he have at his disposal all the neurons which permit the much more complicated patterns of feeling, thinking, and behavior which are compatible with civilized life? Since Lombroso's attempt (1876), many authors have tried to find correlations between physical constitutions and psychopathic behavior. The results have been inconclusive. Glueck and Glueck (1956) found that approximately 60 per cent of persistent delinquents were predominantly mesomorphic. Electroencephalographic studies seem promising, but have led to no definite findings (Ehrlich and Keogh, 1956; Hill, 1952, 1955).

As mentioned in the preceding section on pseudopsychopaths, the prefrontal lobe syndrome at times presents a picture with many similarities to that of the simple psychopath. Since the famous case of Phineas Gage, reported by Harlow (1848, 1868), we have known that prefrontal patients are tactless, impulsive, deprived of anxiety, and given to antisocial behavior. More recently, similar symptoms have been found in some patients after frontal leucotomy. Other organic injuries of the brain or tumors involving cortical or subcortical areas occasionally unchain aggressive and psychopathological behavior. However, as far as can be detected by present methods of investigation, there seems to be no evidence of frontal or cortical lesions in the overwhelming majority of psychopaths.

It is thus appropriate to search for psychodynamic factors which may determine or at least encourage the establishment of the short-circuited mechanism, or which may make this mechanism so powerful as to prevent the use of more complicated patterns. We can offer only hypotheses, which at the present time are supported only by a small number of cases. We know that the young child who goes through the exoceptual or sensorimotor stage at first behaves in accordance with the short-circuited mechanism, but that at a certain phase of his development he learns to postpone gratification. Or rather, he learns to do so *if he is consistently trained to expect substitute gratification at progressively increasing intervals.*

For instance, little George wants a second ice cream. He wants it at all costs; he says he "needs it." But if mother keeps the child on her lap, caresses him and says, "No, George, you can't have it now," little George will be able to accept this deprivation, because it is immediately compensated by the tenderness of mother. Later, in similar cases, he will get the approval of mother as a compensation for the deprivation, instead of direct tenderness. Still later he will get only a promise; that is, the hope that something good will happen to him as a reward for not responding immediately to impulsive urges. Promises and hopes, although abstract visualizations of things which have not materialized, retain a flavor or an echo of mother's approval and tenderness. What we are saying is that in normal development the interaction with a loving or at least well-disposed adult encourages evolvement toward future gratification and higher levels of motivation.

It could be that the future short-circuited psychopath did not go through these normal stages. What appeared to the child as deprivation held no compensations; the postponement was enforced in a crude way. No benevolent mother was there to help the child to make the transition from immediate gratification to postponement. He did not learn to expect approval and tenderness, to experience hope, and to anticipate the fulfillment of a promise. Frustration remains a very unpleasant, even unbearable experience. Thus he continued to exercise his neuronal patterns in circuits which referred to the present and led to quick responses. We often hear statements like the following: "The thief by stealing tries to get substitutes for the love he did not get as a child." We may recognize some truth in this type of explanation, provided we understand what is meant. It is not that the stolen goods are symbolic of maternal love, but rather that the psychopath, not having learned to obtain more abstract values and not having learned to wait for future gratification, concentrates on what he thinks he can get immediately. He gives up the expectation of higher levels of motivation; for him, gratification is possible only at a low level. His self retains a feeling of fulfillment and preserves its own regard by achievements through short-circuited mechanisms.

This infantile situation may explain why a patient has become more adept with mechanisms which lead to quick gratification. However, if the whole psychopathology of the psychopath were included in this mechanism, the person would be quick-tempered, childish, and immature, but not necessarily antisocial. Wanting two ice creams may be immature, but not necessarily psychopathic: to reveal psychopathic tendencies, the child must steal the second ice cream.

Thus the psychopathic mechanism is more complicated than a lack of learning how to postpone gratification. In addition to this, we must remember that the psychopath does not experience enough anxiety or worry about future events to cause him to alter his present behavior. A person may be immature and desirous of quick gratification, but if he has the ability to experience a sufficient quantity of anxiety he will not become a psychopath. A person who has no anxiety can mentally scan all possible ways by which he can obtain quick gratification, and he can promptly translate them into action. For a person who experiences adequate amounts of anxiety, such scanning is not possible. The antisocial possibilities are automatically inhibited or suppressed by the anxiety, and in many cases they remain totally unconscious or repressed.

Again, the parent-child relationship has a great deal to do with this psychopathic lack of anxiety. If, at a certain stage of his development, the parents impress the misbehaving child with the possibility of bad future consequences, if they threaten him with future punishment, and carry out the punishment at a certain interval after the misbehavior, then the child is not likely to become a psychopath. These words may sound strange. For many years, in fact, opposite points of view have been expressed in psychiatry: parents have been told how harmful it is to provoke anxiety in children, and how excessive anxiety, once it has been created, may lead to severe psychoneuroses and to schizophrenia. These statements are substantially correct. However, it may be equally true that the great permissiveness which parents have recently assumed, partly because of their "psychological sophistication," are contributing factors in the recent increase in juvenile delinquency all over the world—and, incidentally, in the decrease in obsessive-compulsive psychoneuroses.

We must once more conclude that parents are in a difficult situation, between psychological Scylla and Charybdis. If they evoke too much anxiety in the child, one sort of mental disorder may be facilitated; if too little anxiety, the likelihood of another sort of mental disorder may be greater. Most parents, however, seem capable of veering away from these two excesses and maintaining a normal route.

At times we do find psychopathic children in very strict and severely punishing families. In these cases, however, the punishment, generally physical in nature, is dealt out immediately after the misbehavior. Thus the child experiences immediate fear and pain, but no anxiety about the future. At times, also we find complicating features in the picture of the simple psychopath. In some cases the short-circuited mechanism is adopted only in limited areas of life. Perhaps the parents were able to elicit a normal amount of anxiety in most areas, but none in these few. It is possible to detect numerous gradations of psychopathy, which deserve specific psychodynamic studies.

In a considerable number of simple psychopaths, we find a basically inadequate personality. For instance, the following picture is common: The patient harbors relatively big aims and wishes, although he is psychologically inadequate to realize them. He tries several times, but always gets into a predicament. Eventually, the relatively quick mental processes which led him to ill-planned adventures lead him to find quick antisocial solutions to his predicaments; for example, to request money from relatives or actually to steal. Here a basically inadequate personality operates together with the short-circuited mechanism.

In some instances of simple psychopathy, sociocultural factors seem to have played a facilitating role. Where the culture partially sanctions violence in some situation, for example, the psychopath may seize on this dispensation when most people would not. That is, a blood feud in a backward and isolated community might encourage the psychopath who has some connection with it to launch into a murder. A psychopathic patient at times will point out that these environmental factors exist in his case, but he cannot see that he is using them as an excuse for antisocial behavior.

THE SIMPLE PSYCHOPATH AND THE PHENOMENON OF WILL

Is the simple psychopath a person suffering from an involuntary reversal of motivation and inability to inhibit the low motivation? Or is he a person who, although capable of choosing and willing, wishes and wills to make what society calls a wrong choice? These questions are of the greatest theoretical and legal importance. If, following the theoretical framework outlined in this book, we conceive the psychopath as a person who periodically reverts to a low level of motivation and integration, where quick gratification is necessary, it is obvious that all spheres of the psyche are involved (see Chapter 3).

It is therefore a matter of individual preference whether the psychopath is included in the category of motivational disorders or in that of disorders of the will. I prefer to place him in the category of patients who undergo a reversal to lower levels of motivation, where conation is governed by the short-circuited mechanism.

The psychopath does not lose his high levels of integration. As a matter of fact, he lives at higher levels most of the time—that is, when he does not act in a psychopathic way. However, when the state of tension builds up, he reverts to the lower level. His cognitive and conative powers seem capable of functioning at high levels, but the need to gratify the wish is so strong that they are ignored.

Technically, the simple psychopath is able to inhibit the low motivation, especially if some variables enter to complicate the already confused picture. For instance, in the presence of a policeman, the simple psychopath is generally capable of controlling his desire for quick antisocial action. In most cases innumerable variables make it impossible to determine the role played by the will. The law generally considers psychopaths capable of understanding and of willing their deeds and therefore declares them responsible for their actions.

2. The complex psychopath

The previous section mentioned how the simple psychopath occasionally has an illumination or insight on "how to do it." The insight of the complex psychopath is more involved and can be summarized as "how to do it and get away with it." To this group of psychopaths belong such groups of people as the "professional" bank robbers and some unscrupulous political leaders.

At first it may seem difficult to explain the mechanisms of the complex psychopath, because they do not seem to fit those which have been described. Finding ways to rob a modern bank, and even more, calculating ways to reach and retain political power, seem to imply an ability to conceive high aims and to use long-circuited mental processes.

We must specify at this point that every mental mechanism has to be considered in relation to an individual's general mental set. Although the emotions which motivate the complex psychopath may not be as primitive as those of the simple psychopath, they are relatively simple in comparison with others that he could experience, and they manifest some characteristics of protoemotions. For instance, desire for possession retains that quality of immediacy and compelling urge which is characteristic of the protoemotion called appetite. At times this desire for possession becomes desire for power over others. The psychology of power is outside the scope of this discussion. We can say briefly that it is a special form of possession; namely, possession or attempted possession of the will or of the whole physical entity of others.

Concerning the use of what appear to be long-circuited mechanisms, we can say that complex psychopaths are very intelligent people, and relative to their intellectual possibilities or to normal ways of reaching goals, the methods they use are quick methods: i.e., eliminating political adversaries by murder. Moral considerations are not allowed to delay their urge for gratification. However, they have to adopt and endure relatively long-circuited mechanisms in order to avoid further delays and make the gratification possible. Here the rest of the mental functions retain their full effectiveness and are used in the service of the relatively quick gratification. Long-circuited mechanisms are in the service of short-circuited ones.

In view of the nature of these cases, clinical experience is limited; and so far this writer has not been able to distinguish psychodynamic factors, or early environmental ones, which differ from those of the simple psychopath. However, the whole philosophy of life of the complex psychopath seems different from that of the simple psychopath. The simple psychopath eliminates the conflict between what Freud called the pleasure principle and the reality principle by completely acceding to the pleasure principle. The complex psychopath operates at a much higher level of motivation. He solves the conflict between "self-realization" and social morality by following without hesitation what seems to him self-realization (see Chapter 9). The complex psychopath believes that he deserves a particular gratification, or that it is congruous with his personal endowment or with the concept of his own self to seek it. He does not care how he is going to get it; the norms of society are not going to stop him and should not apply to him. The maxim he often invokes is that the end justifies the means. But the end, no matter how rationalized, embellished, or disguised, is the gratification of his primitive emotions, and "the means" are his quick methods.

Whereas the simple psychopath can be seen as following a style of life based on the philosophy of Epicurus, or more correctly, on the philosophy popularly attributed to Epicurus, the complex psychopath follows a style of life consonant with some tenets of Nietzsche and some teachings of Machiavelli. Historical figures like Nero, Cesare Borgia, Stalin, and to a lesser degree Mussolini were probably complex psychopaths.

3. The dyssocial psychopath

To this group belong individuals who are occasionally called sociological psychopaths, but the word *dyssocial*, proposed by the Committee on Nomenclature and Statistics of the American Psychiatric Association (1952), seems to me more appropriate. In fact, these patients are not socialized in a usual sense. In place of society in general, they substitute a smaller special society which permits and enables them to be antisocial toward members of the large society. They may be capable of strong loyalties for their own group.

These patients are people who in their youth were often members of juvenile or delinquent gangs. As adults they become members of groups of "professional" criminals. Some authorities consider these patients not as psychopathic personalities, but as members of special occupational groups (Jenkins, 1960).

Jenkins also believes that "the professional criminal is a cultural product." Other authors, like Cohen (1955) and Shaw and McKay (1931), have given great importance to sociological-cultural factors in the etiology and psychogenesis of the dyssocial psychopath. Although I agree that sociological-cultural factors are very important, I do not share Jenkins' view that the dyssocial psychopath is completely separated from the other types. In fact there are many mixed cases: for instance, of people who at times have individually given vent to their antisocial behavior and at other times have done so only when they had the support of a special group to which they belonged.

This type of psychopath belongs not only to gangs of juvenile delinquents or to associations of thieves, but at times to groups which are socially acceptable in particular environments. Undoubtedly one of the most famous, and infamous, of the dyssocial psychopaths was Adolf Eichmann. His group was the Nazi gang, to which he gave his loyalty to the end. Even when he was about to be executed, he invoked his loyalty as a justification of his deeds, saying, "I followed my flag and the law of war." Implicitly he meant that he followed the laws of the German government, which permitted him to kill millions of innocent human beings.

How can we interpret the formal and the dynamic mechanisms of the dyssocial psychopath? Obviously his phenomenology is more complicated than that of the simple psychopath, although he too has a strong urge to satisfy a primitive need for gratification, or for discharge of hostility, by resorting to relatively short-circuited mechanisms (gas chambers, armed robbery, multiple murders, etc.). However, the short-circuited mechanism must be *released* or sanctioned by the authority of a special group. The patient is not simply disregardful of his conscience, superego, or higher levels of motivation, like the simple psychopath. He replaces the normal conscience with the ideology or the laws of his special group.

Adoption of the short-circuited mechanism is thus as important in the dyssocial psychopath as in the simple and complex. Here, however, it has to be accompanied or preceded by an abnormal displacement of conscience (or superego, or parental identifications, or socialized level of motivation, in accordance with the various terminologies). This displacement is probably facilitated by several factors: (1) Early in life the patient did not receive that parental approval, recognition, etc., that he needed to build up his self-esteem; (2) For sociological-cultural-historical reasons, a group is available which can give the patient this approval and recognition, at the same time that it permits him to use short-circuited mechanisms for the gratification of primitive needs. Unusual features occasionally complicate the picture of the dyssocial psychopath. In some rare cases, for example, the group to which he is loyal and whose support he needs is replaced by a single person: a friend, a father-in-law, a fellow prisoner, etc.

Are the mechanisms that are used by simple, complex, and dyssocial psychopaths related to psychotic processes? Psychopaths are generally not considered psychotic either in psychiatric classifications or by the law. Cleckley, by suggesting that they have only a "mask of sanity," perhaps implies that they should be considered insane (1955). If Cleckley means that these people should be considered psychiatrically very ill, that they cannot in some circumstances control their actions, and that the law and our attitude toward them should be revised, then most psychiatrists would agree. However, we must stress that the use of the words *psychotic* or *insane* in reference to psychopaths is ambiguous. A psychotic is not simply a person who is seriously mentally ill, but a person who has undergone a basic symbolic or emotional transformation and accepts his transformation as a normal way of living (Chapter 16). The psychopath has an intellectual awareness that some of his actions are not acceptable to society. His insight, however, is not accompanied by an appropriate emotional tone and remains superficial. Furthermore, his need to carry out the psychopathic act by means of short-circuited mechanism prevails over this insight.

That the psychopath has some insight is also shown by the fact that he makes promises concerning the future. He frequently resolves on good behavior and goes to the extent of showing the therapist that he is fully aware of the troubles he will encounter if he follows his previous behavior patterns. Nevertheless, when the future becomes the present, the impelling need to repeat the short-circuited mechanism overcomes other considerations.

Although some liberal legislators and psychiatrists may believe that the simple psychopath should not be considered legally responsible, since he may be seen as almost impelled to adopt the short-circuited mechanism, it is much more difficult to maintain such an opinion about complex and dyssocial psychopaths. The steps which these patients have to take in order to carry out a criminal act, or in order to gain entrance into the ideologic group which will release the short-circuited mechanism, are long-circuited mechanisms. And long-circuited mechanisms have, at least until we understand them better, the characteristics of acts of free choice, or of deliberation.

4. The paranoiac psychopath

To this last group belong the rare individuals who present a peculiar mixture of paranoiac and psychopathic features. After accurate examination of them, we can state that in addition to being psychopaths they are psychotics in the usual sense of the word.

Paranoid features are seen in many psychopaths who belong to the simple, complex, and dyssocial types. However, these features are rather superficial and inconsistent; often they are obvious defenses or patched-up rationalizations used to justify the abnormal behavior. In the paranoiac psychopath, the paranoiac mechanisms are well systematized and are accompanied by apparently logical cognitive processes. The personality is preserved, and the general picture is closer to Kraepelin's classical paranoia than to the other paranoid syndromes or conditions. For this reason the term paranoiac rather than paranoid is used. No hallucinations or obviously regressive features of the paranoid type of schizophrenia are encountered in these patients. Instead we find periods of drug or alcoholic addictions in some cases.

These patients differ from the usual paranoiac in that their acting out in accordance with their delusions becomes the most salient feature of the syndrome. Undoubtedly many regular paranoiacs and paranoids act out their delusions; but in the paranoiac psychopath the acting out is more extensive. Also, the psychopathic traits generally *preceded* a definite paranoiac symptomatology, or in some cases, periods of acting out with no freely expressed delusions *alternate* with obvious delusional periods. These paranoiac psychopaths are in many instances similar to other cases of paranoia; perhaps they constitute only a variety of this syndrome. In fact, like regular paranoiacs, they are generally single men of superior intelligence who are incapable of sustaining heterosexual relations and who present latent homosexual trends, hidden by sadistic features.

Whereas the dyssocial psychopath needs a group which will release his tendencies to act out, the paranoiac psychopath needs a system of delusions which allows him to act out and to justify his actions. In other words, to justify his use of the short-circuited mechanism the dyssocial psychopath has a long-circuited mechanism based on his allegiance to a group or to a special code. The paranoiac psychopath, on the other hand, finds his justification by creating a long-circuited mechanism consisting of delusions. When the paranoiac psychopath is prevented from acting out—for instance, by imprisonment or hospitalization—he becomes more paranoiac.

If he is discharged, however, he becomes slightly less paranoiac and more psychopathic, especially if external situations permit him to act out.

Some paranoiac psychopaths remain unrecognized for
many years. The brilliancy of their intellect may hide their
pathology. Moreover, the peculiarity of their mental processes
lends itself to demagoguery and may find resonant echo and
wild acclaim in particular historicocultural circumstances. If
future historical and psychiatric research confirms the conclusions of preliminary evaluations, Adolf Hitler is the classic example of a paranoiac psychopath. At first his grandiose
and well-calculated plans were often actualized by resorting
to "the big lie," which, as he boasted, is easily believed. Later
they were actualized by crimes on a scale never before seen
on the surface of the earth.

In order to act out, Hitler needed a paranoiac system.
Prominent in this system were the Jews, who were behind all
evils and had to be exterminated. With his military defeats
and the waning of his grandiose plans, his delusions became
more pronounced and his need to act out more impelling. A
vicious circle thus was repeating itself. Even in the last few
months of his life, he continued to blame the Jews for his defeats. And even then, the loss of all his power was still in the
future and not experienced emotionally by him as a real possibility. The enemy had to be at the doors of Berlin before
Hitler could feel the full import of the disaster. The last sentence of his will, which he dictated shortly before committing
suicide, reiterated his delusions about the Jews.

Not all the paranoiac psychopath's acting out is antisocial.
Some patients become alcoholics, drug addicts, or addicts to
surgery, requesting operations which are unnecessary.

Drug addiction and the psychopathic personality

Drug addiction is a psychiatric problem which is unfortunately acquiring more and more importance as the number
of people suffering from it increases. Addiction will be discussed here only in its relation to psychopathic conditions,
with which it has some traits in common.

Several characteristics of the drug addict are similar to those of the simple psychopath. He experiences a state of tension, characterized by physical discomfort, malaise, short-circuited anxiety, and pain. A short-circuited mechanism—taking the drug—removes all these feelings. Wikler (1953) has clearly described how the primary needs of man—namely, hunger, sexual urges, and aggression, as well as some anxiety and pain—seem satisfied when the patient is on the drug. Contrary to the alcoholic, who drinks in order to release inhibitions and to be aggressive, vindictive, exhibitionistic, and grandiose, the drug addict settles for satisfaction of his primary needs and protoemotions (Nyswander, 1956). He gives the impression of mainly wanting to remove unpleasure. Thus he seems to be motivated at the level of the pleasure principle and to be concerned only with bodily satisfaction.

The psychopathology of the drug addict, however, is not so simple as that of the simple psychopath. The latter has never fully integrated at high motivational levels, which he has eliminated from his life because they seem to him unrealistic and unattainable. But the drug addict, when not on the drug, is fully aware of his anxiety, of his sense of defeat, and of his insecurity. Quite often he is conscious of his own hostility, and fears that it may burst into open violence. Often he is also aware of his early personal history, characterized by a very unstable childhood and shaky self-esteem. The addiction removes all these problems, for they become transformed into only one struggle: to get the drug.

His reversal to a motivation governed by the level of satisfaction (or the pleasure principle) is a form of defense. The needs of his body, at least at the beginning of the condition, replace the higher needs of the psyche, which cannot be fulfilled. The anxiety of interpersonal-symbolic life is replaced by short-circuited anxiety or by bodily tension. Eventually the bodily needs are felt with great intensity, so that the patient seems to live only for the purpose of satisfying them.

Actually the bodily needs are satisfied only in a substitutive way. The drug addict does not experience the pleasure of the gourmet who has been hungry, or of the sexually deprived person who is finally gratified. Predominantly, he achieves removal of the tension and pain caused by the needs, although he may also experience a feeling of calm, relaxation, and exhilaration (being high). In some cases the patient feels that he is making excursions into a pleasant and beautiful unreality. As a rule, therefore, he does not need to escape reality by becoming psychotic. However, a few drug addicts do become psychotic or mildly psychotic when the drug is withdrawn, or after a massive dose, or when the drug itself produces a toxic psychosis (as in the cases of mescaline, lysergic acid, and at times amphetamine). Psychotics or former psychotics practically never adopt the drug habit. In the past, especially in Europe, psychotic patients used to be treated with large doses of opiates, and yet none of them became addicted (Lindesmith, 1947).

Psychotherapy for the drug addict is very difficult, first, because the symptom is gratifying; second, because a rational treatment is self-defeating. A causal nonsymptomatic treatment would have to aim at training the patient to experience anxiety instead of tension. But the patient cannot tolerate anxiety; if we try to increase it, he will convert it into a protoemotion, generally tension, so that the need for the drug will increase. Perhaps we shall eventually devise methods to train drug addicts to accept small doses of anxiety, in order to receive and maintain the warm approval and deep concern of the therapist.

16° THE PSYCHOTIC TRANSFORMATION

In the last few decades psychiatry has undergone significant changes, but schizophrenia has remained its principal theoretical and therapeutic concern. Manic-depressive psychosis, once considered the second major psychiatric disorder, has become much less frequent and is at present attracting less attention. A third psychosis, paranoia, generally is studied as a separate clinical entity, although a considerable number of psychiatrists believe that it is a variety of schizophrenia.[1] Most of this chapter will be devoted to the schizophrenic process.[2] The basic aspects of paranoia and manic-depressive psychoses will also be considered.

[1] Paraphrenia is recognized only in some European schools, where the original Kraepelinian classification has not undergone major revisions. Involutional psychoses will not be discussed in this book, since their basic mechanisms consist of a mixture of the symptoms of schizophrenia and depression.
[2] The catatonic type of schizophrenia will be discussed mostly in Chapter 18.

Schizophrenia

THE PREPSYCHOTIC PERIOD

It is beyond the scope of this book to discuss the psycho-dynamics of schizophrenia in detail. In general, if we ignore the many important personal variables in each case, the life pattern which is apt to lead to the schizophrenic transforma-tion can be divided into three stages. The fourth stage will be the psychotic one.

Stage One. The young child finds himself in a family that for various reasons cannot offer him a modicum of security or basic trust. Early interpersonal relations are characterized by intense anxiety, devastating hostility, or false detachment. The child raised in this condition also has to contend with a delay or blocking in some areas of his development. More than the average child, he has to interpret the world, life, and himself in accordance with immature cognitive proc-esses: images and paleosymbols (Chapter 5), endocepts (Chapter 6), and paleologic modalities (Chapter 7).

Unpleasant images tend to remain a permanent part of his inner life. They become associated with other images and spread an unpleasant affective tonality to all the inner ob-jects. Parents are experienced as clusters of disagreeable im-ages, which are later paleologically transformed into terri-fying phantasy figures. In spite of the anomalies, dreariness, and intense turmoil of this period, relatively few of the chil-dren who undergo it succumb to child psychosis. Most of these children enter the processes of the second stage.

Stage Two. This compensatory outcome is possible be-cause inhibitory mechanisms develop automatically. They stop the functioning of most primary-process mechanisms and allow the secondary process to take their place. Uncanny experiences are repressed from consciousness. The self will be preserved by the adoption of a type of prepsychotic per-sonality which will protect from deep feeling and deep involvement (schizoid personality) or which will permit object relations, although in mutable, unstable, and undependable ways (stormy personality).[3]

The child will have difficulty identifying with the significant adults, but nevertheless will be able to build up some kind of superficial self-image, including identification with one sex rather than the other. These identifications and this patched-up self-image are not rooted in the core of his being; they are superficial reflections of how he feels people deal with him, rather than a well-integrated vision of the self.

The defenses the child builds up do not remove all his difficulties. He introjects, but also greatly distorts and magnifies the feelings and attitudes he felt the family had toward him. He constructs a shaky self-identity and harbors serious doubts about his personal significance and self-worth.

Toward the last period of childhood (prepuberal or preadolescent period), the psychological picture seems much improved. Because of the decrease in his immaturity, dependency, and demanding, the family has learned to live with the child less inadequately. He is now fully aware that the family is not going to constitute his whole world. Moreover, he has learned to appreciate the importance of the future in life, and he hopes in the future.

In the majority of cases, fortunately, there are no subsequent stages. The individual succeeds in building up adequate defenses and more or less adjusting to life, and the psychosis never occurs.

Stage Three. In some cases, however, the defenses which were built up in stage two begin to be less effective, and the person enters a third stage. This adverse turn of events generally starts around the time of puberty, but there are variations in accordance with the prevalent culture, the particular historical climate of the era, and individual events in the patient's life. The defenses which were adequate for the little family world are less reliable now that the patient has extended his contacts with the outside world. The secondary-process mechanisms, which had protected him from the un-

[3] For details concerning the development of a prepsychotic personality, see Arieti (1955, Chapter 3).

pleasant generalizations and paleologic terror of stage one, now increase his discomfort. He now feels that not only his family but the world at large is unwilling to accept his inadequacy.

Not only individual facts, events, and persons, but whole concepts now bother him. Specific events, scenes, and memories—like the creaking voice of mother, the arrogant gestures of father, the smelly kitchen, the dark living room, all sorts of disagreeable little incidents—are interconnected in a gloomy web of feelings. The unpleasant tonality of these memories is now extended to whole categories, for the patient has learned to think in this way—to conceptualize everything. He makes a wrong use of concepts: the categories have an almost absolute, exceptionless finality.

Sexual life is not seen as desirable, but as something which is difficult to control, or something which makes the patient an undesirable partner, an unlovable person, an inadequate lover, and in some cases a homosexual. Thoughts about the future have changed too. Whereas the patient previously seemed to find comfort in his hopes for the future and to acquire present self-esteem by visualizing a fulfilling future life, he can no longer do that. It is when he believes that the future has no hope and may be even worse than the present that the psychological decline characteristic of the third stage reaches its culmination in the preschizophrenic panic. This panic has been well portrayed by Sullivan (1953), who considered it the outcome of injury to self-regard. He described it using such terms as disorganization, terror, perception of danger, need to escape. He explained it as "An acute failure of the disassociative power of the self," that is, of the mechanisms which keep unpleasant memories in repression.

I prefer to distinguish the prepsychotic panic from the psychotic panic, which I consider the beginning of an acute psychosis. In my opinion the prepsychotic panic is more than "an acute failure of the disassociative power," and more than injury to self-regard, although it includes these processes. It is at first experienced as a sort of emotional resonance between something which is very clear (as the feeling of extreme inadequacy brought about by the recent postpuberal expansion of the secondary process and of the conceptual world), and something which is unclear, and yet is gloomy, horrifying.

These obscure emotional forces, generally silent but now re-emerging with devastating clamor, are nothing else but the repressed early experiences and their transformations in accordance with the primary process. In other words, either because of their strength or because of their inherent similarity to primary-process experiences, the conceptual conclusions and the emotional ineluctability reached through secondary-process mechanisms reactivate primary-process mechanisms and their original contents. These re-emerging mechanisms cannot be dismissed. On the contrary, they reinforce those of the secondary process, since they are in agreement with them, and the result is of dire proportions and consequences. The patient cannot repress any longer. He remembers that even before now he has occasionally undergone some unverbalizable experiences (which we would call endoceptual) with undefinable but unpleasant emotional tone. The present experiences are vivid and inescapable. In the totality of his being he sees himself as wholly defeated, deprived of self-worth, and beyond hope. Occasionally he is still able to return partially to an endoceptual level and to dissipate some of his devastating experiences into a nonrepresentational form; but even then an undermining, unexpressible feeling remains.

Only one solution, one defense, is still available to the psyche: to dissolve the secondary process, the process that has brought about conceptual disaster and ominous resonance with the archaic.

Stage Four. It is at this point that the fourth, or psychotic, stage begins. The secondary process can be dissolved in many ways: at times by a rapid regression to primary-process forms, at other times by a slow and partial assumption of regressive forms. In the following sections we shall study this dissolution of the secondary process and re-emergence of the primary process which together bring about the schizophrenic transformation.

THE DELUSIONAL WORLD

One of the first mechanisms adopted by the patient to prevent the agreement between the primary and the secondary process is projection. By projection we mean attributing to external forces something which originates within the self. This mechanism, as well as the others which will be illustrated later, is no longer something which is part of the inner reality or which is used exclusively in dream life; instead, it becomes a mode of dealing with the external world.

The mechanism of projection was first described by Freud in 1896. What Freud did not explain is that projection is actually a returning or giving back to the external, interpersonal world of something which originated in that world. The self-reproach, the low self-esteem, the deep sense of inadequacy were concept-feelings, evaluations, and appraisals that the patient received from the others—the significant adults in his life. During stage two they have partially been neutralized by various defenses; but partially they have remained at a conscious level as parts of the patient's self. During stage three the events of external life and of conceptual development greatly reinforce these negative components of his self-image and finally bring reactivation of the concept-feelings of the first stage which are in agreement with those of the third. In order to avoid the resulting self-image and maintain a tolerable sense of self, the patient projects to the external world the evaluation of the self that he now rejects. In some cases, immediately prior to the outbreak of the psychosis, the patient externalizes concept-feelings of a general and abstract form. The world in general is experienced as hostile; a vague sense of menace is felt almost in the air.

The psychosis starts not only when these feeling-concepts are projected, but also when they become specific and concrete. The indefinite feelings become finite, the imperceptible becomes perceptible, the vague menace is transformed into a specific threat. It is no longer the whole horrible world which is against the patient; "they" are against him. He no longer has a feeling of being under scrutiny, under the eyes of the world; no longer a mild sense of suspiciousness. The sense of suspiciousness becomes the conviction that "they" follow him. The conceptual and abstract are reduced to the concrete, the specific. The "they" is a concretization of external threats; later, "they" are more definitely recognized as F.B.I. agents, neighbors, or other specific persecutors.

Other delusions can be easily recognized not only as projections but also as reductions to a concrete level of what had belonged to a higher level of understanding and feeling. A patient has the conviction that his wife puts poison in his food. He actually used to feel that his wife "poisoned" his life. Thus the abstract poisoning becomes a concrete and specific one; a concept is transformed into an object, a chemical poison, after the inner turmoil has been projected to the external world. Another patient feels that the members of her family are controlling her thoughts with some kind of machinery. During her childhood and adolescence, she used to feel that the adults in her family were trying to mold and control her ways of thinking.

Projection and reduction of some complexes to concrete representations give the patient what seems an easier way of coping with a situation. As unpleasant as it is to be accused by others, it is not as unpleasant as accusing oneself. However, the accusation (for instance, of being a failure) assumes a specific form (such as the accusation of being a spy or a murderer) which seems worse than the original but is more easily projected to others. The patient who believes he is accused feels falsely accused. Thus although the projected accusation is painful, it is not injurious to his self-esteem. On the contrary, in comparison with his prepsychotic state, during which he consciously accused himself, he experiences a rise in self-esteem, often accompanied by a feeling of martyrdom.

The concrete aspect of many schizophrenic manifestations has been studied by Goldstein. According to him, the schizophrenic does not apply the "abstract attitude" in dealing with the world and is left only with "the concrete" (1939, 1943). There is no doubt that Goldstein has opened a path of fruitful inquiry. Nevertheless, we must recognize that his formulations suffer from the fact that originally he worked only with organic patients. Life experienced only or predominantly at a concrete level is a reduced life, but not necessarily a psychotic one. A brain-injured patient with extensive cortical lesions will not be able to solve difficult mathematical problems, for instance, but may function adequately within the realm of a limited reality. Although Goldstein too realized that the concreteness of the schizophrenic is not the same as that of the organic patient, he interpreted the difference simply as a different type of concreteness. Goldstein did not explain adequately what the difference consists of. We find various degrees of concreteness in organic brain diseases and also in mental deficiencies, but these conditions are not necessarily accompanied by psychosis. As a matter of fact, the organic defect may even eliminate the psychosis. It has that effect in psychosurgery, and possibly even in shock therapy, though in a reversible form.

In my opinion, schizophrenia results not from a reduction of the psyche to a concrete level, but from a *process of active concretization,* which follows psychodynamic (or teleologic, or restitutional) trends (Chapter 13). "Active concretization" means that the psyche is still capable of conceiving the abstract but not of sustaining it, because the abstract is too anxiety-provoking or too disintegrating. Abstract ideations are thus immediately transformed into concrete representations.

In this aspect the schizophrenic is similar to the dreamer and, as we shall see in Chapter 21, to the fine artist and to the poet, all of whom transform abstract concepts into perceptual images. The higher level impinges upon a lower form. Contrary to what happens in artistic productions, however, the schizophrenic's abstract level is lost or completely replaced by the concrete form.

To view this mechanism as a process of active concretization is a fruitful approach but does not provide a complete understanding of the problem, unless we clarify how this concretization takes place. The mechanism requires a profound alteration: the adoption of a primary-process type of cognition. Let us consider again the patient who felt at first that his wife was poisoning his life and who later experienced the delusion that the wife poisoned his food. If we examine this concretization, we realize that the concrete form is not a random occurrence, but is related to the abstract form. The two concepts (poisoning of life and poisoning of food) actually are members of a secondary-process or logical class, whose concept is "causing the destruction or warping of the patient's life" (see Chapter 8). The patient, however, tends either to eliminate the concept of the secondary-process class or to transform the secondary class into a primary class, so that the poisoning of life becomes equivalent to the poisoning of food. The abstract is eliminated and the more concrete member of the class emerges.

Thus, again, although the patient is able to conceive the abstract and to make a connection between the abstract and concrete elements which together form a secondary class, the secondary class is transformed into a primary one and remains represented by a concrete member. In other words, the first few stages of this mechanism of regressive concretization still require abstract conceptualization.

The fact that the patient retains abstract conceptualization has made some clinical psychologists doubt that there is a cognitive impairment in every schizophrenic patient. In some cases of incipient schizophrenia, even the most accurate available tests fail to show signs of cognitive impairment. These apparent negative findings can be explained in several ways. First, before the onset of the psychosis the patient's cognitive functions may have been at such a high level that a slight degree of regression or concretization may still allow a level of functioning which is within normal limits. Only people who knew him before he became ill can recognize the difference.

In the second place, especially at the beginning of the disorder, the cognitive alterations take place only when the cognitive content refers to the patient's complexes. He may function at a perfectly normal level when he thinks about psychodynamically neutral matters. In the third place, there is not a complete regression to one level in every case of schizophrenia; several levels and degrees are mixed together, and even in the most regressed patients we find "islands" of cognitive normality.

PALEOLOGIC THINKING

The delusional thinking described in the previous sections mainly adopts the mechanisms of projection and concretization. The concretization, however, may reach degrees which are even more removed from abstract thinking. On one hand, the patient has the urge to escape from the unpleasant anxiety-ridden reality, and he experiences a return of primitive wishes. On the other hand, primitive levels of cognition again become available to him and seem more conducive to satisfaction. These regressive forms of cognition exert a sort of fascination. The patient at first tries to resist them, but finally he succumbs and accepts the new ways of interpreting the world. Now he puts "two and two together"; now he is able to solve "the big jigsaw puzzle." Things which appeared strange, confused, and peculiar now acquire sense.

In many cases this new "understanding" occurs as a sudden illumination, which has been called "psychotic insight" (Arieti, 1955). The patient feels extremely lucid, and has at least a transitory feeling of exuberance, similar to that of a person who has made an important discovery. Although sometimes this new insight results only from the adoption of those mechanisms of projection and limited concretization described in the previous sections, in other cases it is caused by the adoption of a new way of organized thinking or "logic." This new logic is actually a return to the level of cognition which I have called paleologic.

In Chapter 7 we saw how this type of thinking is to a large extent based on the principle of Von Domarus: The person who thinks paleologically accepts identity not on the basis of identical subjects (or wholes), but on the basis of identical predicates (or parts). For instance, a schizophrenic patient thought that she was the Virgin Mary. Asked why she thought so, she replied, "I am a virgin. The Virgin Mary was a virgin; I am the Virgin Mary." The delusional conclusion of being the Virgin Mary was reached because the identity of the predicate of the two premises (being virgin) made the patient accept the identity of the two subjects (the Virgin Mary and herself). Obviously the patient had a great need to identify with the Virgin Mary, who was her ideal of feminine perfection and to whom she felt very close. At the same time she had the need to deny her feeling of unworthiness and inadequacy.

A red-haired 24-year-old woman in a postpartum psychosis developed an infection in one of her fingers. The terminal phalanx was swollen and red. She told the therapist a few times, "This finger is me." Pointing to the last phalanx she said, "This is my red and rotten head." She did not mean that her finger was a representation of herself, but either an actual duplicate of herself, or, in a way incomprehensible to us, really herself.

Another patient believed that the two men she loved were the same person, although one lived in Mexico City and the other in New York. In fact, both of them played the guitar and both of them loved her. By resorting to a primitive cognition which followed the principle of Von Domarus, she could reaffirm the unity of the image of the man she wanted to love.

Derivations of this type of thinking are recognizable in most patients. For instance, a patient felt that when people used the word *water*, they secretly referred to her because "she runs like water." She thought that when people were talking about a certain movie actress, they referred to her because she was "effervescent and blonde" like that movie actress. Another patient felt that when people used the word *candies*, they were referring to her former boy friend. She was on a diet and had *given up* eating candies, just as she had previously *given up* her boy friend. The predicate of "having been given up" led the patient to identify candies and boy friend and to assume that other people would make a similar identification.

Thus any analogy or similarity becomes identity, provided the identity is emotionally attuned to the mood, secret wishes, or fears of the patient. This type of logic often permits him to reach the conclusions he wants, because the same subject has many predicates; he can select that predicate which will lead to the identification he wants or needs. In order to identify with the movie actress, the patient above selected the predicates "effervescent and blonde"; in order to identify with water, she selected the quality of running; but both the actress and the water had a large number of available predicates. In most cases we can recognize the motivation which underlies this type of thinking and actually determines the selection of the predicate. Many patients at this stage indulge in what I have called an orgy of identifications. A French psychiatrist, Joseph Gabel, independently discovered the same phenomenon in schizophrenia and called it a hypertrophy of the sense of identification (Gabel, 1948).

As a last example, take the new patient who was waiting for his first interview with the therapist and saw in one of the magazines in the waiting room an advertisement with the picture of a naked baby. He remembered that there was a similar picture of himself as a baby, and that his father, "the bastard," had recently threatened to show the picture to his girl friend. Seeing the picture of the baby in the waiting room, he thought, was not a fortuitous coincidence. This patient illustrated the phenomenon commonly found in schizophrenics of seeing nonfortuitous coincidences all over. The terrible coincidences for which there was no explanation were pursuing him relentlessly.

The phenomenon of the coincidences is also related to Von Domarus' principle. A coincidence is a similar element occurring in two or more instances at the same time or after a short period of time. The patient tries to glimpse regularities in the midst of the confusion in which he now lives. He tends to register identical segments of experience and to build up systems of regularity upon them. At times the regularity that the identical segments suggest gives sustenance to a complex which, although by now it is disorganized, retains a strong emotional investment.

In the delusions discussed in the previous sections, the mechanism of concretization was still unconscious (for instance, in the patient who believed that his wife was poisoning his food rather than his life). In the paleologic disorder too, the thinking process may be automatic and unconscious. In many cases, however, the patient retains consciousness of his thinking and accepts the conclusions he comes to.

The adoption of Von Domarus' principle in schizophrenia can also be seen as part of the process of concretization.

Whenever the patient functions at the level of Von Domarus' principle, he is able to distinguish a part (or predicate) from a whole (or subject), but is not able to separate the part (or predicate) from the whole (subject). The abstraction is partial. The part which cannot be isolated from the rest has to be associated with the whole, or has to be responded to as to the whole. That is, the inability to abstract from connectedness leads to identification by connectedness. Thus Von Domarus' principle can be reformulated in this way: The more difficult it is to abstract a part from wholes, the stronger is the tendency to identify the wholes which have that part in common.[4]

This process can also be explained as a return to the use of what Chapter 7 called primary classes (pages 108–112). The schizophrenic, following his motivation, switches from A to B so easily because at this level of mentation A and B are members of a primary class and therefore become equivalent. The displacement, which orthodox Freudians consider due to shifting of cathexes, is actually founded on the cognitive equivalence of the members of a primary class.

This interchangeability of the members of primary classes would seem at first to bring about an enrichment in the mental life of the patient. In a certain way we may consider it a restitutional enrichment, as Freud did. However, we must realize that what is gained is much less than what is lost. First of all, the loss of high abstract conceptualization results in a loss of conceptual objects and limits the choice of the patient to concrete objects. Second, the archaic, tangible, primitive objects of his life reassert themselves, and so do his primitive desires. Thus he is restricted both in object choice and in motivational span.

TELEOLOGIC CAUSALITY

A return to a predominantly teleologic causality is evident in many stages of schizophrenia. It is already manifest when

---

[4] Matte-Blanco has interpreted schizophrenic thinking differently (1959, 1965). He believes that schizophrenic thinking "treats relations as if they were symmetrical." In my opinion, Matte-Blanco's principle of symmetry is not accurate. It attributes a mechanism to schizophrenic thinking which is hardly reconcilable with the way the primary process operates.

the patient attributes evil intentions to the persecutors, but becomes more obvious at later stages of the disorder.

The schizophrenic can believe, as the normal person does, that every effect is determined by a cause; but when he is concerned with his complexes, he feels that any event related to them is caused by the volition of other humans (see Chapter 7, page 113). It was not the wind which opened the window, but a malevolent person who wanted to spy on the patient. It was not atmospheric phenomena which brought about a storm; somebody has devised a special machine which changes the weather in order to annoy the patient.

LANGUAGE AND CONNOTATION

The psychopathology of concepts in schizophrenia is evident when a patient's use of language is analyzed in reference to the denotation, connotation, and verbalization of verbal symbols (see Chapter 7, pages 98–106 and Chapter 8, pages 127–135). I have found that, at least for heuristic purposes, it is useful to formulate a second principle of schizophrenic cognition:

Whereas the healthy person in a wakened state is mainly concerned with the connotation and the denotation of a verbal symbol but is capable of shifting his attention from one to another of the three aspects of a symbol, the person who thinks paleologically is mainly concerned with the denotation and the verbalization, and experiences a total or partial impairment of the ability to connote (Arieti, 1948, 1955).

In view of this principle, two phenomena are important in the schizophrenic's use of language: first, the reduction of connotation power; second, the emphasis on denotation and verbalization. These phenomena reproduce in reverse the stages of language development described in Chapters 7 and 8.

For the person who thinks paleologically, verbal symbols tend to lose their function of representing a class, and tend to stand only for the specific objects which the patient is considering at the moment. For instance, he may not use the word "dog" in relation to all members of the canine genus, but only in reference to a specific dog, like "the dog sitting in that corner." Often there is a gradual shifting from the connotative to the denotative level, which becomes apparent in the various stages of the illness when we ask patients to define words. A definition, in fact, requires the formation of a secondary class (Chapter 8, page 127). Following are a few examples of definitions given by patients who represented moderate to very advanced degrees of regression.

One woman who was asked to explain what the word *table* means replied, "What kind of tables? A wooden table, a porcelain table, a surgical table, or a table you want to have a meal on?" She was unable to define the word *table* and attempted to simplify the problem by inquiring whether she had to define various subgroups of tables.

Other patients, when asked to supply a general or categorical definition, replied by giving specific embodiments of the definition. A patient who was asked to define *chair* said, "I sit on a chair now. I am not a carpenter." Another patient answered the same question with "A throne." (He restricted the meaning to this particular type of chair because of a connection with his delusions. He believed that he was an angel and was sitting on a throne in heaven.) At times these definitions reveal not only a constriction to one or a few specific instances of the class, but also the prominence of bizarre associations. Correct but uncommon definitions are also given. For instance, a patient who was asked to define the word *bird* replied, "A feathered fowl." Another patient answered, "A winged creature."

This restriction to concreteness also prevents the patient from giving a metaphorical meaning to proverbs; they are interpreted literally or very concretely. When a patient was asked to explain the phrase, "When the cat's away, the mice will play," she replied, "Mice are devoured by the cat." To the question, "What does it mean: actions speak louder than words?" another patient replied, "A battle in the war." When he was asked to explain this, he added, "There are plenty actions in a battle." The actions which were seen by him as louder than words were military actions. This idea could be interpreted as an unusual association, except that it was given as a definition of a whole class.[5]

[5] Goldman has experimentally confirmed this decrease of connotation power in schizophrenics (1960).

EMPHASIS ON DENOTATION AND
VERBALIZATION

When the word loses its connotation power, as a rule it increases its denotation and verbalization power. At times, perhaps because it evokes images, it acquires a quasi-perceptual quality and a stronger emotional tonality. The word thus becomes almost an icon of the thing it represents. At other times it actually becomes equivalent to its denotation. Schizophrenics, as well as some primitives (Chapter 8), often confuse the word for the thing that it symbolizes.

In most cases of schizophrenia, when the connotation is impaired, it is the verbalization rather than the denotation which increases in significance. Patients often associate words not according to their meaning, but according to their phonetic quality (clang association). This series of words was written by a patient in an order which follows clang association: "Chuck, luck, luck, buck. True, two. Frame! Name! Same! Same! Same! Same!"

At times such series of words, associated because of their similar verbalization, retain a general sense of meaning reminiscent of a primary aggregation (see page 106). For instance, the patient mentioned above who defined a chair as a throne and who believed he was an angel wrote the following "prayer" which he used to recite every morning:

"Sweetness angel, gentle, mild, mellow, gladness, glory, grandeur, splendor, bubbling, babbling, gurgling, handy, candy, dandy, honor, honey, sugar, frosting, guide, guiding, enormous, pure, magnificent, enchanted, blooming plumes." In addition to words that he felt were applicable to God and to angels, he often selected words because of their assonance.

At times the patient loses the proper denotation of a word and gives it another one which is suggested by the verbalization. For instance, a patient who was shown a pen and was asked to name the object replied, "A prison." The word *pen* elicited in him the idea of penitentiary.

Often the verbalization is exploited to fit a certain delusional or referential framework. For instance, every time a patient heard the words *home* and *fair,* he thought they were the slang words for homosexuals, *homo* and *fairy*. He was preoccupied with the problem of sexual identification and believed that people were subtly referring to his alleged homosexuality. The similarity between these words would not have been noticed or seized upon had the patient not been so preoccupied.

Proper names are often the objects of similar processes. A patient whose name was Marcia, and who knew Italian, thought her name meant that she was rotten (in Italian *marcia* means rotten in the feminine gender). Another patient whose name was Stella felt that her name indicated that she was a fallen star. Because they are so involved with verbalization, patients often discover puns all over and feel that these puns are used purposely to annoy them.

HALLUCINATIONS

With the progression of the schizophrenic process, concepts tend to be expressed in a concrete language which consists of perceptual forms. Many gradations are possible. A normal process of perceptualization occurs in dreams, in which thoughts become transformed predominantly into visual imagery which has the characteristics of perceptions. In schizophrenia an abnormal process of perceptualization has its fullest expression in hallucinatory experiences.

In schizophrenic hallucinations, thoughts are transformed into perceptions or images involving every sense, but predominantly the auditory. The patient "hears," "sees," "tastes," etc., without external stimuli. Hallucinations have three important characteristics: (1) perceptualization of the concept; (2) projection of the inner experience to the external world; (3) extreme difficulty in correcting the erroneous experience.

The perceptualization of the concept is a more advanced form of the process of concretization. For instance, a patient who believes that he is a "rotten person" develops the olfactory hallucination that a bad odor emanates from his body. The rotten personality becomes concretized in the "rotten body which smells." As mentioned in the section on delusions, this phenomenon cannot be interpreted as just a return to a concrete level. The patient is still able to conceive the abstract concept-feeling that he is a rotten person, but such an emotionally loaded idea cannot be sustained at its original level and is immediately actively translated into a concrete form. By reducing the concept to a percept, the patient restricts his anxiety to a smaller area of ideation so that it is less disturbing.

The second important characteristic of hallucinations—projection of the subjective experience to the external world—also exists in dreams. The dreamer believes that the action of the dream takes place in the external world. This characteristic which at first seems so strange is actually an intrinsic quality of every normal perception. For instance, when I see an object in front of me, the perception of the object occurs inside me, around my calcarine fissure, but my psychological apparatus projects this perception again into the external world. Thus what is specific in hallucinatory experiences and dreams is not the fact that the subjective experience is externalized, but the fact that an abstract thought has been perceptualized and follows the modalities of perception instead of those of thought.[6]

The third characteristic of hallucinations is the extreme difficulty in correcting the erroneous experience. In other words, it is almost impossible for a person who hallucinates to recognize that the hallucinatory experience does not correspond to external reality. In many cases, however, with

[6] The perceptualization of the concept is a relatively well-known phenomenon in psychopathology. Since Lelut, a French psychiatrist who wrote in 1846 that "The hallucination is the transformation of a thought into sensation," the phenomenon of perceptualization has been described in many ways. A complete interpretation is still lacking, however. Silberer (1909, 1912), influenced by Freud, reported a method of eliciting certain symbolic hallucinatory phenomena. Once while he was lying on a couch, he was thinking of a very difficult abstract subject and an image automatically occurred to him which was almost a concrete symbol of what he was thinking. After this experience, Silberer learned to elicit these quasi hallucinations voluntarily. He reported them in detail, as in the following example: He is thinking about something; but, pursuing a secondary consideration, he departs from the original theme. An hallucination occurs: he is mountain-climbing. The mountains near him conceal the farther ones from which he came and to which he wants to return.

Silberer called these phenomena autosymbolic. They were not real hallucinations, because he knew that they did not represent phenomena of external reality. They were abstract constructs which manifested themselves in concrete forms.

some difficult therapeutic procedures this correction is possible (Arieti, 1962a, 1963).

Recently many works on sensory deprivation, following the pioneer experiments made by Bexton et al. (1954), Heron et al. (1956), and Lilly (1959), have clarified one aspect of the complex problem of hallucinations. These researches found that when the human subject is put into a state of sensory isolation, at first he experiences a hunger for stimulation, then he indulges in reveries, and finally his reveries assume a perceptional quality and become hallucinations.

It seems to me that sensory deprivation is a facilitating mechanism rather than the crucial one in the hallucinatory phenomenon. It does not occur exclusively in experimental conditions: we have a physiological sensory deprivation in the state of sleep. The occipital cortex is not bombarded by external stimuli, and the state of rest facilitates those visual hallucinations which are dreams. In schizophrenia too, some kind of psychological isolation exists. Stimuli from the external world obviously reach the patient somehow, but he is so much less aware of them that they are only superficially registered and are not elaborated in higher mental forms.

SEVERE THINKING DISORDERS

Schizophrenic thinking may reach a degree of impairment more pronounced than that reported in the previous sections. For instance, a patient in the course of some routine examination was requested to answer the question, "Who was the first President of the United States?" He replied, "White House."

At this stage of the illness, thinking regresses to the level of the primary aggregation, which has been described in Chapter 7. A stimulus, such as the question about the first President, does not elicit a specific answer but a whole cluster of previous experiences; that is, a primary aggregation of elements that have not been organized into classes. The only organization consists of belonging to the same elementary grouping. In the example above, "White House" was equivalent to George Washington, because White House and George Washington are elements of a primary aggregation which has to do with Presidents of the United States. Ironically, George Washington never lived in the White House.

Which element comes to represent the primary aggregation is not determined by chance. Often familiarity and primitive motivational factors determine the one that will reach consciousness. "Word salad," a typical thought-language disorder of the very ill schizophrenic, generally consists of verbal elements which replace others that belong to the same primary aggregation.

OPPOSITE SPEECH

Some regressed patients often do or say the opposite of what they intend to do or say. For instance, the patient says "no" when he should say "yes"; "I know" when he should say "I don't know"; "close" when he means "open"; "gone" when he means "arrived"; etc.

Taking the lead from a report by Laffal et al. (1956) on a schizophrenic patient who provided clear examples of opposite speech, Kaplan has reviewed this topic in a very scholarly article (1957). Kaplan concludes that opposite speech indicates a return to a more primitive cognitive level. At this more primitive or undifferentiated level, opposites, like hate and love, hot and cold, belong to the same global sphere and may be interchanged. Kaplan's global sphere corresponds to the primary aggregation described in Chapter 7.

In my opinion, Kaplan's interpretation is correct, but it leaves an important aspect of the phenomenon unexplained: Why, out of the many elements which are included in the primary aggregation, is the one that the patient selects the opposite or antonym of what seems to us correct? Chapter 7 (pages 101–103) discusses the relation between this level of primitive cognition and primary byphasic conation. The schizophrenic symptom of opposite speech clearly appears as a return to that level.

There are other reasons, however, why schizophrenics often *behave* in a way opposite to what one would anticipate in a normal person. This topic will be examined later in reference to catatonic patients (Chapter 18).

ADUALISM

Many of the phenomena, such as hallucinations and delusions, which have been described above are confused by patients with events or things in external reality. More complicated symptoms are thereby formed. For instance, a schizophrenic visualizes a scene in which some people who played an important role in his childhood, and who are now dead, come to visit him in the hospital. As soon as he has these thoughts, he sees the dead people in the hospital visiting him. Actually, he is misidentifying some fellow inmates as these visitors.

Emotionally loaded thoughts are transformed by the schizophrenic into actual things or events, and *the events of the inner life and of the external world become parts of one and the same reality.* Whatever is experienced tends to become true by virtue of the fact of being experienced. This is the phenomenon of adualism, which was described in Chapter 5 (pages 79–81). Adualism is very common in various degrees in all stages of schizophrenia, and at times is prominent even in the early stages.

If we ask severely ill schizophrenics to explain why they believe their strange ideas in spite of lack of evidence, they do not attempt to demonstrate the validity of the ideas. They do not resort to paleologic, as less regressed patients do. Almost invariably they give this answer: "I know," meaning, "I know that it is so." The patient's belief is more than a strong conviction; it is a certitude. Something which he knows or something about which he has some thoughts is for him equivalent to something which exists, almost as if he would actualize the tenets of the idealistic school of philosophy.

Even in the early stages of schizophrenia, the patient is unable to lie about his delusions unless he is recovering or is under drug therapy. To lie requires the abstraction of visualizing what does not exist, and he no longer can do so. The delusions are absolute reality for him and he cannot deny them.

We have seen repeatedly how in psychopathology there is

a tendency to fulfill a wish which, in normal conditions, is difficult to attain. One of the main contributions of Freud was to point out how psychopathological mechanisms are used for nonrealistic wish fulfillment. Their wish-fulfillment quality reaches its culmination when merely to experience a wish becomes equivalent to its actualization. This occurs in schizophrenic adualism: motivational factors induce the patient to indulge in pleasant thoughts and images, but it is the state of cognition which permits him to equate images and thoughts with reality. As a matter of fact, he also experiences anxieties and fears as if they were actualized.

PERCEPTUAL ALTERATIONS

Perceptions too undergo changes in schizophrenia. At times these alterations can hardly be detected; at other times they are obvious. Some occur in the early stages, others in the most advanced.

At the onset of several acute types of schizophrenia, there is an accentuation of the perceptual aspects of external objects. Colors appear extremely bright and intense, as in technicolor movies. Noises and sounds seem loud, distorted, hard to bear.

Another alteration which occurs frequently in acute forms of schizophrenia and appears to a milder degree in chronic cases is the phenomenon that I have termed *aholism* (Arieti, 1961c, 1962a). The very regressed or acutely ill patient is unable to perceive wholes. The disintegration of wholes is gradual and corresponds at a perceptual level to the fragmentation of the primary aggregation described in the earlier section on this topic. At first the schizophrenic must divide big or complex wholes into smaller unities. For instance, a patient looking at the nurse could not see or focus on her as a person, but perceived only her left or right eye or her hand, or her nose, etc. Another patient, who was put into a seclusion cell while she was in a state of dangerous excitement, remembered later that she could not look at the whole door of the cell. She could see only the knob or the keyhole, or some corner of the door.

In later stages, if the excitement increases, the schizo-

phrenic divides even the smaller unities into smaller fragments. Pronounced fragmentation of wholes occurs in states
of acute confusion (as well as in some toxic-infective deliria)
and in very bizarre, almost entirely forgotten dreams of normal people. The patient retains only a vague memory of this
extreme fragmentation. In fact, one of the reasons why it has
not been described in the literature in reference to schizophrenia is the difficulty patients have in remembering it.

These amnesias are probably determined by the fact that
disintegrated wholes have no names and cannot be classified
according to schemata of previous experiences. The mechanism may be similar to what, according to Schachtel (1959),
occurs in childhood amnesias. At times during the very
acute episode, the patient is aware that he is losing the perception of wholes and the capacity to see the world as divided into unities. He then makes conscious efforts to reconstruct these wholes, but the attempts are only partially
successful. The wholes turn out to be different from the original ones, and partial distortions result.

These perceptual alterations occur to a moderate degree in
the chronic schizophrenic. They are responsible for those
disorders in spatial orientations apparent, for instance, in
drawings. The reader will be able to recognize in all these
perceptual alterations a return to the stages of pregestalt
perception described in Chapter 4 (pages 51–55). It is
doubtful that a sense of self as a whole entity is present at
this point.

Other severe types of perceptual alterations sometimes
occur after decades of hospitalization, in what has been
called the terminal stage of schizophrenia (Arieti, 1945a,
1955). The patient shows partial or total anesthesia to pain
and temperature, although he retains reactivity to olfactory
stimuli. Some patients are so insensitive that they can endure
surgical operations without anesthesia. Pieces of ice put over
sensitive regions of the body do not elicit a reaction. Although the phenomenon is not completely understood, it
seems that these sensations are not really lost (in fact, ten-
don and superficial reflexes are retained). Probably what is
lost is only a perceptual elaboration of these sensations. In
other words, the patients may experience agnosia regarding

pain and temperature.[7] It could also be that such patients have lost psychological but not physiological sensation (see Chapter 2, pages 15–18).

THE ENDOCEPTUAL AND PRIMITIVE OBJECT-RELATIONS STAGES

At an advanced stage of regression, the schizophrenic is no longer able to express what he experiences. He has reached a condition of total or almost total inability to communicate. This stage should not be confused with similar but less advanced stages where the lack of communication is due to negativism, withdrawal, or the absence of relatedness. For in the state of advanced regression, the patient's cognitive functions can no longer go beyond the endoceptual level (see Chapter 6). The conceptual and preconceptual parts of the inner objects are now almost entirely dissipated or transformed into endoceptual experiences. Images and paleosymbols exist but cannot be communicated.

At this stage defensive phenomena of an entirely different nature take place in increasing proportions. Regressed patients start to collect objects, such as stones, spoons, cores of fruit, pencils, sticks, etc. This hoarding habit, described elsewhere in detail (Arieti, 1945b, 1955), must be considered a desperate attempt to re-establish object relations. Here, however, the objects are not inner objects, but tangible external objects that have no function other than the psychological one just mentioned.

When patients become more regressed and approach the terminal stage, they start to use the cavities of their own bodies as deposits for the hoarded material. Male patients frequently deposit small objects in their ears or noses. Female patients place objects in their vaginas.

When the last stage of regression is reached, patients do not hoard objects any longer. They pick up whatever small objects are around them and place these in their mouths indiscriminately. This emerging oral tendency does not follow any categorical discrimination, even of a primitive kind.

[7] For further discussion the reader is referred to Chapters 17 and 18 of *Interpretation of Schizophrenia* (Arieti, 1955).

Both edible and inedible objects are incorporated, at times with dire consequences. This habit becomes a problem in custodial care (Arieti, 1944, 1945a, 1955).

At the same time that the patient establishes this oral contact, which is the most primitive form of object relations, he destroys the object by incorporating it. This is the end of any attempt on the part of man to transcend his physical entity and to be in some kind of distinct relationship with the world. However, it may be the last attempt to recapture a sense of self, by regressing to the level of a primitive, stereotyped sensorimotor organism.

CONCLUSION

The preceding sections have outlined the most important cognitive changes that occur in schizophrenia when the disorder runs its progressive course. They did not by any means examine all the schizophrenic phenomena, especially at a behavioral level. Nor did they describe the four main symptomatologic types (paranoid, hebephrenic, catatonic, and simple), as is customary. The aspects of the schizophrenic process which are not dealt with in this book are treated in detail in other works (Kraepelin, 1919; Bleuler, 1950; Arieti, 1955; Bellak, 1958). What we have examined here is the schizophrenic transformation as a process—a phenomenon that reopens the books of phylogenetic, ontogenetic, and microgenetic history.

Unless the patient is successfully treated, or unless favorable circumstances somehow occur, the regression tends to be progressive, because it fails in its defensive function. The schizophrenic transformation reduces the anxiety of the interpersonal world, but does not bring about reintegration at a lower level. The patient's psyche was originally attuned to a high level of social and mental integration, and it cannot adjust at an unnatural level. The schizophrenic then responds to the new maladjustment with further regression. The process repeats itself and the path toward mental dilapidation continues. However, in certain cases, especially in institutionalized patients, life is so reduced or so abnormal as to become adjusted to the maladjustment of the patient. Further regression is then unnecessary. Fortunately, fewer and fewer cases today reach these extremes.

Paranoia

In some psychiatric centers today the diagnosis of paranoia is never made; it is replaced by such classifications as the paranoid type of schizophrenia, paranoid state, and paranoid condition. Kraepelin, who was the first to give the diagnostic criteria for paranoia, divided all paranoiac-paranoid syndromes into three groups. At one extreme he put the paranoid type of dementia praecox (schizophrenia). This type includes cases which present projective and delusional symptoms together with the other regressive symptoms of schizophrenia. At the other extreme he put cases of paranoia, a syndrome characterized by well-systematized delusions, with no tendencies toward regression, remission, or recovery. Hallucinations, according to Kraepelin, may occur in paranoia but are rare; regression may be present also, but only to a minimal degree.

Between these two groups Kraepelin put the paraphrenias, which in American psychiatry correspond roughly to "paranoid states" or "paranoid conditions." Paranoid states are supposed to be delusional syndromes which are fairly well systematized, but not as logically constructed as paranoia. The differential diagnosis between paranoid conditions or states and the paranoid type of schizophrenia is often determined more by the diagnostic orientation of the psychiatrist than by the actual symptomatology.

This section will deal only with paranoia, or pure paranoia, as it is occasionally called.[8] Paranoia is acknowledged to be a very rare disease, even by most of those who recognize its existence. It is said to be much more frequent in the male sex, especially after the age of 35–40. Adolph Meyer described the prepsychotic personality of the paranoiac as

[8] The confusion between these terms is even more pronounced when adjectives and personal nouns are used. A person suffering from pure paranoia is a paranoi*ac*, and not a paranoi*d*, as he is occasionally called. A paranoi*d* is a person suffering from a paranoid state or from the paranoid type of schizophrenia.

characterized by rigidity, pride, haughtiness, suspiciousness or actual distrust, and disdain. A large percentage of these patients are unmarried and show little interest in sexual life; the few paranoiacs who get married are unable to establish a warm conjugal relationship. Some patients disclose indications of overt or latent homosexuality. Contrary to early psychoanalytic formulations, however, homosexuality does not seem a prerequisite for paranoia.

I feel that it is useful to retain this condition as a separate clinical entity, even if we do not understand it completely and do not know how close it is to schizophrenia. We are probably correct to exclude from this group all cases presenting hallucinations and obvious signs of regression. Even if such cases are omitted, however, paranoia is much more common than is usually believed. The diagnosis of paranoia is seldom made for several reasons: (1) Many psychiatrists are still influenced by the early descriptions of this disorder, which portrayed only its most severe forms. Contrary to general belief, however, the majority of cases of paranoia are mild. (2) Many cases are not recognized and never reach the office of a psychiatrist. The patient has no insight into his condition, and people take him for an eccentric, fanatic, or strongly opinionated person, but not necessarily a psychotic. (3) Some paranoiacs eventually act out and are occasionally labeled as psychopaths. Actual paranoiac-psychopathic mixtures do occur, as discussed in Chapter 15.

The paranoiac is a person who at first is possessed by an unconscious wish—or more than a wish, an impelling need—to believe in something which is not supported by ordinary logic. What he must believe in is of great importance to him. For this belief re-creates a meaning to his life—a life otherwise characterized by what he wants to deny: emptiness, lack of accomplishment in spite of expectation, guilt, cruelty, and failure in obtaining and giving love and affection. The belief which the patient now nourishes may concern a great love that he must fulfill, or a great mission that he must complete, or a great hate that he must justify and actualize. It may have to do with unfair suffering that he must avenge, or his own persecution that he must uncover and openly condemn. These clusters of concept-feelings become dominant and are transformed into certitudes in spite of what appears to others lack of corroborating evidence.

The patient does not resort to obvious regressive phenomena in order to demonstrate to himself and to others that what he believes is true. He does not experience the psychotic insight of the paranoid schizophrenic—that sudden illumination which is the result of the acceptance of paleologic forms. The paranoiac starts by accepting some premises as undeniable truths. These truths, however, have to be defended by uncovering hidden connections and by discovering a plan, a plot, or a structure which was not apparent. The patient becomes engaged in collecting material which will prove his allegations. He indulges in prolonged and elaborated investigations, and little by little he connects things to create a well-structured system, which actually consists of misinterpretations and distortions.

These distortions are so well rationalized as to give the impression to the layman, and occasionally even to the psychiatrist, that the patient is perfectly sane. As a matter of fact, he appears as a very intelligent person who has been able to find relations between things and facts that seemed unrelated to more naïve people.

How does the patient find these relations? As already mentioned, he does not resort to paleologic, or to a confusion between identity and similarity. Unlike the schizophrenic, he follows only secondary-process mechanisms. In scanning the several possibilities that may account for a certain fact, he selects and accepts as true the ones which fit his overall system or his preconceived belief. He can view clues and possibilities as sure evidence, so that what should remain a hypothesis becomes a fact if it fits the preconceived notion. In this way the unconscious wish and the impelling need to believe become supported by a cognitive scheme.

To give an example, the patient happens to see X, his alleged persecutor, in the street where he himself works, and he concludes that X has come to spy on him or to harm him. The fact that X is there becomes a proof that X is persecuting him, whereas it should be only a hypothetical possibility, soon to be discarded. Similar clues, of course, are studied by the police in evaluating suspects and are discarded unless supported by other facts. The scientist too conceives hypotheses and wants to determine whether they are valid or not. But for the paranoiac the possibility becomes certainty because it is "proved" retrospectively by what it purports to prove. That is, since X is a persecutor and wants to molest the patient, his being on the street where the patient works is not coincidental but is caused by the fact that X is there to persecute the patient. Since X is there to persecute the patient, it is true that X persecutes the patient. This is circular reasoning, and obviously incorrect; but it is not paleologic.

Such paranoiac thinking, based on premises supported by secondary-process mechanisms, is occasionally also found in paranoid conditions and in the paranoid type of schizophrenia, where it is mixed in with paleologic and other regressive types of cognition. In my opinion, the diagnosis of paranoia is justified only when there are no traces of paleologic or other regressive types of thinking.

The paranoiac system becomes the only inner object the patient cares about. Any therapeutic attempt would have to aim at re-enlarging his attachment to other inner objects. This is a difficult task, because relations with the other objects increase his anxiety and enhance his desire to withdraw again into his paranoiac construction, within which he has become a very efficient manipulator. Although the most typical conditions of paranoia are chronic and progressive, many cases are characterized by episodes that alternate with periods of normal or almost normal behavior. In some instances, the delusional symptoms disappear and are replaced by hypochrondriacal or even psychosomatic complaints. In these cases the paranoiac inner object has been replaced by a mental representation of the body.

Manic-depressive psychosis

Manic-depressive psychosis is a condition characterized by episodes of depression and elation which recur in various forms and cycles. A description of all these forms and cycles will not be attempted here (instead, see Kraepelin, 1921). In the last few decades this condition has become much less frequent (Bellak, 1952; Arieti, 1959b, 1959d). It is a debatable question whether depressions which are so severe as to reach psychotic proportions, but are not followed or preceded by manic attacks, belong to the manic-depressive group or constitute a separate clinical entity. Manic attacks are by far less frequent than depressions. Many patients who have undergone several depressive episodes have never experienced a manic attack.

The attacks of depression are characterized by a triad of symptoms: (1) a pervading feeling of melancholia, (2) a disorder of thought processes, involving retardation and unhappy content, and (3) psychomotor retardation. In addition, there are accessory somatic dysfunctions.

The manic attacks, which are a perfect counterpart to the attacks of depression, are also characterized by three symptoms: (1) a pervading mood of elation, (2) a disorder of thought processes, involving flight of ideas and happy content, and (3) increased and hastened mobility. Accessory bodily changes also occur.

Psychodynamic and psychosocial factors play a very important role in producing the disorder (Arieti, 1959b, 1959d). Without taking them fully into account, any study of the psychosis must be a limited one. The discussion here will be restricted to the major intrapsychic mechanisms of manic-depressive psychosis.

In the attacks of depression, the pervading mood of melancholia is so intense as to confer a characteristic flavor to the whole clinical picture. The gloomy mood invades every aspect of life. As described in Chapter 13, the mechanism of psychodysplasia takes place: A constituent of the psyche, in this case the emotion of sadness, largely replaces all other moods and emotions. The importance of many aspects of life is reduced or, vice versa, exaggerated to fit this pervading mood. Even the mood of hostility is masked, although not always successfully, by the invading depression.

The problems that we have to consider in connection with this syndrome are quite unusual. In fact, we cannot state that there is a return to a primitive emotion. As discussed in Chapter 7, depression is a third-order emotion; that is, a high one. Unless we equate it with simple feelings of deprivation, it is a typically human emotion and seems to presuppose high cognitive processes—complicated evaluations, appraisals, anticipations of the future, etc. There is a sense of despair, as when a loss has been sustained that cannot be compensated. In the psychosis, however, the depression is attributed no longer to something which has occurred independently of the patient, but to something which has happened in relation to him, or in relation to some circumstance for which he feels responsible: he is sick, guilty, a sinner, has caused his family to lose all their money, etc. The depression is generally precipitated by some event which is symbolic of another loss the patient sustained early in life (Arieti, 1959b).

Whether the sad thoughts of the depressed patient are the cause or the effect of the depression is difficult to ascertain. It is a vicious circle which becomes understandable if we take into consideration the patient's whole life. As I have described (1959b), the person who is likely to become manic-depressive has overdeveloped in childhood the ability to accept the symbols of the surrounding adults. This overdevelopment is generally caused by a duty-bound mother's great willingness to give. Such facility for introjection of what is given is retained even when the cognitive content or symbols offered by the adults are accompanied by an affective tonality that is unpleasant.

In the environment to which the young pre-manic-depressive is exposed, the symbols acquired from the adults have a tonality consisting predominantly of feelings of guilt, sin, responsibility, and impending loss. The organization of these symbols, representing such concepts as family, duty, religion, fatherland, work, etc., is also connected with the unpleasant or burdensome tonality. The affective tonality of the symbols may become so powerful that their cognitive aspect remains insignificant, or is confused or lost, or is attached in an unstable way to a vague cognitive ideation of pain and loss.

What are the possible reactions, either normal or pathological, to painful or depressive thoughts? They include (1) rejection of the symbols of society and consequent regression, (2) acceptance of the depression, (3) discharge or escape into action. The first type of reaction requires regression to the individualistic or paleosymbolic forms of cognition. The pre-manic-depressive person is deprived of this mechanism, however; he cannot lose the highest forms of symbolization (or the inner objects) which he has introjected so well. In other words, he cannot regress beyond a very limited extent. Creativity, which would be another escape from conventional symbols, is not available to him either, because it leans a great deal on regressive forms and because it requires a capacity for removal from ordinary external stimulation, which the patient has not mastered.

The patient must retain the introjected symbols. He must accept them even if they are painful, and by doing so he follows the second possibility. Not only does he accept the unpleasant symbols: he accepts them to an exaggerated degree. In other words, in the depressed person the cognitive component of the symbol does not undergo many changes. It is not displaced by an autistic or paleosymbolic symbol, as in the schizophrenic and in some psychoneurotics. The only change common to all these disorders is in the intensity of the emotional tone. In depressions too, of course, the symbols may be displaced, but much less than in other psychiatric disorders, and generally only by symbols which have similar affective components. We have thus a poverty of neosymbols and a quantitative change in the affective component of the old symbols.

The limited possibilities of emotional responses explain the relative simplicity of the formal mechanisms of manic-depressive psychosis in comparison with those of schizophrenia. When a precipitating factor—that is, the reactivation of an early loss—unchains the psychotic attack, the depressive constellations of thoughts re-emerge to sustain the pervading mood. The depressive mood in its turn almost compels the patient to search for other depressed thoughts, so that a vicious circle is established.

As discussed in Chapter 7, depression was retained in evolution (and can be considered as having a purpose) because it elicits attempts to remove the causes which have determined it. A normal person who is justifiably depressed does not want to be depressed, just as a normal person does not

want to experience any form of pain. Depression can be removed if the individual is able to reorganize his thinking, to
change his thoughts into different constellations, so that
those with a sad tonality do not occur. The manic-depressive
patient is not able to do so. A depression which is very severe,
rather than forcing a reorganization of ideas, slows the
thought processes. In this case the teleologic mechanism acts
almost with the goal of decreasing the quantity of thoughts
in order to decrease the quantity of suffering. At times, the
attempt to slow thought processes succeeds so well (as in the
state of stupor) that only a few thoughts of a general and
vague nature are left. These are accompanied by an overpowering feeling of melancholy. The acceptance of the depressed mood and slowing of thought processes which have
an unpleasant emotional tone are thus self-defeating mechanisms. In a vicious circle they aggravate the condition instead of alleviating it.

The third defense for the individual in the presence of depressive thoughts is escape into action and fugitive thoughts.
This defense is available to the manic-depressive patient, although it is not so frequent as the second type of reaction.
The escape into action may be so effective as to prevent the
occurrence of depressive attacks throughout the life of the
patient. Thoughts must be very fugitive, must be changed
very rapidly; because any constellation of organized thoughts
about practically any topic sooner or later brings about the
depression. Pleasant thoughts are searched for; actions that
may replace ideas are sought.

The patient resorts to this defense either in order to prevent the depression or in order to escape from it (as when he
slips from the melancholic into the manic state). At times he
succeeds in using the defense in an acceptable or at least tolerable way by retaining, or even increasing, normal abilities.
The capacity to recall masses of detail which is shown by
some hypomanic patients may be useful if it is channeled
into activities that require accurate descriptions. Often,
however, the wealth of details is useless and irritating.

The manic attack should not be viewed solely as an escape
from depression or from the tension which produces mental
pain. The manic also tries in a positive way to extend or en-

large his contacts with the world. Such contacts must remain superficial, however, if depressing connections are to be avoided. Pain elicits in the organism a reaction of *moving away* from the source. In psychotic depression, of course, no moving away is possible, not even from one's thoughts. In pleasure, there is not only a moving away from the source of pain but also a *moving toward* the object which will confer pleasure. The increased motility of the manic must be considered as an attempt to *move toward* the source of pleasure.

The manic mechanisms, however, fail because of their pathologic proportions: in order to avoid unpleasant constellations, thoughts must be so rapid that they cannot be organized or, therefore, capable of leading to rewarding actions. The pleasant ideas cannot be sustained and eventually leave the patient with the realization that they are futile. When the manic fervor is exhausted or cannot be sustained any longer, depression ensues or returns.

It is still not clear why some patients are able to avail themselves of the manic defenses and others are not. Perhaps constitutional, cultural, and dynamic factors play roles which cannot yet be ascertained. It has been reported that in primitive cultures the manic attacks are more numerous than the depressions.

17 ⊛ THE PSYCHONEUROTIC SPLITTING

The personality as a whole entity and the sense of self is preserved in the conditions called psychoneuroses. The patient
is aware of the pathological nature of his symptoms and is
unwilling to accept them as natural parts of himself. The expression "splitting," which is generally applied to schizophrenia, may in a different sense be used also in reference to
the psychoneuroses. This expression, in fact, may aptly point
out the division or incongruity between the psychoneurotic
symptomatology and the healthy parts of the psyche—a division generally well recognized by the patient.

Psychoneuroses have been classified in many ways. The
types which are generally given the status of clinical entities
are anxiety reaction, phobic condition, obsessive-compulsive
syndrome, and conversion hysteria.

The psychoneuroses constitute the field of psychiatry in
which Freud has made his greatest contributions. These contributions in the main have remained unchallenged, and in
the history of psychodynamic psychiatry, may be considered

the *avant-postes* from which larger conquests have been made. However, the following observations have been made repeatedly since Freud's original contributions: (1) social and interpersonal factors have much more importance than at first believed; (2) in many instances the traditional psychoneurotic syndromes do not constitute autonomous clinical entities, but are parts of a larger pathology, to be included under such terms as neurotic syndrome and character neurosis. In some cases, however, the bulk of the symptomatology adheres to the original descriptions, and the splitting mentioned above is clearly apparent.

A comprehensive exposition of the psychoneuroses is not offered here. It would be impossible to cover the field without reference to the interpersonal-social determinants and without repeating the important findings of Freud about the intrapsychic mechanisms of these conditions. This chapter has a modest aim: to reconsider some of the well-known psychoneurotic mechanisms from the points of view of the studies reported in Part I.

Before taking into consideration the classic psychoneurotic syndromes, we shall briefly examine the phenomenon that Sullivan named parataxic distortion.

Parataxic distortion

Parataxic distortion occurs not only in the psychoneuroses, but to a moderate degree in normal conditions too. In some individuals it is so pronounced as to make several psychiatrists think that probably a special neurosis, called "parataxic neurosis," could be recognized.

For example, a patient is behaving with apparently unmotivated anger toward elderly red-haired women, and he does not know why. In the course of psychoanalytic treatment he remembers that when he was a young child, his mother, who was a widow and had to go to work, would leave him in the custody of a red-haired aunt. The aunt was unsympathetic, resentful at having to take care of him, and rather hostile; yet he had to stay with her often, particularly during school vacations, so that holidays became an unpleasant time for him instead of a joyful one.

Another patient, the director of a company, used to be extremely lenient, almost subservient, with an elderly salesman, "forgiving" all the salesman's mistakes that were costing the firm money. The patient did not know why he had to take so much unpleasantness from this salesman. During the course of the analysis he discovered that he was behaving toward the man as he had always behaved toward his own father, whose peculiarities he had to tolerate because, after all, "One has no choice about one's father. One cannot fire him."

In Freudian terminology, this type of behavior is included in the phenomenon of transference. However, the term *transference* has come to be commonly used to designate the attitude or affects that the patient transfers specifically to the analyst. Sullivan would call this type of distortion parataxic. As Clara Thompson wrote (1950), parataxic distortions "are reaction patterns taken from the past and applied indiscriminately to the present situation where they are not suitable." Parataxic distortion, therefore, would be any attitude toward "another person based on fantasy or identification of him with other figures." Thompson goes on to say that a way of recognizing parataxic distortions in our thinking and feelings is by comparing our own evaluation with those of others. In parataxic distortions there is no "consensual validation"; other people do not agree with our distortions, because they did not have the early experiences which led to the formation of the parataxic patterns.

Sullivan's and Thompson's concept that a parataxic distortion occurs when the patient identifies a person of his present life with a significant figure of his past is fundamentally correct. It is based, as I have already mentioned, on the earlier Freudian concept of transference. "Identification" in this context means responding to a present situation in a way which is similar or identical to the way the patient responded to the original situation. For instance, in the first example above, it means responding to red-haired women as the patient used to respond to the aunt; in the second example it means responding to elderly salesmen as the patient used to respond to his father. But this interpretation, although correct, is incomplete. We must clarify the mechanisms that make such implausible identifications possible.

In these cases of parataxic distortion, a response takes place which follows a primary-process type of organization: the patient responds in the same way to any member of a primary class (see Chapter 7). His cognitive capacities are not arrested at a primitive level, however. The first patient knows that a red-haired woman is not necessarily his aunt, but he responds *as if* all red-haired women were his aunt. The second patient knows that a salesman is not his father, and yet he responds to him as if he were his father. There is a discrepancy, a splitting between the intellectual and the emotional-motor response.

There are many questions to be asked and problems to be solved in relation to this phenomenon. Why do these primary responses occur? How are Freudian dynamic interpretations to be correlated with structural mechanisms? In the case of the first patient, obviously the aunt inflicted a trauma on him. The unmastered emotion or affect remained connected not with a whole (the aunt), but with some characteristics or parts (her being an elderly woman and red-haired). These characteristics became releasing elements or parts around which a primary class was formed.

Since the symptom (or the primary class) was retained for many years, it has probably fulfilled a purpose. This symptom, which is based on a fixation, actually alleviated anxiety, or removed worse injury to the self-esteem. For if the noxious agent is a red-haired woman and not necessarily the aunt, the child feels he has nothing to do with his being rejected. The aunt does not reject him, but red-haired women have to be avoided, because they are creatures who evoke this bad effect in him. In the same way, the director of the firm will not feel uncomfortable about having to act in such a peculiar way toward his father, because after all, that is the way one reacts to elderly men.

The formation of the primary class, or the identification (or reaction to a releasing element), is not known to the patient. What is known, of course, is only the external behavior, the response. Contrary to what is suggested in many psychoanalytic reports, the memory of the early experiences (for instance, of the aunt or of the father) is not repressed. What is unconscious is the connection between the present behavior and the origin of the behavior.

Freud, too, wrote that the origin of obsessive-compulsive symptoms is known to patients. For instance, he described a patient who remembered the traumatic experiences she underwent on her wedding night. What she did not know, however, was that there was a connection between these experiences and her compulsions (Freud, 1920). The patient must become aware of the connection, as a first step toward recovery from the symptom.

However, even knowledge of the origin and of the present purpose (or secondary gain) of the symptom does not make the symptom disappear. A common situation in psychotherapy is generally summarized by the statement that the patient understands his symptom intellectually, but not emotionally. The symptom is not lost, because its repetitive occurrence is based not on repression but on the formation of a primary class. The primitive mechanism is automatic, like a reflex or conditioned reflex, and occurs when the releasing element is present. In addition to becoming aware of the symptom's origin and secondary gain, the patient must break the formation of the primary class or overcome the releasing quality of the releasing element in order to free himself of the symptom. For instance, our first patient must train himself to see elderly red-haired women on their own, one by one. If his general anxiety has become less overpowering and less in need of automatic defenses, he will be able to stop the propensity to behave in accordance with primary-process mechanisms.

Anxiety response and phobias

A primary generalization, or formation of a primary class, occurs not only in parataxic distortions but also in typical neuroses. For instance, in the condition which in various classifications is called anxiety neurosis, anxiety state, or anxiety reaction, anxiety rapidly spreads to many situations which normally are anxiety-free.

One of the most frequent anxiogenic situations is anticipation: the attitude of anticipating becomes transformed into the attitude of being anxious. Although for the normal person not every anticipation is anticipation of danger, it tends to become so in anxiety neurosis. If we call E any normal event—for instance, anticipation—and PR a primary response characterized by excessive anxiety, we have the following schema:

$$E \longrightarrow E' \longrightarrow E'' \longrightarrow E^n$$
$$\downarrow \quad \downarrow \quad \downarrow \quad \downarrow$$
$$PR \quad PR \quad PR \quad PR$$

The schema shows that not only E, but an increasing number of events, things, and usually harmless stimuli lead to the primary anxiety response. At times these stimuli are not easily perceived, because they are endocepts. In such cases we have the impression that the anxiety is "free-floating."

Whereas in anxiety reaction the source of anxiety is an enlarging primary class of stimuli, in phobia the noxious stimuli tend to remain specific. The patient is afraid of specific things, like horses, bridges, people wearing certain uniforms, etc. Actually, when we treat a phobic patient we discover that he is a very insecure person in a general sense. He is afraid of interpersonal relations, especially those that require intimacy and closeness. He is ill at ease in his family life and is afraid to search for personal significance outside his home environment. The vague threats and the state of general anxiety which he experiences subliminally or endoceptually become channeled into one or a few specific, concrete fears: the phobia (or phobias). This phobia becomes the common denominator or the common phobic pathway of many anxiety situations. The mechanism can be graphically represented in the following way:

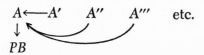

A', A'', etc., are the anxiety-provoking situations which become displaced to A (phobogenic stimulus) in order to elicit phobic behavior (PB). We have here the phenomenon of discrimination (Chapter 4). It is interesting to determine, if possible, why of all the anxiety-provoking stimuli or situations only *A* is selected as the channel of phobic behavior. A teleologic or purposeful mechanism occurs here too through concretizations. For instance, it is easier for the patient to admit that he is afraid to walk on streets than to say that he fears making excursions into life. It is easier for people like little Hans (Freud, 1909) to feel that they are afraid of horses than to face the fact that they are afraid of relationships with their father or their family in general.

In phobias the concretization assumes the form of reification, or transformation of an abstract concept or interpersonal relationship into an I-It relationship (Chapter 13, page 221). One could object that in phobias too there is a certain kind of animism, since a special power is attributed to particular situations and to inanimate things. Too, animated entities, like animals, often become phobogenic objects. However, relationships with subhuman animals are much less complicated than relationships with human beings. The phobogenic animal is not seen as a plotting or malevolent creature who wills evil things, but mostly as a disturber of the organism. Some rare patients present phobic reactions in which human beings are involved—for instance, fear of elderly women. These symptoms must be considered intermediate between phobias and delusions. In phobias, as in delusions, the stimulus—for instance, the horse—becomes a paleosymbol (see Chapter 5). The phobogenic meaning exists only for the patient.

Whereas in anxiety reaction there is an emotional reaction to something which is not necessarily present, in phobia the phobic reaction occurs when the object is present. Is the phobogenic object (for instance, the horse) a symbol or a sign? Inasmuch as the horse must be present to elicit the fear, it is a sign. We have seen in Chapter 7 how paleosymbols tend to become transformed into signs. However, the horse is a special type of sign: many things which are not present (and which are not parts of horses, or related to horses in any unusual way) become represented by the horse. The horse becomes or tends to become symbolic of everything in life which is fear-producing. It is thus a member of a primary class made up of fear-producing situations or things. In phobias, however, only one member of the primary class becomes a paleosymbol and a sign and elicits the abnormal response. In Freud's case of Hans, the horse is the chosen member. When the horse is present, it becomes a sign upon which the paleosymbolic meaning has been imposed. Whereas the phobogenic member of the class (the horse) is reinforced by its emotional effect, the other members lose the effect and their anxiety-provoking meaning may become unconscious.

Inasmuch as the paleosymbol immediately becomes a sign, it differs from signs made by men at secondary-level thinking. For instance, an arrow that indicates the direction of the traffic need not be actualized by concrete events in order to retain its signalistic value, since a motorist may disregard the meaning of the sign. In the case of the phobic patient, he is compelled to release the phobic behavior in the presence of the phobogenic object.

We must emphasize again that a pure phobic condition—that is to say, a condition in which the distress occurs only in the presence of the phobogenic object—is rare. In by far the majority of cases, the phobic condition perpetuates a state of intense anxiety: the patient lives in the anxiety of sooner or later having to face the phobogenic object.

Obsessive-compulsive psychoneurosis

Obsessions are emotionally loaded ideas that recur very frequently to consciousness and cannot, as a rule, be removed by any voluntary effort. Most of the time the patient recognizes their illogicality, but this knowledge does not help him to get rid of them. Occasionally the obsessions consist not of thoughts but of visual (and in rare cases, olfactory) images. Typical obsessions are the idea, held by a young mother, that she is going to kill her child with a knife; the visualization that a close member of the family is going to die in an automobile accident; the thought that at a certain date or age something terrible will happen to the patient or to a member of his close family. In many instances profane or blasphemous words or visual images recur mentally and make the patient feel guilty, impure, unclean, etc.

Compulsions are actions determined by inner urges which

seem irresistible. The patient feels he must act in a certain way, ostensibly in order to prevent certain events from happening or to promote the occurrence of other events. Compulsions are carried out with reluctance and conflict, for the patient is aware of their abnormal nature. At times they are used as defenses against obsessions, almost as if they had a magic power. For instance, a woman may have the obsession that her child is going to die, but that if she washes her hands a certain number of times, the child will survive. It is easy to realize that the obsessions stand for more important conflicts which the patient wants to deny. For example, the fear of killing one's own child is a concretization of a chain of apprehensions: uncertainty about being a good mother, a good wife, an adequate person, etc., and therefore fear of inflicting psychological harm on the child. Often the obsession is more complicated, and only long analytic treatment can reveal its hidden symbolic content. The obsession, like the phobia, may become the common pathway for many anxiety-provoking situations.

A schema like the one used for phobias could be applied to obsessions.

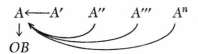

All anxiety-provoking situations or ideas (A's) are discharged through the same obsessive idea A, which elicits the same unpleasant obsessional behavior (OB). The situation is more complicated than the diagram indicates, however, because the patient generally has more than one obsession. A similar mechanism occurs in compulsions. Anxiety situations may be relieved through the magic of one compulsion, but in several instances multiple compulsions become connected to form a complicated ritual.

Whereas in phobias the patient feels hopelessly overcome by a gigantic external threat, and considers avoidance of the fear-provoking situation the only available defense, in obsessive-compulsive psychoneurosis the patient is afraid of the internal pressure of the compulsive orders which comes from his inner self. Actually, the patient is afraid of something else; for instance, of hurting the child by being a bad mother.

Guilt feeling plays an important role in obsessive-compulsive psychoneurosis. In a certain way the ritual is an atonement, and consequently a reassurance that the outcome will be favorable. For instance, the patient feels that if she washes her hands a specific number of times, the peril will be eliminated.

Both obsessions and compulsions tend to lose their paleosymbolic value and to become concrete signs or things. This aspect may be difficult to understand in obsessions. For instance, an obsessive thought or image, let us say of a profane thing, produces a psychological disturbance in the patient. The medium of the obsession seems symbolic: it consists of verbal or sensory images. However, the effect of the obsession is to disturb the patient; it is emotionally equivalent to pain or to unpleasure. Just as in art (Chapter 22), the medium of an obsession is not only a symbol, but almost a concrete substitute for what it represents.

Ostensibly some obsessions are not restricted to the present (for instance, the patient's idea that something terrible will occur five years from now) and seem therefore to require those abstract processes needed for visualizing the future. In these cases, however, the thought itself is something which exists in the present and tortures the patient here and now.

Compulsions have more clearly concrete forms. They must be performed in a specific actual way (not just as mental representations) in order to be considered effective.

At times, the compulsive action has an obvious relation to the anxiety that it aims to eliminate. For instance, by washing her hands a mother *cleans herself* spiritually, and as a result her child will not die. In her repressed fantasies, the death of her child would be caused by (or would be a retribution for) her uncleanliness or sinfulness. In some cases, however, it is impossible to retrieve the connection between a particular anxiety situation and the compulsive action which is supposed to relieve it.

Sometimes the compulsion derives from a temporal contiguity or simultaneity with events which are anxiety-relieving or anxiety-provoking for the patient. For instance, a patient used to go home from work by bus every day. He could walk from the bus stop to his home by different routes. One day he went through a parking lot, a route he did not ordinarily use. Later that day something "good" happened to him, and he decided that he should walk through the parking lot every day, because the result of doing so would be good. On another occasion he was walking through a block in a different part of his route, and something unpleasant occurred to him. From that day on he avoided that block. The final result of many such chance occurrences was that in going from the bus stop to his home he was compelled to take not the shortest possible route but a complicated zig-zag journey.

This example demonstrates that some compulsions do not have any similarity to the anxiety-provoking situation but are based on a different mechanism. The patient wants to force on nature or on the unpredictable and anxiety-provoking future a new law which will reduce his anxiety. If he passes through a given block, a pleasant thing will happen. Since on one occasion A (walking through that block) was followed by B (pleasant occurrence), *A will always be followed by B*. The patient is ready to make an inductive conclusion. Actually, however, what he follows is a caricature of the inductive method, because his reasoning is based on the least possible evidence (the occurrence of B only *once* after A). The patient knows that this pseudoinductive evidence is not valid, but he is looking for a guide to his actions in order to avoid an endoceptually experienced danger. His anxiety is so great that in order to re-establish a minimum of inner security, he is willing to accept a pseudoinductive reasoning and the corresponding concretizing action.

Hysterical syndromes

Fenichel called hysteria "the classical subject matter of psychoanalysis." "The psychoanalytic method was discovered, tested, and perfected through the study of hysterical patients; the technique of psychoanalysis still remains most easily applicable to cases of hysteria, and it is the psychoanalytic treatment of hysteria that continues to yield the best therapeutic results" (Fenichel, 1945, page 230).

Although Fenichel's statement remains valid, hysteria has declined in importance not only in the field of general psychiatry, but also in that of psychoanalysis. For one reason, patients with the classic hysterical symptomatology described by Charcot and Freud have become strikingly less frequent. Freud's teachings, spread throughout culture at large, may have hastened this decrease. In many cases hysterical and other psychoneurotic symptoms are found mixed together.

In brief, the syndrome of hysteria is generally characterized by the loss of some functions, like walking, talking, hearing, or seeing, in spite of the fact that no organic cause is responsible for such loss. Other symptoms may occur, such as apathy toward one's illness (generally called *la belle indifference*), bending of the body (*arc-de-circle*), amnesia, etc. A psychological disturbance is "converted" into a physical or apparently physical one. According to Breuer and Freud, forgotten traumatic events produced a disturbance that later expresses itself in conversion symptoms. The symptom is a distorted substitute for sexual gratification, which the hysterical person is incapable of achieving in a normal way. The recall of the traumatic forgotten events will produce abreaction, or discharge of pent-up emotions, with the consequent disappearance of the symptoms.

The apparent physical symptoms offer "secondary gains." For instance, rather than face his problems at his job, a patient develops a functional paraplegia, which will make him unable to walk and to work. We have here a double mechanism of concretization. Not only is the psychological symptomatology transformed into an apparently physical one, but the imitated symptomatology is as distressing as the real physical one. The paraplegic hysterical patient is indeed unable to walk. The symptom does not become an imitation or sign of impairment; it becomes the impairment itself. Szasz has given particular importance to this imitative function of the hysterical symptom (1961). For him, the hysterical syndrome is a nonverbal or nondiscursive language—a primitive language (protolanguage) which consists of iconic body signs. Hysterical manifestations are like icons; that is to say, like pictorial reproductions of symptoms usually found in patients affected by physical illnesses.

The interpretation of a symptomatology as a language is in my opinion problematic. Undoubtedly the symptoms are symbolic. Generally, however, the word *language* is applied to those large groups of symbols which are used for communication with others. The need to communicate that he is sick is undoubtedly very strong in the hysterical patient, but he wants to convince himself more than others. If he is physically sick, he will not be distressed by his psychological difficulties. Furthermore, he will be justified in not assuming responsibilities or not exposing himself to anxiety-provoking situations. Hysterical symptoms seem to be based on paleologic forms of concretization which refer to the functions of the soma: imitation of (or similarity with) body impairment becomes equivalent to body impairment.

18° *PSYCHOPATHOLOGY OF ACTION*

Classifications

Psychopathology of action is a difficult field to define. It does not include the pathology of motility found in many neurological conditions, such as apraxias, dysmetrias, paralyses, pareses, tremors, etc. It is not the pathology of behavior in general, but only of a special type of behavior; namely, that which is *ordinarily* under volitional control. Psychopathology of action must also be distinguished from psychopathology of conation, which includes all goal-directed but not necessarily willed behavior. The field of pathology of action does not even include the study of the making of "wrong choices." For instance, the psychopath often makes what appear to others wrong or immature choices. In the light of our present understanding of his disorder, his difficulty lies more in the realm of motivation than in the realm of action. The psychopath seems capable of *willing* his wish; that is, of giving to himself the executive order to consummate the wish.

Even the compulsive patient who is apparently compelled to perform some actions against his will is not impaired in his volitional system. From a technical point of view, it seems that he could resist the compulsions, if he would accept the anxiety which would be caused by not following the compulsion. But he prefers not to accept this terrible anxiety. Whereas the psychopath wills to attain his pleasant aim, the compulsive patient wills to avoid the unpleasant feeling.

Although various forms of pathology of action are found in most psychiatric conditions, it is only in some that they constitute the main feature. The following classification of these disorders is a tentative one, urgently in need of drastic revisions. It will not take into consideration the usual psychiatric categories, like psychosis and psychoneurosis, but instead will refer mainly to the type of pathological action. Three main groups will be distinguished:

1. *Psychokinetic disorders* (other than neurological). The word psychokinetic is a synonym for psychomotor. Since the latter term is commonly used in connection with epilepsy, I shall use the former to avoid confusion. This group includes conditions characterized by movements or actions which in normal persons are inhibited or limited by the will. Among these conditions are also some which consist of motor representations of thought processes that are not fully expressed.

2. *Paravolitional disorders.* In these conditions, the most typical of which is the state of hypnosis, apparently normal actions are not directly willed by the patient.

3. *Dysvolitional disorders.* The patient is impaired in his capacity to will—that is, to put his decisions into action—as in catatonia.

Psychokinetic disorders

Psychokinetic disorders are found in a large group of clinical entities ranging from slight abnormalities of the personality to serious psychotic states. Psychokinetic symptoms can be seen in the kinetic person, who has to move and do things almost incessantly; in the impulsive type of character neurosis; and more obviously, in manic and hypomanic states. Some hyperkinetic conditions are insignificant and produce little alteration in the life of the patient; others have severe crippling effects.

The first condition that we shall take into consideration is the general *hyperkinetic syndrome*. This syndrome is often distinguishable from the picture presented by the *kinetic* person only because the motor activity is less organized. The kinetic person appears normally integrated in spite of his increase in motor activity, but the movements of a patient suffering from a hyperkinetic syndrome are uncoordinated and may contain adventitious parts. The motor excess is obvious even to the layman.

Most patients with a hyperkinetic syndrome are children. It is still debatable whether this condition is caused by (1) minute brain damages occurring at birth, (2) minimal postencephalitic lesions, (3) biological or temperamental propensity to restlessness, or (4) psychological difficulties with the mother or mother substitute.

In a small number of cases, the existence of postencephalitic lesions has been established. Often a psychological difficulty with the mother or with both parents is apparent. However, it seems that at least in some cases a motor hyperactivity existed since birth and increased the difficulty between the intolerant mother and the child. The mother who is not able to accept the child's hyperactivity makes him anxious, and his anxiety expresses itself in increased restlessness and disorganized patterns of motor behavior. A feedback mechanism is thus established.

Some of the children who develop a hyperkinetic syndrome are at the stage of development in which the phantasmic life of inner objects expands rapidly (see Chapter 5). Their inner life is unpleasant, because it reflects their unsatisfactory relations with the mother or other surrounding adults. The children thus tend to escape from the phantastic world by reverting to the sensorimotor level and becoming fixated to it. They become more concerned with the external exoceptual life than with the inner one. A few of these children later developed more serious disorders. A large number of them, however, improve, recover, or eventually become able to channel their motor excess into useful outlets. They may become kinetic persons.

The hyperkinetic syndrome is found in adults, too. In many instances it originated in childhood, as described above. In a few cases it becomes more marked in adulthood. It is distinguishable from manic or hypomanic states because it is not accompanied by euphoria or by the other symptoms of manic-depressive psychosis. As already mentioned, often it can hardly be distinguished from the picture presented by kinetic personalities. The patient may show increased mobility only in some situations of increased anxiety, embarrassment, shyness, etc. And even normal, or slightly neurotic, persons assume particular postures, gaits, etc., in such situations (Shatan, 1963).

In many patients the motor unrest assumes more definite and circumscribed patterns: *tics* and *spasms*. Tics are sudden, brief, inappropriate, and irresistible movements which involve a relatively small part of the body or circumscribed groups of muscles, and which tend to have a cyclic recurrence. Examples of tics are various movements of the head, raising one shoulder, blinking, clearing the throat, twisting the mouth, turning the neck, making peculiar noises with the mouth, etc. Most of the time, the will of the patient is not capable of controlling these movements. Tics have been studied most intensively in children (see, for instance, Kanner, 1942; English and Pearson, 1937). Although they occur in some cases of postencephalitic conditions, no organic pathology is found in the majority of patients.

Generally, tics are defenses against affects which for some unclear reasons cannot be channeled into better-organized forms. They are motor outlets, transformations of mental unrest into movements. It is often assumed that when hostility cannot be sustained as such, it tends to be transformed into tics. However, any kind of emotion, even joyful excitement, is capable of engendering tics in the patient who is apt to develop them. Even the normal affective components of usual thoughts elicit tics in some *tiqueurs*. Thus we must postulate an as yet unknown mechanism which in some children and adults facilitates the transformation of emotional excitement into tics.

Closely related to the tic phenomenon is *stuttering*. In this speech impairment, the proper movements for normal phonation are displaced by adventitious movements, perseverations, and blocks.

Another condition that in general borders on the conditions just mentioned is Gilles de la Tourette's disease, named after the physician who first described it (1885). Although this syndrome is occasionally called *maladie des tics*, it should not be confused with the tic conditions mentioned so far, because it is much more severe. Important contributions on this subject recently have appeared in the American literature (Ascher, 1948, 1966; Eisenberg, Ascher, and Kanner, 1959, Schneck, 1960).

According to Ascher (1948), Gilles de la Tourette's disease is a relatively uncommon disorder, having been reported in only 4 cases among approximately 9,000 inpatient and 50,000 outpatient admissions to the Henry Phipps Psychiatric Clinic. The condition is characterized by compulsive jerkings involving the musculature of the face, neck, and extremities, often accompanied by coprolalia, echolalia, and occasional imitation of movements of other people (echokinesis). Some cases recover or have a recurrent episodic course. In others, the motor phenomena are accompanied by a progressive decay of the personality; for instance, the patient does not seem to be troubled by the symptoms, which are very distressing to the observer. This characteristic, as well as the apparent total involvement of the personality, has suggested to some authors that a basic schizophrenic disorder underlies this motor syndrome. Moreover, in some cases it is almost impossible to distinguish the manifestations of Gilles de la Tourette's disease from schizophrenic stereotyped mannerisms. The writer has seen pictures similar to the one generally called Gilles de la Tourette's disease in a small number of patients who have been hospitalized for several years for chronic schizophrenia, as well as in a few patients who had had schizophrenic episodes, from which they had seemingly recovered.

The German psychiatrist Leonhard (1960, 1961) has

differentiated a condition that he calls *motility psychosis.* Whereas manic-depressive psychosis predominantly influences affectivity and schizophrenia predominantly influences cognition, motility psychosis is a purely psychokinetic illness. Hypermotility and hypomotility may both occur, but the hypomotility type is much rarer. In both types the change is quantitative: motions are increased or decreased in number, but are not disorganized. In the hyperkinetic type, the excessive movements also involve facial expressions and gestures. "They look at everything, listen to everything and handle everything" (Leonhard, 1961). Although these patients may appear silly and immature in their behavior, to such a point that they may give the impression of being hebephrenic, they do not belong to the schizophrenic group. They may recover soon and completely from individual attacks, then undergo further episodes later in a cyclic form.

A large group of kinetic phenomena occurs in schizophrenia: they are the well-known peculiar *mannerisms* and *stereotypies.* A stereotypy is an apparently non-goal-directed movement which is carried out in a uniform, stylized, repetitive form. Also characteristic of schizophrenia are the *bizarre acts* which in some cases constitute the bulk of the symptomatology. In these acts we often recognize a symbolic meaning or the translation into a motor phenomenon of a thought or concept that the schizophrenic could not tolerate as such.

Thus a patient, at the beginning of an acute psychotic episode, used to walk on the edge of the sidewalk in a conspicuous and ridiculous manner. Later in the treatment he was asked why he used to do so, and he replied: "I was in danger; my condition was unstable." Obviously he had to translate his feeling of psychological instability into a physical status, which could be more easily controlled. In fact, he obviously succeeded in walking on the edge of the sidewalk without falling, by carefully placing one foot after the other, but had not been so successful in the path of life. Another patient used to go into stores and put the light on and off repeatedly, to the consternation of all people who were there. At a time when he felt powerless, this act would give him a feeling of power and connection with the world that was escaping him.

Some self-mutilations and self-injurious acts of schizophrenic patients can be interpreted in a similar way. The self-injurious action is used to transform a mental pain into a physical one (Arieti, 1963).

Now, if we reconsider from a general point of view all the psychokinetic conditions that we have examined, we can see a common denominator: a motor activity which escapes voluntary control and which results from various degrees of psychological unrest. There is a tendency for the psyche to operate at an exoceptual level more than is usual (see Chapter 3). If the patient, as a result of treatment, can reduce his inner unrest, he will also be able to decrease the motor abnormality.

More serious than the increase in exoceptual activity is the tendency in psychokinetic disorders to translate some anxiety-provoking concepts into exocepts, as in some forms of schizophrenia. In these cases the exocept is not a normal exocept, but a concept which has been reduced or concretized into an exocept. Inasmuch as the patient accepts the exocept at a reality level and has no insight into the abnormal nature of it, the phenomenon is a manifestation of regression and must be considered psychotic. The exoceptual behavior of the schizophrenic is not an acting out.

"Acting out," an expression used originally by Freud to refer to the patient's compelling urge to repeat original situations or feelings in the therapeutic transference, was later applied to the pleasure-seeking actions of the psychopath. As discussed in Chapter 15, the psychopath's desires coincide with the results of his actions at a realistic level. His exoceptual activity is not a motor concretization of concepts.

Paravolitional (or parabulic) conditions

In paravolitional conditions the patient experiences his own behavior as being completely outside of his control or will. Contrary to what happens in most psychokinetic disorders, his actions are well integrated from a motor point of view. Nevertheless, he experiences them as foreign to his usual state of consciousness. These conditions can be divided into two categories: (1) those caused by physiological-neurological alterations, for instance by epilepsy; (2) those occurring in states of altered relatedness, as in hypnosis. Although both are outside the scope of this book, I shall describe them briefly for continuity's sake.

In many forms of epilepsy or of temporal lobe pathology in general, patients undergo twilight or dreamy states and fugues, during which they perform actions over which they have no control. They retain a certain level of awareness; for instance, they are capable of following traffic rules and avoiding accidents. Nevertheless, they cannot stop the course of their actions until they wake up from the twilight episode. When they do wake up, they have no memory of what they have done. At times during these trances they indulge in antisocial behavior.

Similar processes occur in patients suffering from somnambulism. Although they are in a state of sleep, they can perform well certain actions which seem to be completely outside their control and for which they do not assume responsibility.

In dreams too, the dreamer hallucinates that he is behaving in a certain way without being able to control his behavior. He may, however, feel guilty for what he has done and feel relieved when he wakes up.

The most common paravolitional condition caused by altered relatedness to others, *hypnosis*, has already been mentioned in Chapter 12. In the hypnotic state there is an almost complete abolition of the subject's will. Although it is said that it would be impossible for a hypnotist to induce an honest man to commit a crime, the fact is that the hypnotized person is induced to do many things that he would not normally perform. The hypnotizer becomes the governor of his will. As stated in Chapter 12, probably this condition is based on a return to that primitive type of volition which consists of accepting the will of others. There is no regression of the total personality, but only regression of the patient's volitional faculty.

Latah is a condition characterized by forced imitation of the actions of others, or echokinesis. Its occurrence has been reported in Malaya, northern Japan, Siberia, and various parts of Africa. In Western countries it is extremely rare in pure form, but it has been observed in syndromes which also present the characteristics of Gilles de la Tourette's disease. The writer has seen some rare and partial cases in patients who otherwise seem to fit that prepsychotic type of personality which he has described as "stormy" (Arieti, 1955).

In latah, the patients, mostly women, at first repeat words heard from others; finally in a pantomime fashion they imitate the gestures and actions of other people, even if they are harmful. The psychopathology of latah is difficult to account for. Arieti and Meth (1959) stated: "Latah may be interpreted as an attempt of the patient to free himself of his anxieties by surrendering himself totally to others. Frightened children often mimic other people." Mimicking may be an anxiety-relieving mechanism to which people raised in some cultures may find relatively easy access.

In some collective psychoses, which occurred relatively frequently in Europe from the eleventh to the seventeenth centuries, and which occasionally are still found in isolated villages, the patient assumes the dominant idea of a special group to which he belongs. For instance, like the other members of the group, he believes that he has been transformed into an animal (lycanthropy) and behaves as that animal would. He may start to bite like a dog or mew like a cat. In other cases he must imitate the bizarre behavior of the group (dancing in St. Vitus' dance, or convulsing in tarantism or tarantulism). In these collective psychoses the patient must accept the will of the group and renounce his own (Arieti and Meth, 1959).

Dysvolitional disorders

In dysvolitional disorders the will mechanism is impaired to such an extent that a return to early stages of volition takes place. The catatonic phenomena that occur in the catatonic type of schizophrenia belong to this group. These phenomena are so different from other schizophrenic manifestations that some authors consider catatonia an independent entity. Although I am discussing catatonic phenomena separately from the rest of the schizophrenic process, which was reported in Chapter 16, I agree with the basic Kraepelinian concept that catatonia is a type of schizophrenia.

The progressive regression which takes place in the other types of schizophrenia is found in catatonic conditions too; but whereas in the other types the regression is mostly in the cognitive area, in catatonia it predominantly affects conation. Actually, even in cases which seem of pure catatonic type, the other schizophrenic symptoms appear in different combinations.

The catatonic patient, often quite suddenly, but in some cases gradually, becomes unable to will. At times his will impairment is complete; at other times it is partial and consists of an arrest or return to previous stages of the phylogeny-ontogeny-microgeny of the will. The patient often cannot move or moves very little, or else his movements are transformed in peculiar ways. However, contrary to a superficial impression, the catatonic does not undergo a motor disorder, but a will disorder. If he cannot move, it is because he cannot *will* to move.

Why the catatonic should suddenly become so affected is not at all clear. Psychodynamic factors which are interpersonal in origin, and which can be mentioned only briefly here, are certainly very important. The patient generally is confronted with an important decision to make, but such a task seems to overwhelm him. Generally his early life was characterized by difficulty in making choices, coming to decisions, translating thoughts and wishes into actions. Often his parents either made him feel guilty for his actions or prevented him from developing the ability to choose, decide, and take action. Mother was there to make the choice. If the child made it instead, it would turn out to be the wrong choice, so that he would have to be punished for it or feel guilty.

When the disintegration of the will takes place at the onset of the psychosis, the patient experiences strange phenomena. A process which seems very important to the author, but which he could find in only *one* patient out of the many that he has examined, is the substitution of an action for an analogic one. For instance, this patient (who subsequently sank into full catatonia) noted that instead of dropping a shoe, he would throw a stone; instead of moving a chair, he would move a piece of wood, etc. He knew that he was performing the wrong action, but he could not avoid doing so. It seems almost that when the concept of the movement was being formed, it was channeled not into the proper exocept, but in an analogic one: that is, into an exocept which, together with the appropriate exocept, would form a primary class of exocepts.[1]

As a rule, however, the catatonic does not even reach this stage of will formation, but others which have been described in detail elsewhere (Arieti, 1955). He may not will at all, remaining immobile like a statue. From the few patients who have been able to report their catatonic experiences this writer has learned that a tremendous fear of their actions did not permit the patients to will them. A special significance was attributed to any action, such as the possibility of determining portentous events. Horrible things would result as a consequence of the action, perhaps even the end of the world. The patients seem to have returned to that stage which is more typical of primitive people: fear to will (Chapter 12). Thus immobility results. Catatonia is a removal of action in order to remove the panic connected with the willed action. Sometimes this panic is generalized. When it is extended to every action, the patient may lapse into a state of complete immobility (catatonic stupor). At other times it is an obsessive-compulsive anxiety rather than definite fear which does not permit the patient to move. Is it better to move or not to move, to talk or not to talk, to choose this word or another one? In the midst of this terrifying uncertainty the patient decides not to will at all.

In some cases, as if in answer to an order, the patient starts a movement but then stops, as if a counterorder had prevented him from continuing. Having decided to obey, he is then afraid to will the act involved, and he stops. At other times there is a series of alternated opposite movements, like a cogwheel movement, superficially similar to those observed in postencephalitic patients affected by muscular rigidity. In the middle of a movement the patient becomes afraid of willing that action, decides not to perform it, and arrests his mo-

---

[1] For a more detailed illustration of this case the reader is referred to the original work (Arieti, 1961a).

tion. But to decide not to perform the action is also a volitive act. The patient becomes afraid of it and starts to make the movement again. To do this is also a volitive act, and he is again afraid. This series of attempted escapes from volition may go on for a long time. It is a horrifying experience, which only a few patients are able to relate.

The fear of volition accounts for other characteristics encountered in cases of catatonic schizophrenia. In order to avoid anxiety and guilt, the patient cannot will to act, but returns to that stage of volition (described in Chapter 12) in which he accepts commands by others. He may passively follow orders given by someone else because the responsibility will not be his: there is a complete substitution of the other's will for his own. *Waxy flexibility*—the retention of body positions, no matter how uncomfortable, into which the patient has been placed—can also be explained in this way. When the patient is put into a given position, the will or responsibility of someone else is involved. If he wants to change his position, he has to will the change, and this engenders anxiety or guilt.

Quite often the reverse seems to occur: the patient will resist the order, or will do the opposite. This is the phenomenon of negativism which has baffled many investigators. Such willed disobedience may be seen as a return to the stage in which will consists of resisting the will of others. However, resisting the will of others or resisting one's own will may also indicate a return to that stage of will formation characterized by the inhibition of spontaneous, easy, or reflex movements (see Chapter 12). At times the catatonic loses his usual inhibiting attitude and acts in an opposite way —that is, as if he were not concerned at all with responsibility, or as if he were defying previous feelings of fear and responsibility. His behavior consists of a sequence of aimless acts. This is the state of *catatonic excitement*, during which the patient may become violent and homicidal. In the majority of catatonic patients several symptoms, corresponding to the various degrees of regression of the volition process, are superimposed, and the resulting picture is a mixed and confusing one.

Theoretically, the catatonic could avoid his difficulties and the agony of his not willing to will by reverting to the level of the pleasure principle, with its immediate sensorimotor behavior, or to the level of wish fulfillment. Apparently, however, he cannot find these simple solutions. He cannot become a psychopath, or a delusional person in the wish-fulfilling sense. Perhaps the tremendous fear of his own wish for hostility, or the fear of what he is capable of doing in the catatonic excitement, does not permit him to regress to those simple solutions. We could say that although he cannot will, he cannot indulge in wishing. Although he cannot wish, he can fear. He lives only in the fear of what he could do, and the only choice, which he thinks he is not choosing, is not to do.

PART III

The Rise of Creativity: From Primary to Tertiary Process

19 ⊙ THE STUDY OF
THE CREATIVE PROCESS

Creativity has recently been the object of much research and has been defined in many ways.[1] By the term *creative process* I mean a special process that transcends the usual psychological formula of Stimulus-Response and brings about a desirable enlargement of human experience.[2] Although symbol-making man is fundamentally different from the infrahuman animal which has a limited number of responses, he too tends to respond in fixed ways. Whether his response occurs immediately after the stimulus or whether it follows a complicated set of symbols and choices, man tends to react in accordance with a repertory of responses provided by his usual psychological faculties or by the common style of his culture. If his responses are mediated by cognitive processes,

[1] Cf. Anderson (1959), Eidusun (1962), Getzels and Jackson (1962), Ghiselin (1952), Gruber, Terrell, and Wertheimer (1962), Hammer (1961), Koestler (1964), Kubie (1958), P. Smith (1959), Stein and Heinze (1960), Taylor and Barron (1963).
[2] This definition is a modification of an expression used in a different context by Von Bertalanffy (1964).

they generally follow the mechanisms that in Freudian theory are ascribed to the secondary process. As we have seen in previous chapters, these mechanisms correspond to the terminal stages of microgenetic development, or, in common words, to ordinary logical thinking.

The creative process enables man to liberate himself from the fetters of the ordinary secondary-process responses. But creativity is not simply originality and freedom. It also imposes restrictions. Although it uses methods other than those of the secondary process, it must not be in disagreement with the secondary process. Otherwise the result would be bizarre, not creative.

The desirable enlargement of human experience may be aesthetic pleasure, as in art, or usefulness, understanding, and predictability, as in science. At the same time that this process discloses new dimensions of the universe, it expands man too, who can enjoy and inwardly retain these new dimensions.

The creative process has an additional important characteristic. It tends to fulfill a longing or a search for a new object or for a state of experience or of existence which is not easily found or easily attainable. Especially in aesthetic creativity, the work often represents not only the new object, but this longing, this indefinite search, this sustained and yet never completed effort, which has either a conscious or an unconscious motivation.

A sharp distinction must be made between the creative process and the creative product. In contrast to what could be said about the creative product, the creative process is not only shorn of newness and sublimity, but to a considerable extent consists of ancient, obsolete mental mechanisms, generally relegated to the recesses of the psyche where the primary process prevails. Part II examined these mechanisms as they reappear in various mental disorders. They reappear in the creative process also, in strange, intricate combinations with secondary-process mechanisms, and in syntheses which, although unpredictable, are nevertheless susceptible of psychological interpretation. It is from appropriate matchings with secondary-process mechanisms that these primitive forms of cognition, generally confined to pathological conditions or to unconscious processes, become innovating powers. I have proposed the expression *tertiary process* to designate this special combination of primary- and secondary-process mechanisms (Arieti, 1964, 1966). For accuracy's sake, I must point out that in a certain number of creative processes the matching is not necessarily between primary- and secondary-process mechanisms, but between faulty or archaic and normal mechanisms, all of which belong to the secondary process. For these combinations, too, I shall use the name tertiary process.

The following chapters will try to differentiate in the various fields of creativity the specific modes by which the mechanisms match and innovation emerges. The fields of creativity are many, but we shall take into consideration only a few important ones. We shall study wit and the comic; aesthetics, with particular emphasis on poetry; religion, and mysticism; and finally, science.

It may appear surprising that this study gives first consideration to wit and the comic—apparently "lower" forms of creativity. Actually, even for researchers as different in background and methodology as Freud and the novelist Koestler, the study of wit has been the path to a better understanding of creativity. For me also, some notions on wit and the comic which I discussed in an earlier paper (written in 1948–1949 and published in 1950) led to many of the ideas on creativity developed in the following chapters (Arieti, 1950).

Some important aspects of the creative process, such as the influence of the environment or of previous creative works, are beyond the range of topics covered by this book.[3] Because of this imposed limitation, some major fields of creativity, such as ethics, politics and economics, which are more closely connected with interpersonal processes, will not be discussed here.

[3] For some elementary principles of cultivation of creativity, see Arieti (1966).

Originality versus creativity

As already mentioned, the characteristic of uniqueness or originality in a new work is not enough to qualify it as a creative product. There is a difference between originality and creativity that becomes particularly evident when we study dreams.

In dreams unexpected connections occur. Some combinations of scenes and events do not seem to have taken place ever before in nature or in dreams of other people. On some rare occasions dreams have been reported as conducive to direct acquisition of insight, or even to the formulation of inventive procedures that generally occur in waking life, when the mind has access to the secondary process.[4] Some dreams should not be considered just a reflection of the dreamer's state of psychological pathology or of his health, but as psychological attempts to solve conflicts. For instance, recovering schizophrenics dream about conflicts or situations which had appeared in delusional forms during the acute attack of the psychosis (Arieti, 1963). The dream often offers a solution at a less unrealistic level than the delusion did.

In spite of all these characteristics, dreams cannot be considered products of creativity. With a few exceptions, they are of value only to the dreamer himself. They are private experiences that cannot be fully or correctly reproduced. They consist mostly of primary-process mechanisms which are not sufficiently integrated with those of the secondary process, so that they cannot be shared or communicated in the original form. When they are told to others, and even more, when they are interpreted, they acquire a medium which comes from the secondary process. But then they are

---

[4] For instance Sinnot (1959) reports that the Nobel prize winner, Otto Loewi, saw the proof of the chemical mediation of nerve impulses in a dream. On awakening he could not remember the dream, which fortunately was repeated the following night.

Antonio Ludovico Muratori, a scholar of the eighteenth century, reported that on the night of December 30, 1743, he had a dream in which he composed the following Latin verse, a pentameter, that ordinarily would require complex use of metric technique if composed in waking life: *Et quam multa queas, fac quoque multa velis.* ("If you can do much, you must will much." That is, you must equate your will and wish to your ability to actualize them.)

no longer dreams; they are translations of dreams. Nevertheless, Freud's work on dreams will remain one of the foundations of the study of the creative process, because it revealed the existence of the primary process and some of its main characteristics. However, Freud did not pursue the study of the primary process in relation to the cognitive mechanisms necessary for creativity. He saw the primary process predominantly as a carrier of unconscious motivation.

Creativity must be distinguished not only from originality but also from those feelings of being surprised and affected by the new and being receptive to new ways that are experienced by many people. Although these feelings are prerequisites for creativity, they do not constitute its specific essence, according to the definition given at the beginning of the chapter.

General Theories of Creativity

Theories on creativity may be divided into specific and general ones. The specific theories are supposed to be valid only for particular fields; the general ones aim at individualizing the common mechanisms that occur in every process of creativity. It is impossible within the limits of this book to review all or most general theories of creativity. I shall only make a few remarks about the ones which are closest to my own approach.

NONPSYCHOANALYTIC THEORIES

Wertheimer interpreted "productive thinking" in accordance with the tenets of the gestalt school (1945). According to him, the creative process moves from a structurally unstable or unsatisfactory situation S_1 to a situation S_2, which offers a solution. In the passage from S_1 to S_2 a gap is filled; a better gestalt is formed. Wertheimer says that in all productive thinking there is grouping, organization, and structuralization. Dividing wholes into subwholes and seeing subwholes together, without losing track of the whole figure, are for him important steps in creative thinking.

Wertheimer also describes another mechanism of the creative process in which some features of S_2 are envisioned to start with by the creative person. From these few features the creative person must recapture the whole S_2. According to Wertheimer, the process starts as a search not just for any relation which would connect the elements, but "for the nature of their intrinsic interdependence." The entire process of creativity is for Wertheimer "one consistent line of thinking."

In my opinion Wertheimer's concepts are correct, but refer only to some general aspects of creativity and do not attack the core of the problem. His concepts have the merit of asking pertinent questions, but do not provide the answers. What are the mechanisms that fill the gaps? How does one move from a few aspects of S_2 to the whole S_2? Wertheimer ignores the difference between ordinary logical solution of problems and creativity. He does not stress the occurrence of unusual processes.

In a recent book on creativity (1964) Koestler expands concepts already expressed in his previous book *Insight and Outlook*, which dealt predominantly with wit and the comic (1949). Koestler's fundamental concept is that of *bisociation*. Bisociation, which according to him underlies every creative process, is "any mental occurrence simultaneously associated with two habitually incompatible contexts." It is true that in many innovations we find a mental construct which usually appears in two habitually incompatible contexts, but Koestler does not explain how the two habitually incompatible contexts are united in the creative work. He does not seem to recognize that some contexts use forms and mechanisms of the primary process.

PSYCHOANALYTIC THEORIES

Without having a full realization of it, Freud was responsible for a breakthrough that led to a better understanding of the formal psychological mechanisms of the creative process (see Chapter 20). Nevertheless, Freud did not study these formal mechanisms. He intended to contribute to the study of creativity by reaffirming the importance of unconscious processes, especially of unconscious motivation.

According to Freud, creativity originates in conflicts,

which spring from more fundamental biological drives, and consists of attempts to solve these conflicts. Freud compares literary work to daydreaming. Only unsatisfied people have fantasies or daydreams; happy people don't. "Unsatisfied wishes are the driving power behind fantasies; every separate fantasy contains the fulfillment of a wish, and improves an unsatisfactory reality" (Freud, 1908).

Just as the child finds wish-fulfillment improvement over reality in play and games, in which he generally impersonates the role of an important adult (leader, general, parent, etc.), the adult creates a work of art in which he can satisfy his daydream wishes. However, people are often ashamed or embarrassed of their daydreams, just as they are of their drives which give rise to their nocturnal dreams. In nocturnal dreams, the censorship diminishes the shame by making the manifest aspect of the dream very different from its meaning. In creative works, daydreams are also disguised. "The essential *ars poetica* lies in the technique by which our feeling of repulsion is overcome. . . . The writer softens the egotistical character of the day-dream by changes and disguises, and he bribes us by the offer of a purely formal that is, aesthetic, pleasure in the presentation of his fantasies" (Freud, 1908).

According to Freud, childhood experiences are very important in accounting for the creative product. Personal experiences explain the peculiar characteristics of the creative work. For instance, in one of Leonardo da Vinci's famous paintings the Virgin Mary and Saint Ann both appear with the infant Jesus, in contrast to the usual representation of the holy family in Italian paintings. This characteristic is not due to chance. Leonardo had the unconscious need to reproduce a childhood experience: he was raised by two mothers—his real biological mother, a peasant woman, and his father's legal wife, in whose home he grew up. According to Freud, Leonardo's conflicts over his own homosexuality also explain some of his creative activities.

The role of sexuality in creativity is always prominent, Freud believes. He traces the creative person's desire to know the unknown back to the child's sexual curiosity, which begins with the third year of life. According to Freud the child's inquiring over sexual matters has three possible outcomes. The first is "energetic repression," favored by educational and religious inhibitions. The second outcome occurs when sexual investigation is not totally repressed, but is coped with by thought processes or by compulsive defenses. This transformation occurs when the intellectual development is sufficiently strong. In the third outcome, which is "the most rare and most perfect type," sexual curiosity is *sublimated* into that curiosity which leads to creativity. Freud's concept of sublimation, or diversion of sexual energy from the original aim, plays an important role in his concept of creativity. It is apparent that Freud was mainly concerned with the importance and relevance of motivation in creativity, not with the essence of creativity itself.

Motivation, conscious or unconscious, is indeed very important, but it is hard to believe that the whole phenomenon of creativity can be reduced to a motivational mechanism. A more urgent problem is to determine why and how a few gifted men are able to transform their motivations and the effects of their early or late personal experiences into creative productivity. Moreover, as Freud himself recognizes, it is particularly in the mediocre work of art that the personal conflict-born motivation is very important—for instance, in second- or third-rate paintings, plays, and psychological novels, which openly reveal the neurotic idiosyncrasies of the author. These works often remain mostly at a clinical level and hardly enter the aesthetic field.

Within the theoretical framework of the Freudian school, Kris is perhaps the most prominent author who has studied creativity not exclusively from the point of view of unconscious motivation. To Kris must be given the credit for having stressed the importance of the primary process in the formal mechanisms of creativity (Kris, 1952). He considers the use of the primary process in creativity as "a regression in the service of the ego." In my opinion the use of the primary process is not necessarily to be viewed as manifestation of regression but of an emerging accessibility or availability, which only occasionally is connected with regression. However, this difference between my view and that of Kris may be secondary and semantic in nature, based on a difference in our use of the word regression.

The main divergence between Kris' formulations and mine is in the attempt to explain how this "service of the ego" takes place. To me, it is not enough to say that such mechanisms as displacement and condensation occur or are made syntonic with ego function; we must understand how this syntonization is carried out. Kris remains to a large extent in the energetic-libidinal framework of Freudian theory. Having given importance to the system preconscious rather than the unconscious in creativity, he states that the preconscious process becomes subject to free or mobile id cathexis and is drawn into the primary process. On the other hand, "The reverse (unconscious material becomes preconscious) occurs when id derivations are cathected with ego energy and become part of preconscious mental processes . . ." (1950).

Still in the framework of orthodox Freudian theory, Kubie (1958) adds support to Kris' idea that creativity is a product of the preconscious and not of the unconscious, as had been assumed by many psychoanalysts. Conscious mental activity may hinder the creative process by the rigid use of symbolic functions. The unconscious may hinder it with an even more rigid anchorage in unreality.

Jung too has made a significant contribution to the problem of creativity, especially in reference to the aesthetic process. Philipson has written an interesting book, *Outline of a Jungian Aesthetics,* which will be my guideline in these brief comments on Jung's contributions (Philipson, 1963). Jung believes that the creative process, at least when it pertains to art, occurs in two modes: the psychological and the visionary. In the psychological mode the content of the creative product is drawn from the realm of human consciousness. Although the vast realm of human experience—in its relation to such things as love, family, environment, society, crime, human destiny in general—usually appears in the content of the work of art, this mode of creativity "nowhere transcends the bounds of psychological intelligibility." Everything in it "belongs to the realm of the understandable." The psychological mode submits the material to a direct, conscious, and purposeful aim.

The visionary is the mode that concerns Jung more deeply. In this second mode the content does not originate in the lessons of life, but from timeless depth, from what he calls the collective unconscious. The collective unconscious is the depository of the archetypes—primordial experiences which have repeatedly occurred in the course of generations. The archetypes may surpass man's understanding. They may be many-sided, demonic, and grotesque.

In the visionary mode the creative person is at the mercy of the re-emerging content. He is in a passive situation. "The work brings with it its own form, what he [the author] would add to it is declined; what he does not wish to admit is forced upon him." In the visionary mode the creative person is more conscious of an "alien" will or intention beyond his comprehension. Especially in the visionary mode, the emerging product of creativity is an *autonomous complex,* which, like a neurotic complex, is a detached portion of the psyche which leads an independent life. Its psychic energy has been withdrawn from conscious control.

The creative process thus consists of an *unconscious animation of the archetype.* The primordial image, connected with the archetype, compensates for the insufficiency and one-sidedness of the creative person's experience of life, or even of the spirit of the historical time in which the creative person lives. In other words, the great work of art transcends life experiences, personal factors, and the historical period in which its producer happens to live. By reawakening the wealth of experiences dominant in the collective unconscious, the creative process confers on the work of art a universal significance. The artist's lack of adaptation to his environment becomes his real advantage; it facilitates the re-emergence of the archetypes—induces him to enter into a mystical participation with the ancient sources.

It is easy to recognize that Jung's concept of the collective unconscious colors his whole theory of creativity, just as the concept of libido colored Freud's. Jung is definitely right in pointing out that the great work of art cannot be seen only as the result of personal life experiences, mediated by the usual cognitive mechanisms. However, he believes that what transcends personal experience originates in the collective unconscious. In some ways, the collective unconscious occupies the role that the primary process has in the Freudian system. However, the mechanisms of the primary process, like our microgenetic mechanisms, are more easily seen in their functional nature than as deposits. Although in one of his writings Jung denies that the archetype is determined in regard to its content (1959), in most of his work he conveys the impression that he believes it is so. He finds in the archetype "an invariable nucleus of meaning."

In spite of their appealing quality, we may recognize in Jung's concepts a unilateralness which does not do justice to the creative process. Jung sees the greatness of the creative work in the reactivation of the archetype. The creative product could be compared to an old treasure which is exhumed. The unpredictable newness of the work of art, although an important inherent characteristic of any work of creativity, is not accounted for.

As an example from the neo-Freudian schools we shall take into consideration Schachtel's contribution. Schachtel recognizes that the creative person is not embedded in the clichés provided by society, but is subject to new experiences. Contrary to Freud and Jung, Schachtel does not give importance to pre-experiential modes, like those implied in the concepts of primary process and of the collective unconscious. Nor does he see the creative process as a drive discharge function. The creative person's new ways are the result of being *open to the world.*

The concept of the German philosopher Max Scheler (1928), that man as a spiritual and creative being is no longer subject to primitive drives but is "open to the world," may have influenced Schachtel. Openness to the world is an important attitude, just as courage is for military men. But openness to the world is not sufficient for creativity, just as courage alone does not make a good strategist or logician. According to Schachtel, "The main *motivation* at the root of creative experience is man's need to relate to the world around him" (italics are Schachtel's). Schachtel writes that "The quality of the encounter that leads to creative experience consists primarily in the openness during the encounter and in the repeated and varied approaches to the object, in the free and open play of attention, thought, feeling, perception" (Schachtel, 1959). Schachtel accurately describes some general attitudes of the creative person, but does not account for the newness of the creative work, or for the inner forces or mechanisms which substitute new and significant forms for society's worn-out clichés.

Motivation and creativity

As stated in the previous section, motivation, although necessary, is not the specific ingredient of creativity. Practically all behavior of man is motivated, but only a small part of it can be called creative. However, we cannot ignore the fact that creativity too is motivated. The rest of the chapter will be devoted to this aspect of the creative process.

We have already seen that in Freud's theory infantile events play a significant role in motivating creativity. According to him, the creative person experiences a need to represent his conflicts or his ungratified wishes by artwork. However, it is evident that early in life a large number of people experience conflicts and frustrations, similar, for instance, to those of Leonardo. Yet the Leonardos are extremely rare.

Early experiences can play a determining role in stimulating and directing the individual toward a certain kind of activity. The child who grows up in an environment lacking stability and consistency may become an inventor in the field of mathematics, where he searches for and finds a feeling of certainty for some aspects of the world. The child who feels falsely accused may become a promoter of innovations that guarantee civil liberties. Another child may feel that only if he becomes a great man will he deserve and obtain his mother's love (see Chapter 14). However, in this author's experience, a different kind of relatedness to the mother is a more frequent antecedent of creativity: the love of a good mother, which is accompanied by the faith that the child will be a worthwhile and creative individual. The child introjects this feeling from the mother; he accepts her prophecy. Now he must prove that mother is right. The image of the trusting mother will sustain him throughout his life, in moments of doubts, tribulations, and impulses to withdraw from the pains of the innovating search. Freud himself is an example of this type. As he wrote to Jones, he felt that his mother's love and faith were a valuable support during his creative struggles.

Again, we could repeat that although the maternal influence is of great importance and in some cases necessary, it is impossible to say that it is a sufficient causative factor. Too many are the mothers who nourish similar feelings for their children; too few are the children who respond to such feelings by becoming creative. As a matter of fact, this maternal influence leads to competition with real or symbolic siblings oftener than to creativity.

Later, in adolescence, other motivational forces develop at higher levels of cognition and reinforce the creative person's original primitive motivational trends. A few adolescents start to think that their own self-expansion will continue if they reach beyond the limits of what seems to them a restrained and small reality. The creative adolescent becomes aware of the vast discrepancy between the human condition and the ideals that his conceptual cognitive powers permit him to envision. Also, a state of aloneness, or a detached or quasi-schizoid personality, may not permit the young and gifted individual to savor life as much as he would like and may predispose him to crave for something that he does not have or see: an object which does not exist in his psychological reality. It is by searching for this object that he will continue to grow and give an acceptable meaning to his life. He recognizes in himself the reality described by Vico: *finitum, quod tendit ad infinitum,* or "a finitude which tends toward infinity" (see Chapter 8, page 148).

This realization, based on secondary-process mechanisms, reactivates old feelings and longings which were mediated partially or totally by archaic and primary-process mechanisms (for instance, feelings of omnipotence, as described by Silverberg [1952]). The search for the new psychological object is started, but what the result will be we do not know. It is not necessarily a rewarding achievement. It may end in frustration, in anger at society or at a few people, in resignation and acceptance of the limitations of human existence, or in a resort to diversions of any kind. It may even lead to mental illness, if other circumstances happen to be conducive to abandoning painful secondary mechanisms and finding refuge in primary ones. Finally, it leads to creativity, if a possibility exists of combining primary and secondary processes in a constructive way. The new object will then be formed.

Because of my familiarity with their writings, I find it useful to examine as examples of creative motivation the two major Italian poets, Dante and Petrarch. Their works may to a considerable extent be interpreted as the expression of a search for a special object—a type of love which at first has the characteristic of ordinary love but later becomes mystical and transcendental. This love seems to be realizable on earth, and yet it always escapes the pursuer. A longing for it, which is possibly based on the reactivation of infantile longings and strivings, becomes connected with, and therefore transformed by, the most ideal concepts. The medieval Christian concept that nothing noble, beautiful to the spirit, and therefore really worthwhile is actualizable on earth, becomes part of the conception of a love which is not attainable.

Dante's love for Beatrice has many paleologic, archaic, obsessive, and schizophrenic-like elements (see Chapter 21, page 396). The poet met Beatrice Portinari three times in his whole life. No intimacy, no prolonged interpersonal contacts, not even an exchange of views seem to have occurred between the two. And yet it is on these puny segments of historical reality, rather than on his prolonged contacts with his wife and the mother of his children, the earthy Gemma Donati, that he has based his two great works *La Vita Nuova* and *The Divine Comedy*. These momentary and casual street encounters must indeed have been passionate personal experiences, but the memory of them through the years, together with Dante's creative potentiality, transformed them and gave them unpredictable power.

At the same time that Beatrice remained a real person in her physical essence, she became the symbol of love and goodness. As many critics have pointed out, often Dante speaks of her as he would speak of God, and at times perhaps without realizing it, he identifies her with Christ. He calls her the daughter of God. The historical events of the casual encounters with her become surrounded by an atmosphere of mysticism where the number 9 assumes a magic flavor. Dante had an obsessive-compulsive attitude toward this number. He lets us know that he was 9 years old when he met Beatrice for the first time and that it was 9 years later when he met her again, at 9 o'clock. This obsessional attitude toward the number 9 recurs frequently throughout his writings. In three visions which foretell Beatrice's death, the number 9 appears in one way or another.

The first part of *La Vita Nuova* is mainly the expression of a presentiment and expectation of Beatrice's death. But Dante does not even bother to give a descriptive account of the actual occurrence of her death. Her death makes her more alive in his artistic reality. She becomes the image of love and goodness, and finally the guide who will accompany him up to his encounter with God.

Also unusual is Petrarch's love for Laura. Laura was a married woman who lived in southern France, between Avignon and Vaucluse.[5] Her actual encounters with the poet were very few and, in the eyes of the world, inconsequential. There is no indication whatsoever that Laura reciprocated the feelings of the poet. Reading Petrarch's writings, one could even imagine that he was not too distant from that form of paranoia called erotomania. He idealized this woman, but not to the degree that Dante idealized Beatrice. Laura remained fundamentally a terrestrial creature, although endowed with unusual qualities; for instance that of beautifying whatever she touched—trees, water, grass, etc. Her death is described in detail by Petrarch in one of the best pieces of Italian poetry: even death looked beautiful when, like a soft snowfall, it descended over Laura's lovely face.

This account of Dante and Petrarch is not intended to give the impression that the two poets were suffering from psychosis. On the contrary, they both possessed unusual mental lucidity and were in full control of secondary-process thinking. I wanted to indicate that in addition to presumed ungratified infantile wishes which we cannot retrace, they had

[5] It may be a matter of curiosity for the psychiatrist to know that Laura belonged to the family de Sade, from which the famous Marquis later descended (Bishop, 1963).

a conscious motivation: expansion of their own self by the search for an ideal—a complex of feeling and concepts which they called love. This search, promoted by flimsy external events, drew its sustenance from the poets' personal encounters with a conceptual world of both external (or cultural) and internal origin. The searching itself created the object which was searched for. The two poets succeeded in finding the ideal love, but only as an aesthetic entity. That the aesthetic object which they created prevented the formation of a delusional, psychotic object is a remote possibility. It is more likely, however, that in the spirit of medieval mysticism and of scriptural acculturation, the poetical allegory tended to assume the validity of historical truth (Singleton, 1954). Beatrice and Laura existed for the poets, as they had imagined them to be. The poetical visions were as pregnant with truth for the poets as the revelatory experience was for the men who knew God.

And yet these poetical visions included obsessive and paranoid elements, as well as other abnormal mental constructs. How unusual cognitive forms are integrated with normal mechanisms and become products of creativity will be the subject of the following chapters.

20 ⦿ *CREATIVITY IN WIT*

Wit has aroused deep interest in a considerable number of philosophers, psychologists, psychiatrists, and neurologists. Often it has been studied as a form of art; at times as a psychological process; occasionally as a special expression of the spirituality of man.

In his important monograph "Wit and Its Relation to the Unconscious" (1916), Freud succinctly reviewed the theories that had been previously advanced and showed their inadequacies. For instance, Fischer (quoted by Freud) had defined wit as "the ability to combine with surprising quickness many ideas," but had not shown how these ideas are combined. Freud wrote that many authors had found the basis of wit in "sense in nonsense" or in the "succession of confusion and clearness." Freud recognized the vagueness of these formulations, which had not explained how there could be sense in nonsense or clearness in confusion.

An important contribution which Freud overlooked is that of the neurologist Hughlings Jackson, who in 1887 delivered an address on "The Psychology of Joking" at the opening of the Medical Society of London (reprinted 1932). Long before Freud, Jackson compared puns with dreams, but he did not pursue this comparison as far as Freud eventually did. Jackson found that in both puns and dreams "two very dissimilar mental states pretending to be stereoscopic" are in reality "diplopic"; that is, they show two different overlapping visions instead of one.

In a monograph published in 1924, Gregory added a rich bibliography to that of Freud. After reviewing the literature on the subject, Gregory came up with the interesting remark that "Wit is a quick, vivid illumination of a truth." Froeschels, a philosopher as well as a physician, dealt with the problem only from a philosophical point of view (1928). He considered witticisms the means by which unexpressed philosophical truths that actually have been known to us from the time of our birth become "ripe for expression."

Koestler applies to the problem of wit his concept of "bisociation" by which he tries to explain all forms of creativity (1949, 1964). Bisociation is "any mental occurrence simultaneously associated with two habitually incompatible contexts." [1] Although it is true, as we shall see later in detail, that many jokes contain a mechanism which can be called bisociation, this mechanism per se is not sufficient or specific enough to create a joke. In schizophrenic productions or drawings, for instance, we often find the simultaneous association of two or more habitually incompatible contexts. And yet it is only in rare cases that these productions are witty or comical.

Freud's contribution to the psychology of wit

Of all the discussions of the phenomenon of wit, the one by Freud seems to me the most illuminating and the most farreaching in its implications. Because of their significance and because I take issue with some of them, I shall review Freud's major findings and concepts in detail.

---

[1] Kraepelin, quoted by Freud, advanced a similar theory. According to Kraepelin, wit is "the voluntary combination or linking of two ideas which in some ways are contrasted with each other" (Freud, 1916).

Freud became interested in the problem of wit when he noticed that certain dreams resembled jokes, especially when they were interpreted (1916). Instead of disregarding this apparently accidental similarity, he studied it more and more and discovered numerous analogies between witticisms and dreams. He analyzed the various techniques of wit and found them similar to those he had described in his book on dreams as parts of the dream-work. He noticed, for instance, that formation of mixed words or "condensation with substitutive formation" occurs in witticisms as well as in dreams. For example, in a well-known witticism by Heine the word "famillionaire" condenses two meanings, familiar and millionaire.

Freud found double meanings or plays on words to be among the preferred techniques in jokes. This is one of his examples: *A physician, leaving the bedside of a wife whose husband accompanied him, exclaimed doubtfully: "I do not like her looks." "I haven't liked her looks for a long time," was the husband's rejoinder.* With the word *looks* the physician referred to the patient's condition of health; the husband to his wife's appearance.

According to Freud, other jokes are based on ambiguity, such as the following one, which was popular during the trial of Dreyfus, the French Jew unjustly accused of treason by the French army. *"That girl reminds me of Dreyfus. The army does not believe in her innocence."* The technique is based, Freud said, on the experienced uncertainty about the meanings attributed to the words *innocence* and *army*.

Freud realized that the technique of a piece of wit is very important. He wrote that the wit "invariably disappears when we remove the effect of these techniques in expressions." Freud divided the techniques into three groups: techniques of (1) condensation, (2) application of the same material, and (3) double meaning. He then divided each of these groups into several subgroups. Freud thought that all these techniques must have something in common which confers a witty character on the expression, and he made an attempt to find this common denominator. At first he thought it may consist of the condensation or tendency to economy, as when a single word in the witticism gathers several different or even opposite meanings. He realized soon, however, that the nature of wit does not lie in the tendency to economize in expression, because "laconism is not necessarily wit." The intellectual work required in putting together several meanings in order to make a witticism often requires more energy than is saved by the economy of expression.

Freud then turned his attention to puns. Whereas in a play on words, both meanings are expressed in the identical word, in the pun only a certain phonetic similarity or structure is necessary. A pun reported by Brill is quoted as typical. *At a party someone spoke disparagingly of a certain play and said, "It was so poor that the first act had to be rewritten." "And now it is rerotten," added the punster.*

Freud also examined other forms of wit whose technique cannot be classified under the three groups mentioned. He found that a displacement of the focus of attention from the original theme to another, as he had described in dreams, is a technical aspect of some jokes. He gave the following example: *A needy man borrowed twenty-five dollars from a wealthy acquaintance. The same day he was found by his creditor in a restaurant eating a dish of salmon with mayonnaise. The creditor reproached him, "You borrow money from me and then order salmon with mayonnaise. Is that what you needed the money for?" "I don't understand you," responded the debtor. "When I have no money I can't eat salmon with mayonnaise. When I have money, I mustn't eat it. Well then, when shall I ever eat salmon with mayonnaise?"*

According to Freud, the technique of this joke does not lie in words or a play on words, but in the displacement of the psychic accent. The creditor does not blame the debtor for eating salmon *on the day* he borrowed the money, but reminds him that he has no right to think of such luxuries at any time. Another common technique, according to Freud, is "the representation through the opposite," as in the following example from Heine: *This woman resembles the Venus de Milo in many ways. Like her, she is extremely old, has no teeth, and has white spots on the yellow surface of her body.* In this case, ugliness is depicted by making it agree with the most beautiful.

It is not necessary to report here all the possible techniques described by Freud. He described them accurately, but in spite of his attempts he failed to find what is the common and *essential* characteristic in all of them. His conclusion was that the same techniques are to be found in dreams. Freud proceeded then to study the *tendencies* of wit, which are not to be confused with the techniques. Whereas the techniques deal with the formal structure of the joke, the tendencies are more closely connected with the content. Freud thought that wit may be harmless when it has no hidden meanings and its pleasurable effect is due only to its technique. On the other hand, it may be "tendency wit" when its content cannot be safely expressed in an explicit way. Freud pointed out how tendency wit permits expression of feelings and ideas which otherwise would be repressed, as in hostile and obscene jokes. He showed clearly how sexual exhibitionism, invective, and rebellion against authority are made possible by the technique of wit.

Freud then reached the conclusion, which is one of the most significant of his contributions on this subject, that the pleasure in tendency wit results from the fact that a tendency whose gratification would otherwise remain unfulfilled is actually gratified. Freud tried to demonstrate that the search for and discovery of an outlet for hindered motivation was the main aim of the joke, just as it was for the dream. The joke permits release of the inhibition and sets free some repressing energy. Freud, however, could not find economy of psychic expenditure in "harmless witticisms," that is, in witticisms in which he could not recognize any repressed tendency in need of gratification.

After evaluating other doubtful hypotheses, he expressed the idea that pleasure in some "harmless" witticisms is due to the discovery or recognition of the familiar, where one expects to find something new instead. Recognition of the familiar occurs, for instance, in witticisms which use unification, assonance, antonyms, and words with double meanings as techniques. Freud thought that the source of pleasure in rhyme, alliteration, refrains, or assonance in poetry is the discovery of the familiar. However, it seems to me that if it were so, there would have to be some other fundamental characteristics which make a difference between the pleasure derived from a poem and the pleasure obtained from a joke. Although Freud had to admit that in some cases the gratification of a forbidden tendency is not the mechanism responsible for the pleasure experienced in hearing a witticism, motivation in wit remained his main preoccupation. Thus he saw witticisms as related more to dreams than to works of art.

Paleologic and faulty logic in wit

Some of the primary-process mechanisms that were described in Chapter 7 and again in Chapter 16, especially the first (or Von Domarus) and the second principles of paleologic, seem to me to form an integral part of many jokes. Let us reconsider some of the examples from Freud; for instance, the witticism of the poet Heine, who in talking about a lady said: "This woman reminds me of the Venus de Milo in many ways. Like her she is extremely old, has no teeth, and has white spots on the yellow surface of her body." Heine in reality wanted to say that the lady was ugly; but to say that would have been an act of hostility. Heine therefore resorted to a method which would allow him to gratify this hostility, although not too overtly. The method he resorted to is indeed unpredictable and bizarre: he identified the ugly woman with the most beautiful—the Venus de Milo.

How could this logically impossible identification be made? By abandoning Aristotelian logic and reverting to the paleologic of the primary process. The woman and the statue of Venus are identified because they have some predicates in common, namely, being old, having no teeth, and having white spots on the yellow surface of the body. Freud believed that the technique of this joke consists of "representation through the opposite." Ugliness is made to agree with the most beautiful. Trying to identify a subject with its opposite reinforces the effect of the joke; but in my opinion, the *fundamental* factor in the joke is the possibility of an impossible identification. The identification is made possible by the application of Von Domarus' principle, according to which two different subjects are identified just because they have one or more predicates in common. This logical mechanism, which we have studied in schizophrenic thinking, where it is commonly found, appears also in witticisms of normal people.

To take another of the quoted examples from Freud: *The physician leaving the bedside of a woman says to her husband, "I do not like her looks." The husband of the woman adds, "I have not liked her looks for a long time."* In this little joke a mental conflict is portrayed in an unusual fashion. The husband experiences some feelings of aversion for his wife—feelings that he has to repress until an unpredictable opportunity presents itself for letting off steam in a more acceptable manner. The physician uses the word *looks* as a symbol of the concept, "physical appearance, as indicative of a state of health." The husband uses the word *looks* as a symbol of the concept, "physical appearance, as indicative of a state of attractiveness." The two concepts are identified because they have the same verbal symbol. The identification here is made possible by the application of the first and second principles of paleologic (Chapter 16, pages 274–279).

Another of Freud's examples is "That girl reminds me of Dreyfus. The army does not believe in her innocence." Freud reasoned that this joke mainly utilizes the technique of ambiguity; but it is obvious that here again an improbable identification is made, with the application of the first and second principles of paleologic. Dreyfus and the girl are identified because they have a common predicate, "innocence not believed in by the army." The predicate is common to both subjects only in that the same verbalization is applied to two different concepts. In the case of Dreyfus, *innocence* means "state of not being guilty of treason"; in the case of the girl, it means "lack of sexual experience." Also, the word *army* has a different meaning in the two cases. In the case of Dreyfus, it means "general staff"; in the case of the girl it means "group of men," with emphasis on their being male. The ambiguity of this joke, which was the quality emphasized by Freud, is due to the difficulty encountered in making the three or four paleological identifications and certainly adds charm to the joke, but it is not the fundamental ingredient.

An example with a more complicated mechanism is the

joke reported by Freud about the man who had borrowed twenty-five dollars and who was found by his creditor in the act of eating salmon with mayonnaise. When the creditor reproaches the debtor and asks him whether that meal was what he needed the money for, the latter answers, *"I don't understand you. When I have no money I can't eat salmon with mayonnaise. When I have money, I mustn't eat it. Well then, when shall I ever eat salmon with mayonnaise?"* What is the latent meaning of this joke? Here is the problem of a poor fellow who, being a human being, thinks that he too is entitled occasionally to eat salmon with mayonnaise, in spite of his economic condition. When the debtor is reproached by the creditor, he has to find a way to justify himself. He cannot find an acceptable logical justification and resorts to paleologic: if he is not allowed to eat salmon when *he has no money*, he should be allowed to eat salmon when *he has money*. This reasoning would be correct if "to have money" were identical with "to have borrowed money," but they are not. It is generally assumed that borrowed money should not be spent so freely. The debtor has conveniently identified the two types of money, just because they can be spent.

In other jokes the mechanism can become even more complicated. It is not founded on "pure" paleologic, but consists of transitional stages from paleologic to logic, or of discarded and obsolete ways of thinking, as in the following example (not from Freud): *Mother goes for a walk with her little boy. They come to a nudist camp which is surrounded by a high board fence. The little fellow peeps through a low hole. Mother asks: "What do you see?" Boy: "A lot of people." Mother: "What are they, men or women?" Boy: "I don't know; nobody's got any clothes on."*

In order to justify his ignorance logically, the child resorts to a childish form of thinking. He thinks, as occasionally very young children do, that people wearing masculine garments are necessarily men, and people wearing feminine garments are necessarily women. The child could have another source of information, which is the most reliable and which in this case is unexpectedly available: the direct observation of the anatomical characteristics of the nudists. However, he is not able to resort to this method because he is not familiar with (or because he wants to deny) the anatomical differences between the two sexes. From his point of view his answer is logical, but is in contrast with the adult way of approaching the question. Furthermore, by answering as he does, the child reveals naïveté (or according to another interpretation, his repression of the facts of life). Many other factors are involved in this joke, such as the contrast between the surprising availability of the source of information and the nonuse of it, and obviously there is a sexual tinge.

The transition from paleologic to logic is almost complete in the following contemporary American joke: *A woman sues a man by whom she claims she has been raped. The plaintiff and the defendant are in front of the judge. The judge looks at both of them and sees that the woman is tall and stout, the man short and thin. With some astonishment he asks the woman, "Is this the man who raped you? How did he do it?" The woman answers, "He pushed me against a wall and he raped me." "How is it possible?" asks the perplexed judge. "You are so tall and he is so short!" "Well," says the woman, "I bent my knees a little bit."*

The woman is logical. If she bends her knees, the sexual act is possible. In the attempt to use logic in self-defense, however, she accuses herself, because the bending of the knees implies her willingness to be a partner and automatically excludes the act of rape. Though in this case no paleologic is involved, it is still the logical mechanism which is the basis of the joke—a logical mechanism which is used by the woman in self-defense and which, on the contrary, turns out to be a self-accusation.

In some jokes the mechanism consists of comparing two different ways of thinking and of discarding one of them, or often of accepting an absurd way of thinking, like that of mental patients. For example: *A deluded patient visits a psychiatrist. "Doctor, Doctor, help me!" he says. "Look, I am full of bugs," and tries to brush off the parasites from his clothes. "Be careful," replies the psychiatrist, quickly recoiling, "don't brush them on me."* The story is witty because the psychiatrist accepts the patient's way of thinking, whereas he is expected to reject it. The meaning of the joke is obviously this: "Psychiatrists are not necessarily superior to or healthier than their patients. Like their patients they may be fooled—and may also be unbalanced."

Some jokes rely more on a nonverbal medium, like drawing, but are based on the same formal mechanisms. For example, a cartoon that appeared some time ago in a periodical showed a middle-aged couple arriving at a railroad station. On his shoulders and in both hands a porter carries the luggage, consisting of so many heavy bags as to make it hardly believable that one man could carry so much. The wife tells the husband, "Darling, keep an eye on the porter. See that he doesn't run away." The woman's attitude is somewhat logical: she wants to make sure that the porter, a man whose honesty has not yet been proved, does not rob her of her belongings. In the circumstances, however, the remark is absurd, because the porter could not run away with such a heavy load.

From all these examples it is apparent that if, for the time being, we overlook the emotional tendency which seeks gratification, we can conclude that jokes require apparent ways of proving something, such as sustaining an allegation, a hostile attitude, or a desire. *The sustaining of the story is made possible by the adoption of special cognitive mechanisms.* At times these mechanisms consist of microgenetic or primary processes, often the paleologic type of cognitive organization; at other times of logical processes with false premises, or of ways of thinking which, although logical, imply some additional facts that would automatically invalidate the allegation. These are the same mechanisms which we have encountered in microgenetic and pathological processes. In special cases, the technique consists of comparing two different ways of secondary-process thinking and rejecting one of them.

As the mentally ill person or the dreamer resorts to primitive cognitive processes to sustain wishes or hostile attitudes, or to avoid anxieties, so the joker resorts to these regressive mechanisms. Their degree of regression varies. At times they are based on the principle of Von Domarus; at other times on the principle of altered connotation-verbalization balance (or the second principle of paleologic); at other times on mechanisms which are logical per se, but whose premises are false.

The nature and perception of wittiness

Although the previous section discussed the special cognitive mechanisms which must be used in forming a joke, it did not intend to suggest that the wittiness of a joke is due simply to the use of primary-process paleologic or of faulty logic. More than that is necessary. Let us examine again the Dreyfus joke, and let us assume that the girl who was identified with Dreyfus was Jewish. If a person said. "This girl has something in common with Dreyfus; she is Jewish," this would be a logically correct statement but platitudinous. It would be a statement made with a secondary-process mechanism. Or if a schizophrenic patient said, "This girl is Dreyfus; she is Jewish," this would be a paleologic primary-process identification because of a common predicate (being Jewish). It would be delusional, but not witty.

Thus it is not the use of primary-process palelologic or of faulty logic which confers the witty character to a joke. In my opinion, *one perceives a stimulus as witty when he is set to react to logic and then realizes that he is instead reacting to paleologic or faulty logic.*

The listener is temporarily deceived because he first apprehends the intellectual process of the joke as logical. A fraction of a second later, however, he realizes that the intellectual process is not logical at all, and he laughs. The listener discovers that he is not reacting to logic but either to paleologic or to faulty logic. Logic, faulty logic, and paleologic may be very similar and, when they are put together as they are in the joke, may deceive us as identical twins do. It is just a fleeting deception, however. As soon as we become aware of it, we laugh.

If we know that we are going to listen to a joke, we prepare ourselves to be temporarily deceived. At the same time, we are invaded by curiosity; how will the raconteur be able to solve the difficult situation in which he put himself? How could he, for example, prove that an ugly woman is like the

Venus de Milo? We shall indeed experience surprise when we realize that such proof is based on unsuspected modes of thinking. Surprise confers charm to the witticism. The confusion between similarity and identity, which we have dealt with so much in this book, may occur *twice* in the joke: the first time, when the joke is based on paleologic or Von Domarus' principle (and Von Domarus' principle leads to mistaken identity); the second time, when paleologic or faulty logic is confused with logic.

In the creation of a joke, the creative process is based on the following facts: (1) Primary-process mechanisms, or cognitive mechanisms which are usually discarded because of their faults, become available to the creative person. (2) Out of the primary-process and/or faulty cognitive mechanisms which have become available, the creative person is able to select those which give the fleeting impression of being valid secondary-process mechanisms. The amused response on the part of the listener occurs when he recognizes logic-paleologic discordance.[2] The creative process of wit consists of putting together the primary- and secondary-process mechanisms and automatically comparing them. It is the comparison which reveals the discordance and provokes laughter. The discovery by a creative person of an apparent concordance in a logic-paleologic discordance constitutes the tertiary process of the wit he creates. It constitutes the creative process of the joke.

On the other hand, the perception of wit—or more specifically, the typical response to the perception of wit—consists of the discovery of logic-paleologic discordance in what for a brief interval seemed concordance. It seems to me that to have recognized this point is a very important step in the psychological understanding of wit. However, we have not yet understood the reasons for the subjective responses to wit. That is, we have not yet understood why the recognition of logic-paleologic discordance in an apparent concordance is

[2] If faulty logic is used instead of paleologic, then there will be a logic–faulty logic discordance. In the following discussion in this chapter we shall take into consideration only logic versus paleologic and secondary-process versus primary, because these seem the most typical and most frequent combinations in creativity of wit. However, the same notions could be repeated for logic versus faulty logic and secondary versus faulty secondary process.

followed physiologically by a pleasant subjective experience or reaction. This reaction, which is more or less specific, entails a feeling of amusement and tends to make the listener smile or laugh—at times even in a forcible and spasmodic way.

Here we have reached the border between objectivity and subjectivity, that border between body and psyche which at this stage of our knowledge we are unable to cross. In some ways we are like the physicist who has discovered that a certain length of light wave will bring about the perception of the color red, but cannot understand why such a wavelength becomes transformed into the subjective experience of redness. Or we can compare ourselves to the chemist who knows that compounds with a chemical formula corresponding to glucose or to saccharin are perceived as sweet, but does not know why.

In many psychological phenomena a degree of understanding similar to the one that we have reached in the study of wit is easy to obtain. For instance, we know that embarrassing stimuli make people blush, although we do not know why the experience of embarrassment is accompanied by a dilatation of the capillaries of the facial region. In the case of wit, it was much more difficult to determine the specificity of the wit-producing constellation of stimuli, as it consists of a relatively complicated cognitive construct.

It is possible to understand now why most paleologic expressions of schizophrenics (and occasionally of other psychiatric patients) are bizarre but not witty. The language of the schizophrenic is often so remote from reality that no similarity or possibility of confusion with logic is left. Only when such confusion is possible for the listener are expressions witty. Occasionally schizophrenic language is witty; as a matter of fact, it is to some witty expressions of schizophrenic patients that I owe the origin of my interest in the psychology of creativity. For instance, a patient examined many years ago had the habit of wetting her body with oil. Asked why she did so, she replied: "The human body is a machine and has to be lubricated." The word *machine*, applied in a figurative sense to the human body, had led to her identification with man-made machines.

The creative process as it has been described in this chapter is not involved in what this patient said. She did not know that her explanation was witty; she meant it literally. Her delusional remark is witty only for us. In this case we, not the patient, create the joke, because we recognize her illogicality in the apparent logicality. Apparent witticisms of schizophrenics have been reported in the literature. These witticisms generally result from paleological identifications or from extreme literalness, which follows reduction of the connotation power and emphasis on verbalization (Chapter 16, pages 278–281). One of Levin's patients believed that she was in a ward for colored people (1936). Asked why she thought so, she replied, "Because I was brought here by Miss Brown" (the nurse who had accompanied her to the hospital). A patient of Bychowski, asked where her husband was, replied: "On our wedding picture" (1943).

Apparent witticisms are also found in nonschizophrenic psychotics. In organic patients they generally represent attempts to cover the inadequacy or deficit due to the illness. Witty expressions were particularly numerous in expansive cases of general paresis, which now have become extremely rare (Arieti, 1950). They occur also in Korsakoff's psychosis, senile psychosis, cerebral arteriosclerosis, brain tumors, especially of the frontal lobes, epilepsy, especially in twilight states, mental deficiencies, and the cerebral type of Buerger's disease (Arieti, 1950).

The comic

As mentioned in the previous section, the individual who perceives wit undergoes a pleasant experience which entails a feeling of amusement and tends to make him smile or laugh. Actually this response occurs not only to witty stimuli, but to a much larger category, comical stimuli, of which the witty ones constitute only one subgroup. We must therefore try to determine the nature of the comic and distinguish it from that of wit before proceeding.

Many philosophers since ancient times and a considerable number of contemporary psychologists have investigated the nature of the comic. In this chapter no attempt will be made to review their theories. Each author believes that he has found the entity to which people respond with laughter, smiles, or a humorous attitude. However, when one tests the validity of each proposed theory, he sees that it seems correct for some aspects of the comic but completely wrong for others.

Perhaps helped by what we have already established about the nature of wit, we shall now examine the nature of the comic. Since wit is a special subgroup of the comic, what we shall determine about the comic must also apply to wit; but the reverse does not hold.

An observation made several decades ago which led me to the formulation of a theory (Arieti, 1950) was that when Italians hear or read something Spanish for the first time in their lives, they laugh or smile—that is, they react as perceivers of a comical stimulus. Obviously, there is nothing comical per se in the beautiful Spanish language. There must be something in the situation which makes the Italians react in this way. An Italian who listens to Spanish for the first time recognizes that he is listening to a foreign language with different grammar and a different vocabulary. Yet in some expressions the two languages are so similar that the Italian is often able to understand the meaning of what is said. In other words, he often understands the meaning not because he has studied Spanish, but because he knows Italian. He is prepared to respond to Spanish, but he often finds himself responding to Italian—the Italian which appears in the Spanish—and he experiences a comical sensation.

This observation and subsequent similar ones led me to formulate the following hypothesis: *The subject perceives a comical stimulus when he is set to react to A and then finds himself reacting to B, because of a confusion between the identity and similarity of A and B.*

To test this theory, let us consider another common situation in comedy—the mistaken identity of persons. For example, in Shakespeare's *Comedy of Errors* two brothers, unknown to each other, are identical twins and are continuously confused with each other, even by their wives. To increase the confusion they have the same name, one being

referred to as Antipholus of Ephesus and the other as Antipholus of Syracuse. Each Antipholus has a servant who is
an identical twin of his brother's servant. Each servant is
called Dromio. The situation is extremely comical and causes
the audience to roar with laughter, because when one thinks
he is reacting to the presence of Antipholus of Ephesus he is
instead reacting to Antipholus of Syracuse, and vice versa.
When the audience thinks it is in the presence of one servant,
it is in the presence of the other. The wife of one of the twins
allows certain intimate expressions to a man who she thinks
is her husband, but the man does not even know her. This
comedy by Shakespeare is a very close imitation of the
comedy *Menaechmi* by the Latin Plautus (254–184 B.C.).
Plautus in his turn imitated the Greek Menander (343–291
B.C.).

From ancient times, the error of misidentification of person has been one of the most powerful stimuli of the comical.
The simplest form of mistaken identity of A for B occurs in
the case of two persons who look very much alike—as with
identical twins. Even today in plays, movies, and vaudeville
shows, twins appear frequently as a source of the comic. The
comical element is maintained if the two persons are identified not only because they look alike, but, for instance, because they have a predicate in common, as when A has the
same name or dress as B, or is located geographically in a
place where B is supposed to be.

The audience tends to laugh when a character C, in a theatrical performance, is set to react to A and instead reacts to
B, thinking that B is A. The spectators do not accept C's apparent identification of A and B, and are compelled to laugh.
Moreover, the spectators themselves are set to react to A but
find themselves reacting to B; they become aware of the mistaken identity and laugh. The performer C, however, allegedly does not know that the person whom he thinks is A in
reality is B; so he cannot laugh. He continues to identify paleologically—somewhat like the schizophrenic. It is because
the audience cannot accept the paleological identification
that it continues to laugh.

Let us examine what happens in other comical situations.
The intensity of the comic persists, but is diminished when A

and B are in the same person. For instance, in plays and masquerades there is a tenuous comical element because we know that the person who acts or is dressed like A is not A but B. In the horse pantomime we laugh because we are set to react to a horse and instead find ourselves reacting to two men functioning as the legs of the horse. In the caricature we look at a picture of a person anatomically distorted, and yet recognizable. We recognize the similarity in the dissimilar. The caricature uses exaggeration of traits to make a B of an A, generally a distorted and undesirable B, but in spite of the deformation we recognize A and we smile. Images seen in distorting mirrors produce the same effect. We react comically also to a photograph which had not turned out well. Generally we react comically to the inadequate, but only when the inadequate has unconsciously deceived us in the paleological identification. For instance, a child who uses big words like a grown-up makes us smile, because at first we react to him as to a man, and then we realize that he is not a man. In a certain way, however, we feel that there is a man in him; this feeling is reinforced because we know that a child is potentially a grown-up. We are deceived until we focus our attention on the fact that he is a child.

The concepts of identity and similarity, which have been discussed so many times in Parts I and II of this book, once more appear very important. We may look at the problem in a different way. A principle which logicians generally call Leibniz's law states: "X is identical to Y if X has every property that Y has and Y has every property that X has."

Von Domarus' law or principle, which is followed by the person who thinks paleologically, can be reformulated in this way: "X is identical to Y if X has at least one property that Y has and Y has at least one property that X has."

My theory of the comic can then be reformulated to say: "A subject is a perceiver of a comical stimulus when he realizes that he tends to identify X with Y not in accordance with Leibniz's law, but in accordance with Von Domarus' law." Of course, for such a realization the person does not need to know that Leibniz's and Von Domarus' laws exist, just as he does not need to know that he adopts Aristotle's laws of thought whenever he thinks logically.

Wit is a particular type of the comic, inasmuch as the required confusion between similarity and identity necessarily occurs in the field of cognition. The two subjects which are unwarrantably identified are logic and paleologic (or faulty logic). The listener at first is prone to identify the faulty logic of the joke with valid logic by virtue of Leibniz's law. Soon he discovers, however, that he identifies the two forms of thinking in accordance with Von Domarus' law.

We must therefore repeat that the confusion between similarity and identity may occur twice in witticisms: the first time when the joke is based on paleologic or Von Domarus' principle (and Von Domarus' principle leads to mistaken identity); the second time when paleologic or faulty logic is confused with logic (that is, when Von Domarus' principle is confused with Leibniz's principle).

Gratification of tendencies in wit

The previous sections have investigated the formal cognitive mechanisms inherent in wit. We shall now consider the aspect of wit to which Freud devoted the most study: the gratification of tendencies in relation to the content of the wit.

A joke, according to Freud, does not try to impart new knowledge. It has a special aim, which is disguised under the obvious aim of amusing the listener: it attempts to gratify a wish which is generally suppressed or inhibited. The joke is an attempted gratification or pseudogratification, or at least a partial or vicarious gratification, which is obtained by resorting to special cognitive mechanisms. These mechanisms represent the wit-work which, like dream-work, transforms the content of the joke into one which is more acceptable. Both the repression and the gratification achieved in the joke are not so marked as in dreams. The gratification is due to the fact that verbal expression of the forbidden becomes permissible, and with this expression a certain excitement and release of emotions is obtained.

There are several tendencies whose gratification is sought by means of witticisms. One of the most common is sexual in nature. Frank admission of sexual drives, as well as of sexual exposure and consummation, is made possible in telling a joke. That sexual jokes are extremely numerous is understandable because of the repression to which sexual drives are subjected by society. However, since the repression in the joke is very weak, sexual jokes too are forbidden in numerous milieus and, of course, all of them cannot be published. Homosexual jokes are relatively rare because the repression in the joke is indeed too feeble to compensate for the ostracism to which this form of sexuality is subjected.

As far as the technique is concerned, sexual jokes do not differ from others. Often they resort to very primitive paleological laws, as in the following example taken from Freud: *A wealthy but elderly gentleman showed his devotion to a young actress by many lavish gifts. Being a respectable girl, she tried to discourage his attentions by telling him that her heart was already given to another man. "I never aspired as high as that," was his polite answer.* The technique of this joke consists of the paleological identification of two concepts, because they have the same verbalization in the word *high*. The gentleman used the word in an anatomical sense, not in a figurative sense, as he pretends. The latent meaning of the joke is obviously this: "Let's do away with this false sentimentality. My attentions are caused only by my sexual desire for you."

A second group of jokes, perhaps even larger than the group with sexual content, consists of what may be called hostile jokes. In these jokes the tendency is toward the expression of anger, enmity, disparagement, and denigration. It is not a surprise to find so many hostile jokes, since civilization requires repression of hostility as much as of sexuality. The target of hostility in the joke is attacked not directly, but through wit-work. The reader will remember the witticism about the husband who shows his feeling toward his wife by agreeing with the physician about her looks. Heine's joke about the Venus de Milo has a similar tendency. Jokes expressing rebellion against socially recognized authority may be included under this category. The jokes about psychiatrists which appear so frequently in the American press express resentment of the prominent position that psychiatry has acquired. "Psychiatrists are human like their patients and may be unbalanced too," most of these jokes imply. In many situations the hostile joke becomes an actual act of hostility, ranging over a gamut of variegated tonalities from bland teasing to vitriolic expression. The individual with a schizoid personality, who is particularly sensitized to environmental hostility, is often said to have no sense of humor. This is because the schizoid person, alert as he is to external antagonism, is not deceived by wit-work and recognizes the hostile element in wit (Arieti, 1955).

I might mention that some parents and teachers who disapprove of physical punishment instead punish children by using witticisms or by emphasizing the comical aspects of the situation. However, unless the humor is of a very bland type and accompanied by affectionate concern, it may have even more disturbing effects than other types of punishment, as disclosed by patients under intensive psychotherapy.

Hostility engendered by prejudice may also be ventilated through jokes, as revealed by the following example: *A Jewish gardener answered an advertisement for a job in a nunnery. The Mother Superior told him that since he was Jewish she'd have to give him a week of trial service. At the end of the week the Mother Superior came up to the gardener and said, "Well, you have done pretty well, but there are several habits I want you to lose. I don't mind so much your lighting cigarettes from the holy candles, or washing your hands in the holy water, but for God's sake, stop calling me 'Mother Shapiro.' "*

This joke, apparently innocent and harmless, has a touch of anti-Semitism. Its latent meaning is in the accusation, made time and again, that Jews do not want to lose their Jewish habits and traditions, even when they sharply contrast with those of the majority. The gardener should be very grateful to the Mother Superior. He has found employment in a Catholic cloister, a place where it is hardly conceivable that a Jew would be hired. He should feel a sense of obligation and try to conform as much as possible. What does he do instead? He lights his cigarettes from the holy candles and washes his hands in the holy water. These habits are overlooked by the Mother Superior because they disclose only the gardener's poor judgment. What the Mother Superior cannot tolerate is being called "Mother Shapiro." Shapiro is a common Jewish name, and the gardener, who is used to pronouncing it, confuses it paleologically with "Superior." Even in the cloister which has been so generous to him, he remains a typical Jew.

In a third important, though not quite so large, group of jokes, the tendency which is expressed is the frank admission of human frailty as a truth that has to be accepted and defended. This tendency, though justified, has to be repressed generally because of the ways of living which civilization imposes upon us. Typical of this group is the joke described earlier about the man who was caught by the creditor in the act of eating salmon with mayonnaise. The debtor had to resort to wit-work in order to assert his human rights and defend his wish to eat salmon with mayonnaise once in a while. To him this desire had the validity of a truth. Several jokes, especially those belonging to this group, assert what may be considered natural truths. In a certain way they are reminiscent of those dreams which do not express the fulfillment of irrational and immoral wishes, but the fulfillment of some of our good impulses which, for social reasons, have to be repressed. They also show that, at least in some cases, the assertion of Gregory that "wit is a quick, vivid illumination of a truth" is correct. And they support the plausibility of Froeschels' statement, mentioned at the beginning of this chapter, that witticisms are means by which philosophical truths congenitally known but not yet expressed become "ripe for expression."

A fourth group which is quite common consists of jokes which express the unrealistic effort of the inadequate man to cover his own inadequacy. This effort is not really fulfilled in the joke, which therefore in a certain way becomes a hostile joke. Nevertheless, since it is especially the covering of one's inadequacy which is emphasized in these jokes, they deserve to be classified separately. The following example is from Koestler (1949): *Mr. Dupont, an elderly notary, has for years suffered from the annoying habits of his clerk, Jules. Returning home unexpectedly from a journey he finds Jules in bed with his wife. Mr. Dupont surveys the scene with a mournful eye and says, "That's enough, Jules! Once more and you're fired."*

According to one way of thinking, the notary's action is

logical. The clerk is warned; one more mistake and he will be fired. However, another way of thinking, more acceptable in our society, requires that Mr. Dupont be more energetic in seeking immediate and drastic retaliation against Jules. But Mr. Dupont is a weak, inadequate person, a man unwilling to defend his honor with strong action. What he really wishes is to find a method to keep peace and save his face.

In my opinion, these four tendencies are the principal ones expressed in jokes, but probably there are many more. Often several tendencies are combined in the same joke; at times all four even appear. An example is found, for instance, in the joke about the tall woman who sues the short man on the charge of rape. In this joke there is certainly a sexual exposure, which satisfies the sexual tendency. There is also hostility toward women, for the joke illustrates very well what many men think of such charges made by women—that sexual intercourse with conscious adult females is not possible without their consent, or without a certain degree of acquiescence.[3] From the point of view of the man there is assertion of his own rights; he is unfairly accused of having raped the woman. Finally, the joke shows how the woman attempts to cover up her own inadequacy or the inadequacy of her story.

However, we must remember that the gratification of these forbidden tendencies in jokes does not preclude the gratification of a fully conscious tendency or motivation: that of enjoying their witty or comical aspect. We enjoy the wit in addition to the other gratifications which the contents of a joke offer us. This situation is similar to that of other art media which confer an aesthetic pleasure not necessarily related to the content. In wit, however, the hidden tendency is stronger than in other forms. This fact, as well as others that will be mentioned in the following section, really places the joke in a halfway position between dreams and art forms.

[3] Except, of course, under threat of violence. But how could some men, like the one reported in this joke, physically less endowed than the woman, threaten her?

Relation between content and form

We must thus agree with Freud that the gratification of forbidden tendencies is a fundamental aspect of jokes. Now, however, we shall take into consideration another aspect of jokes which makes them particularly suitable as an introduction to the study of the creative process: the relation between form and content.

In jokes we can easily recognize an almost perfect harmony between form and content. It is hard to imagine a different product which in waking life would permit the gratification and, practically at the same time, the rejection of a forbidden tendency. In the dream the visual hallucination transports the dreamer into a world of illusion that exists as long as the dream lasts. In the joke the illusion can exist in waking life too, but is even more fleeting. For a fraction of time, we allow ourselves to believe what the secondary process will almost immediately recognize as absurd and to be rejected. Moreover, it is because we know in advance that our intellect will soon reject what the joke asserts that we allow ourselves to hear it and fugaciously believe it. In jokes we pretend, as we do in other games.

In wit there is a *going backward* (or regression) of part of the cognitive faculties. Wit is in certain respects related to children's play. In play there is the same permissiveness: the children allow themselves to go backward to a realm of fantasy, which is lived. In wit, however, the going backward (or regression of cognition) is temporarily accompanied by the assumption of *going forward* (sustaining a new point).

At this point we can re-examine the statement that jokes occupy a position halfway between dreams and other works of art. They do; nevertheless, they are genuine works of art, even if their purpose or tendencies are similar to those of dreams. Whereas the dream is only for the dreamer or for the dreamer's dream life, the joke is understood by others and accepted socially. Whereas the dream consists mostly of primary-process mechanisms and does not substantially reach the secondary process, the joke attains an overlapping of the two processes which is necessary for the evolving of the tertiary one. Let us remember, however, that in the joke also, two processes are not fused or integrated. One of the two, generally the primary, is soon rejected.

On the other hand, we must recognize that no matter how refined jokes are in their technique, as a group they belong to a primitive form of art. The close relation between jokes and mere psychological functions is revealed not only by the use of primitive cognitive mechanisms in jokes, but also by their propelling necessity to gratify an unadmitted emotional drive, at least for a fleeting instant. In higher forms of art, this gratification is not so direct. It is attenuated by the aim to create an independent life for a new object, the work of art; to maintain an "aesthetic distance" from it (see Chapter 21); and most of all, to experience aesthetic pleasure.

Accessory factors

The emphasis given in this chapter to the use of some special cognitive mechanisms in the formal structure of witticisms should not obscure the existence of accessory factors which are part of the technique of jokes. Some of these factors were first recognized by Freud, but whereas he believed that they constituted the basis of wit, I think they are merely accessory mechanisms. They are not essential to elicit a comic response but lend additional charm to the joke. The ability to find them and to unite them is an expression of the artistic level of the person who wrote the joke.

Some of these secondary factors have been implied in the previous discussion. For instance, what Freud calls *ambiguity* can be interpreted as the suspense and effort necessary to make the paleological identification. *Displacement of the psychologic accent* is based on the fact that often the paleological identification needs a predicate or a characteristic which is secondary, adventitious, or loosely associated with the original meaning.

Representation through the opposite also confers charm and beauty to a joke. We can take again as examples the joke of the ugly woman who was identified with the symbol of beauty, the Venus de Milo, and the joke about the young child who could not determine the sexual identity of people, because they were naked.[4] In these cases representation through the opposite increases the element of surprise; but the intellectual element—demonstration of something which cannot be demonstrated by the usual cognitive mechanisms —is the fundamental factor. In many jokes these secondary characteristics are elaborate and at times exaggerated in order to increase the suspense and the element of surprise. A good example is the following joke:

There were twins, about seven years of age. One had been born a pessimist, the other an optimist. Came Christmas, and their father gave the pessimist a nice little automatic plane that would do all sorts of tricks; and he filled the optimist's shoe with some horse manure. On Christmas morning an uncle came to visit, and asked the pessimist: "Well, how did Santa treat you?" "Terrible," was the answer. "I got a little plane that will do everything by itself—no fun for me, nothing to do." "And you?" asked the uncle of the optimist, "How was Santa to you?" "Couldn't have been nicer," said the little boy. "He brought me a little live pony; only before I woke, unfortunately the pony ran away . . . !"

The emphasis on the opposite attitudes of the twins gives charm to this joke. However, most of the content is technically unnecessary. The really witty part consists not in the attitude of the pessimist—mention of which may be even completely eliminated—but in the attitude of the optimist— that is, in the optimist's interpretation of the presence of manure as proof that he had received a pony as a gift. At a latent level this joke is a pessimistic one, inasmuch as it shows how unfounded is the optimism of one of the twins.

Another characteristic mentioned by Freud—*condensation*—is an important accessory factor, just as it is in dreams. The more condensed the latent meaning, the more significant is the joke. This condensation is due to the paleological identifications or compositions which were mentioned before. Condensation also occurs in the emotional content. For instance, at least four different tendencies and emotional drives

---

4 In some not yet clarified ways, representation through the opposite may be connected with the origin of opposite meanings described in Chapter 7, pages 101–103.

are condensed in the joke about the tall woman and the short man.

In extremely rare jokes the cognitive technique is more complicated, or is even at variance with the ones more commonly encountered. Let us consider the following unusual example: *A young man by the name of Peter went to his mother in a very agitated, mournful state. "What happened?" asked the mother. "Mother," replied Peter, "I am in love with the daughter of Mr. Smith, our neighbor, and I cannot marry her." "Why?" asked the mother. "I went to Father," said the son, "and told him of my love, but he replied, 'You cannot marry Mr. Smith's daughter. Mr. Smith's daughter is my daughter.' "Is that all?" replied the mother. "My son, don't worry. You can marry Mr. Smith's daughter." "How is it possible?" asked Peter, perplexed. "Very possible, son. You are not your father's son."*

There is some humor in this joke, but not much, as the mechanism is the reverse of the one usually adopted. The young woman involved, who is at first identified as a sister, is discovered not to be a sister after all, and therefore eligible for marriage. The joke is unusual because it is the information given by the mother which permits the logical (not paleological) possibility for the gratification. The mechanism thus is the reverse of the one usually adopted. The humoristic value is consequently diminished. The two unexpected confessions of the parents make the story interesting.

Puns, proverbs, and parables

One example of a pun—about the play which had to be rewritten and was "rerotten"—has already been mentioned in the section on Freud's contribution to wit. Another example may be taken from a speech of President Truman delivered during the 1948 political campaign.[5] Alluding to the fact that the Gallup and other private polls, which predicted the victory of his opponent, discouraged Democrats from going to vote on election day, he called them "sleeping polls." He obviously meant that they acted as sleeping *pills*. Other

[5] Speech given in Cleveland, October 26, 1948.

examples, mentioned by Freud, are the Latin *amantes-amentes* (lovers-lunatics) and the Italian *traduttore-traditore* (translator-traitor).

All these examples are witty, and yet, in the order presented here, they decrease in comic power. What meanings do these expressions really convey? The play is both rewritten and "rerotten"; the polls are in a certain way (sleeping) pills; the lovers (*amantes*) act foolishly and therefore are like lunatics (*amentes*); the translator (*traduttore*) does not convey the real meaning of the original text, and he is therefore a traitor (*traditore*).

It is obvious that in these examples the latent meaning is not sustained by paleological identification alone. In other words, there is no contrast between the logical and the paleological form. The paleological identification is used either to add something to the logical meaning or to give additional support to it. These witticisms are not like the one about the woman who was identified with the Venus de Milo, for such identification is only possible from an exclusively paleological point of view. In the case of the play which was rewritten and "rerotten," the meaning of the expression is still mainly sustained by paleological identification, and therefore there is still a considerable amount of humor. In fact, the punster was more interested in conveying the notion that the play was "rerotten" than the notion that it was rewritten.

The more the logical meaning is accepted, the less is the need for paleological sustenance. The humoristic power decreases, but the expression acquires greater effectiveness. *When the logical thought is entirely accepted, there is very little witty effect, if any.* Thus the use of paleologic does not have the purpose of confusing for the sake of humor, but of conveying the message through a stronger medium. Modern advertisements often use this paleological reinforcement.

Puns and proverbs, in which the paleological meaning mainly reinforces the logical one, may be compared to those rare dreams whose manifest content coincides with the latent. A beautiful example of paleological reinforcement is found in Benjamin Franklin's historic statement, "We must all hang together, or assuredly we shall all hang separately." This sentence has great vigor and strength because it follows both logic and paleologic. It has practically no comical effect because the meaning is not sustained by paleologic alone. Franklin wanted to convey the message, "We must remain united," but he did not use this ordinary phrase. He said instead that we must hang anyway, so let's hang together rather than hanging separately; but to "hang together" means to remain united, and "hanging separately" means to be executed on the gallows. In a fleeting preconscious moment, all the meanings of the words "to hang" are identified. When they are recognized as being different, the artistic effect is experienced.

To take another example which has been considered with veneration throughout the centuries, in the Gospels it is written that people who wanted to confuse Jesus asked him whether it was proper to pay taxes to Caesar. Jesus requested that money be shown to him and then asked whose image was on the coin. They replied "Caesar's." Jesus then said, "Render therefore unto Caesar the things that are Caesar's, and to God the things that are God's." The Gospels say that the people were astonished at such an unexpected answer, just as an increasing number of people have been throughout the centuries.

Jesus' answer is enigmatic and has been interpreted in many ways. And yet we immediately perceive its great force, and we sense that it conveys a great meaning. Why is it so? It is difficult to examine Jesus' sentence from an exclusively formal, strictly literal, and concrete point of view, because as soon as we hear it we become inundated by its profound and various abstract meanings. Nevertheless, it seems that if we make an effort we can recognize in this sentence a concrete and literal basis, as we do in parables in general. The image on the coin was Caesar's only as it represented the likeness of Caesar, not because it belonged to Caesar. In other words, only the image was Caesar's, not the ownership of the coin. Therefore, if we take this sentence in an extremely literal, concrete sense, Jesus would be wrong, having based his statement only on a play on words—on the fact that the expression "Caesar's" would paleologically acquire the meaning "being property of Caesar." The coin then would have to be given back (rendered) to Caesar, its rightful owner. But taxes would have to be paid even if the coins did not show the image of Caesar.

Why does the story not appear humorous, in spite of having a partially paleologic foundation? The expression reinforced the important message which Jesus wanted to convey to the people: that money *did* belong to Caesar, not in a literal but metaphorical sense. Money is a material thing, and belongs more to Caesar and to the materialistic world of Rome than to the spiritual world of Jerusalem. Jesus' followers should not be concerned with such things, but only with "things which are God's and must be rendered to God." Jesus was trying to counter the discontent of the people by showing, in an unusual, unpredictable way, that it was right to pay the unfair tribute to Caesar. With his words he did not take a pro-Roman position, nor did he take a rebellious one and come out against payment of taxes. At the same time, in a new and highly artistic way he supported the old religious Hebrew tradition which stressed the antithesis between God and Moloch. Moloch is a contemptuous word for king, a king being interested only in temporal, earthly values. In this parable, Caesar is Moloch.

We can see in this example the fusion or contemporaneous occurrence of several levels of meaning. Had Jesus simply resorted to a play on words, his remarks would have been witty, but not epoch-making. Had he tried to placate discontented taxpayers, his intent would have been a noble one but not a revelation. Jesus wanted to reveal what for him was the highest truth. This revelation was made not through a scientific demonstration but through paleologic reinforcement. Paleologic reinforcement is the opposite of logic-paleologic discordance. It does not belong to the comic, but to the general realm of art and occasionally of science, as will be demonstrated in the following chapters.

21 ° *THE AESTHETIC PROCESS*

For many the work of art is a perfect and indissoluble unity, capable in its totality of eliciting a particular subjective experience. These people follow Croce's tenet that it is impossible to separate form from content. Such "dissection" would actually destroy the aesthetic value.

This point of view is understandable in aestheticians as well as in admirers of art, inasmuch as they are interested in the end result of the creative process—the only one which evokes the aesthetic effect. Such an approach, however, does not lead to a psychological understanding of the creative process. The psychologist does not deny that the work of art constitutes a unity where the content is indissolubly intertwined with a particular form. But he is aware that this intertwining is completed at the last stages of the process of creativity, and that these stages are preceded by many others, some conscious, others unconscious, which at times unfold in rapid succession, at times in slow.

The psychological analysis of a work of art may temporarily suspend the aesthetic appreciation, but it eventually leads to a deeper understanding and more intense experiencing of that work. The previous chapter shows how we may differentiate in wit the various forms, the special contents, and the conditions which lead to the comic response. This chapter will follow a similar pattern in relation to the aesthetic process and aesthetic response.

Clive Bell called the aesthetic form "significant" (1913). With this term he strongly emphasized that the quality which confers to a work of art its artistic essence is the "significance" of the form. Bell's concept, although important, does not greatly increase our understanding, because it does not explain what makes a form aesthetically "significant." This chapter will illustrate how the tertiary process adds aesthetic significance to forms and contents. Although my aim is to clarify the aesthetic process in general, I shall take as my central example the tertiary process as it evolves in poetry. Some consideration will be given to other forms of art.

The similar in the dissimilar: the metaphor

We have repeatedly seen in this book that one of the pillars of human cognition is the ability to associate similars and then to distinguish similarity from identity. The person who creates a witticism sees a similarity between a logical statement and a paleological one and, by temporarily making the listener believe that this similarity is an identity, creates a joke.

The poet also sees a similarity in the dissimilar in the process of creating a metaphor.[1] Aristotle wrote, "The greatest thing by far is to be a master of metaphor; it is the one thing that cannot be learnt from others; and it is also a sign of genius, since a good metaphor implies an intuitive perception of the similarity in dissimilar" (*Poetics*, xxii).

Poetry, of course, is not based exclusively on metaphor, but metaphorical language is one of its fundamental components. Let us take as an example Blake's beautiful poem "The Sick Rose":

[1] The grammarians' distinction between metaphor and simile is unnecessary in a psychological study and will not be retained in this book.

O Rose, thou art sick!
The invisible worm,
That flies in the night,
In the howling storm

Has found out thy bed
Of crimson joy;
And his dark secret love
Does thy life destroy.

Ostensibly the poem is about a beautiful flower which has been invaded and soon will be destroyed by an ugly worm. But there are many more levels of metaphorical meaning. What comes easily to mind is that the rose stands for a beautiful woman and that the worm stands for a fatal illness which soon will destroy a promising human being. In fact, the poet addresses the rose as a person. He says: "Thou art sick!" Such comparisons between flowers and women and worms and illnesses do not occur only in poetry, but also in dreams and in schizophrenic ideation.[2]

We have seen, especially in Chapter 16, that in psychopathologic conditions and in dreams common predicates lead to metamorphosis—to identifications of what seem to normal or waking people dissimilar subjects. In poetry there is no *metamorphosis*, but *metaphor*. The poet knows that the rose is not a woman, but he feels the woman is like a rose. In order to compare the sick flower to the sick woman, the poet has accessibility to the formation of a primary class. As described in Chapter 7, a primary class consists of equivalent or interchangeable members. Now, is a primary class involved in the making of a poetic metaphor? Yes and no.

The poet does not *actually* substitute the sick rose for the sick woman. The sick rose is not the sick woman; but in the sick rose he sees the sick woman. In schizophrenia the interchangeability or displacement is complete instead of partial: in one of the examples given in Chapter 16, the patient becomes the Virgin Mary. In neuroses the situational behavior of the patient is interchanged or displaced: in one of the ex-

[2] Names for women often denote flowers, of course.

With the image of the "invisible worm," Blake's creativity prophesies the bacteriological era in science which will discover "invisible" germs in sick animals and plants.

amples in Chapter 17, the patient responded to every red-haired woman as he would to his aunt.

In the schizophrenic the primary class of virgin women was an unconscious class. In neuroses the primary class is also unconscious (for instance, the patient does not know that he has formed a class of red-haired women to whom he will respond indiscriminately in a certain way). He knows, however, that his behavior is unwarranted, unwanted, and neurotic.

In poetry, the displacement—for instance, from the woman to the rose—is conscious. The poet wants to react to the sick woman as he would to a sick rose. Whereas in psychopathologic conditions and in dreams the displacement is from the real object to the symbolic, in poetry it is from the symbolic object (the rose) to the real (the woman).

The difference is deeper than that, however. As already mentioned, the rose does not *replace* the woman as the Virgin Mary replaces the patient, who is no longer the patient but who has undergone the delusional metamorphosis of becoming the Virgin Mary. In the poem we see the woman *in* the rose. The woman and the rose are fused together; but it is not that bizarre fusion found in schizophrenic drawings and delusions. The woman and the rose, although fused together, retain their individuality. The retention of their individuality permits a comparison, but does not lead to identification.[3] This is possible because by putting the sick rose and the sick woman together we become, at least partially, *conscious* of a *class:* the class of "beautiful life destroyed by illness." As a matter of fact, it is enough for the human cognitive faculties to be aware of only two members of a class to become aware of the whole class.

But is this class primary or secondary? Both, and in a certain way, neither. In the act of being created, the class is primary, since finding common predicates among different subjects and identifying by virtue of these common predicates is a primary-process mechanism. The primary process tends to remain primary: the rose and the woman tend to interchange or to remain together, but inasmuch as the concept of the class "beautiful life destroyed by illness" emerges,

[3] In Chapter 10's terms, the number is two, not one.

their fusion does not become complete. They remain distinct. However, the level of the secondary class is not fully reached in the poem, or it does not remain independent of the primary-class origin. The poet does not deal on a cognitive level with "beauty destroyed by illness." Only the student of literature may translate the poem into secondary-level content. The poem itself oscillates between a primary level and a secondary level which is inferred. Thus here is an important difference between art and psychopathology: *Whereas in the psychopathologic use of the primary process there is no consciousness of abstraction* (as a matter of fact, the power of abstraction is impaired, and the mind has to find concrete channels), *in art the use of the primary process does not eliminate the abstract. On the contrary, it is through the medium of the primary process that the abstract concept emerges.*[4]

A physician would not make a study of comparative pathology in a woman and in a rose in order to clarify the outcome of a fatal illness, or in order to lead to the formation of a new class. Why does a poet need the example of a rose invaded by a worm to tell us that fatal sickness in a beautiful woman is a horrible thing? Why does he need to resort to his unusual accessibility to primary classes?

The poet discovers that things abound with similarities. New similarities take on new meanings, because each recognized similarity is a concept and implies the formation of a new class. The formation of new classes or categories is one of the main ways of expanding knowledge, a method which the aesthetic fields have in common with science (Chapter 23).

Let us remember what happens in jokes: the joke is based on the eventual recognition that logic and paleologic (or faulty logic) are not identical, but only similar. The recognition of the logic-paleologic discordance leads to the comic reaction. In some puns and parables there is more agreement than disagreement between logic and paleologic. In poetry, however, paleologic and logic agree; paleologic actually reinforces logic.

---

[4] In some forms of art the abstract concept is not immediately available. We shall discuss this important topic later.

Indeed, art depends to a great extent on *paleologic rein-forcement*. At the same time that a work of art elicits the abstract concept, it sustains itself upon the paleologic reinforcement, or identification with a concrete example. There is almost a perfect welding of the abstract concept to the concrete example, of the replaced object to its metaphor. The concrete object of the metaphor is not only a symbol; it is a participant in producing the effect. In paleologic as used by the schizophrenic, the object which is replaced or symbolized fades away (at least from consciousness) or is replaced by its symbol. For instance, in the examples above, the aunt fades away and a red-haired woman emerges; the virgin patient disappears and is replaced by the Virgin Mary, etc. In dreams, too, what is symbolized is no longer present. For instance, in a dream a gorilla may stand for one's father. The image of the father is completely absent, and only psychoanalytic work can recapture it. In art the replaced object fades also, but not entirely. It fades away only in its concrete essence; its presence is felt in its absence. For instance, the woman is not mentioned in Blake's poem, but her presence is felt. She indeed exists in the artistic assumption. At the same time that she is eliminated by the art-work, she is there as a rose. Symbol and reality hold hands.

There are other factors to be considered in the study of the metaphor: (1) accessory techniques, (2) multiple meanings, and (3) the universality of metaphor in symbolism.[5]

In a brief poetic passage we may find only one metaphor; but in highly wrought artistic works more than one metaphor appears. In Blake's poem the rose stands for a beautiful woman who is sick, and we are, so to say, invited to pity her fate. This is actually a recurring theme in literature. In French literature there is the ailing woman named after the flowers she liked so much: *la dame aux camelias*. In Italian opera, Mimi of *La Bohème* is not a sick flower but a sick maker of artificial flowers. Her beauty is compared to the crimson beauty of dawn and of sunset. Something vaguely associated with this image is also found in Dante. In the first

---

[5] In this chapter metaphors are studied only as aesthetic forms. However, they can be analyzed in a much larger perspective (see Foss, 1949; Kaplan, 1960; Wheelwright, 1954, 1962).

of the dreams reported in his early book *La Vita Nuova,* he describes how Beatrice appeared to him in the arms of a male figure, Eros or Love. Beatrice is partially covered by a red cloth. The whole scene takes place in a cloud, red as fire. Dante knows that Beatrice is going to die because of something Love had made her eat.

In Blake's poem, many metaphorical meanings are suggested in addition to the woman and the rose. As in Dante's dream, the invader is a male (*his* dark secret love). The bed of crimson joy conveys the image of femininity and sexuality from the point of view of a male (crimson are the cheeks, lips, and perhaps the vagina of the woman). The rose becomes more female, the worm more male. Accessory predicates which lead to additional identifications increase the artistic value, just as they do in jokes.

But there is much more in the poem. The invisible worm that flies in the night, in the howling storm, which with his secret love invades the bed of crimson joy and destroys life, may suggest evil producing sexuality, a sadistic passion, a "dark" love; not something appropriate for crimson joy.

At this level of understanding the poem would represent a drama between two people, woman and man—the usual battle of the sexes. But the poem can be interpreted at a much more abstract level to represent beauty and evil, which must but cannot coexist in the same universe, since evil often ends by destroying beauty. The worm may represent the seed of spiritual decay. And yet the worm may even appear not so evil in its evil, because it is capable of loving and it is only its love which leads to destruction. Moreover, the worm too is prompt to leave "the howling storm," that is, the horrible and tempestuous world, but inasmuch as it too is part of that world, it will end by producing evil.

We could find other levels of meaning. The rose and the woman appear like sisters, in the sense in which Francis of Assisi saw brotherhood and sisterhood in the disparate existences of the universe. The new class or "family," to which the rose and the woman belong, reasserts the universal encounter with life, love, sorrow, decay, and death. We enter thus into an indefinite realm of symbolism, for the classes of symbolized objects accrue by a sequence of paleologic analogies which are like more and more windows, more and more doors, which open into unguessed aspects of reality, into unpredicted worlds. In the great work of art we can seek and find more and more analogic expansions. Thus, though the new object has been found, the longing and the search continue. The finiteness of the new object contrasts with the indeterminacy of the search. And yet the search itself becomes part of the newly created work, of the new unity, an aesthetic entity which in its totality appears for the first time in the universe. This is occasionally referred to as the unfinished statement of the work of art.

The person who appreciates the great work of art has the feeling that the work grows in him as he becomes involved in a prolonged capturing of emerging marginal meanings. Thus he feels that he too is creative, has to add to his experience and understanding.

The apparent and implied subject matter of great poems is vast and of universal relevance. At times the poetry of an author involves a whole aspect of human existence. For instance, Homer's works deal with the heroic aspect of man. Nevertheless, in poetry the content per se plays a relatively secondary role. To refer again to Blake's poem, we have seen that its theme is a recurrent one and so in itself cannot be responsible for the striking beauty of the poem. Some aestheticians have repeatedly emphasized this point. Ciardi, for instance, has titled a monograph on poetry "How Does a Poem Mean?" (1959). The how instead of the what reveals his basic idea. Ciardi wants to demonstrate that the aesthetic meaning is inherent in the way (or how) a poem is constructed, not in its content.

Again in regard to Blake's poem, we can say that all of us respond to phonetically beautiful words and to their rhythms; we pity beautiful women who become sick and die; we are all concerned with evil that destroys beauty; we are also receptive to the sensuous beauty of flowers and have some distaste for earthy worms. Everything was ready for the fitting together of all these elements. Blake did this by harmoniously blending primary and secondary processes, as in a symphony, never heard before, of unsuspected predicates. The synthesis Blake achieved can be easily communicated and shared. The originality of the new poetic object contrasts with the response to such an object, which is almost a general one.[6]

Can a poetic fusion of primary and secondary processes be compared to a discovery? In a certain way, yes; but only to a special type of discovery. An aesthetic discovery may not make us know things that we did not know before. However, it creates a new affective experience.

Schizophrenic language and dreams, too, have different meanings and different levels of cognition. However, in dreams and in psychopathological conditions these different meanings are discordant; furthermore, often they do not coexist but replace one another. That is, the dreamer and the talking schizophrenic are only aware of what they see in the dream or of what they say at a manifest level. They need the therapist to recapture all or many of the meanings. If there is a holistic quality, it is in the atmosphere of the dream or in a sort of primitive affective gestalt. Although the schizophrenic experience is also a new experience, it is actually a reduction to a concrete level—a restriction, not an enlargement; unless some new understanding or the recapturing of the abstract meaning is obtained through recovery or therapy.

At times the artist has almost as great a capacity for imagery as the dreamer does, or he has the schizophrenic's capacity for "orgies of identification" (Chapter 16). He is able, however, to use them in unpredictable syntheses which become works of art. For instance, Victor Hugo in his poems compares the stars in multiple, and, to the average person, inconceivable ways: to diamonds, other jewels, golden clouds, golden pebbles, lamps, lighted temples, flowers of eternal summer, silvery lilies, eyes of the night, vague eyes of the twilight, embers of the sky, holes in a huge ceiling, bees which fly in the sky, drops of Adam's blood, and even the colored spots on the tail of the peacock.[7]

---

[6] This section focuses on the use of the metaphor. The other aesthetic elements blended together in Blake's poem will be taken into consideration in subsequent sections.

[7] See also Huguet (1904) and Konrad (1958).

Concretization of the concept (or perceptualization)

Another important aspect of the aesthetic process is the concretization of the concept. We have already examined this process in detail in psychopathological conditions—schizophrenia especially, but also phobic and obsessive-compulsive psychoneuroses.

In dreams and in schizophrenia, when a concept cannot be sustained at an abstract level it undergoes a transformation. We have seen that in dreams and in psychoses the capacity for abstraction is not completely lost; otherwise there would be no abstract content to be transformed into a concrete representation. The abstract ideation, however, cannot be sustained at an abstract level. In dreams, thoughts are transformed into visual images. In schizophrenia, high mental processes are transformed into specific thoughts which have a concrete content or into forms equivalent to perceptions—for instance, hallucinations (Chapter 16).

The concretization of the concept at times acquires the form of a metaphor. For example, if a patient believes that his wife poisons his food when actually he feels she "poisons" his life, this phenomenon may be considered a metaphor. Actually, there is no displacement here from one concrete object to another (as in the case of the aunt and the red-haired woman, or of the woman and the rose, as in Blake's poem). What is concretized here is an attitude or an aspect of behavior (the attitude which the patient feels that his wife has toward his life).

As in this example, in the aesthetic process too we shall speak of concretization or of perceptualization when something which is difficult to objectify in definite terms is transformed into concrete, tangible symbols. What is transformed is generally a subjective state, a life attitude, general or specific behavior, a mood, or so on. In the aesthetic tertiary process the concrete representation not only is not incongruous with the original abstract concept but actually reinforces it.

Our terms *concretization* and *perceptualization* correspond to the terms *image* or *imagery* used in aesthetics. With these words some aestheticians refer to something which has a wider range than the metaphor. At times the expression *metaphorical language* is used. However, in a psychological study it is preferable to maintain the distinction between metaphor and the more general phenomenon of concretization.

At times it is indeed difficult to distinguish a metaphor from a more general concretization. Metaphors are, of course, concretizations too, but very limited ones: they may still be interpreted as displacements or interchanges between members of a primary class. In many cases simple metaphors and larger areas of concretization are associated. For instance, as long as Blake compared the sick woman to a sick rose, we can speak only of metaphor, but when the woman came to represent beauty and the worm to symbolize evil, we can speak also of concretization.

Poets quite often express themselves through concretization. A typical example is the Italian poet Pascoli, who unfortunately is not well known in English-speaking countries. In some of his poems he ostensibly describes natural phenomena or countrysides, in some ways as Frost later did; but these descriptions must be interpreted as concretizations of high concepts through imagery. In one of his most celebrated poems, a *fallen oak* concretizes people who are ignored or hated as long as they are alive, then are recognized in their full value and even sanctified after their death. In the poem "In the Fog," we are confronted with an allegory about the fogginess of life, at the same time that the description of the country under the fog stands on its own merits as a realistically vivid representation. The following poem is titled "My Evening" ("*La Mia Sera*"):

Il giorno fu pieno di lampi;
Ma ora verranno le stelle,
Le tacite stelle. Nei campi
C'è un breve gre gre di ranelle.
Le tremule foglie dei pioppi
Trascorre una gioia leggiera.
Nel giorno, che lampi! che scoppi!
  Che pace, la sera!

The day was full of lightning, but
now the stars, the silent stars, will
appear . . . while in the fields little
frogs say "gre gre." Joy moves the
wavering leaves of the poplars. What
lightning! What thunder in the day!
What peace in the evening!

Si devono aprire le stelle
nel cielo si tenero e vivo.
Là, presso le allegre ranelle,
singhiozza monotono un rivo.
Di tutto quel cupo tumulto,
di tutta quell'aspra bufera,
non resta che un dolce singulto
  Nell'umida sera.

    The stars must open up now in so alive
       and tender a sky.
    There, close to the merry frogs, a brook
       sobs monotonously.
    Of all that dark tumult, of all that
       bitter storm
    Only that sweet sobbing remains in the
       humid evening.

E quella infinita tempesta,
finita in un rivo canoro.
Dei fulmini fragili restano
  cirri di porpora e d'oro.
O stanco dolore, riposa!
La nube del giorno più nera
fu quella che vedo più rosa
  nell'ultima sera.

    That infinite storm ended in the sing-
       ing brook.
    The fragile lightnings became golden
       and purple clouds.
    O tired sorrow, do rest! The darkest
       cloud in the day
    Is the one which seems to me the pinkest
       in the evening.

Che voli di rondini intorno!
che gridi nell'aria serena!
La fame del povero giorno
prolunga la garrula cena.
La parte, sì piccola, i nidi
nel giorno non l'ebbero intera.
Nè io . . . e che voli, che gridi,
 mia limpida sera!

> Now the swallows fly all around; what
> shouts in the serene air!
> The hunger of the poor day prolongs the
> garrulous supper.
> During the day the nests did not have a
> small portion of food.
> Nor did I; and what flights, what shouts
> in the limpid evening!

Don . . . Don . . . E mi dicono, Dormi!
mi cantano, Dormi! sussurrano,
Dormi! bisbigliano, Dormi!
là voci, di tenebra azzurra . . .
Mi sembrano canti di culla,
che fanno ch'io torni com'era . . .
sentivo mia madre . . . poi nulla . . .
 sul far della sera.

> *Don . . . don . . .* The bells say, Sleep! They
> sing: sleep; they whisper: sleep.
> They softly repeat: sleep, over there . . .
> voices from the blue darkness.
> They seem songs of the cradle, which
> makes me be as I was . . .
> I felt my mother . . . then nothing, while
> evening was coming.

This poem cannot be interpreted, of course, merely as a description of a stormy day followed in the evening by a change in the weather. There is also an allegorical meaning. The tempest which seemed endless (infinite) has ended in a melodious singing brook, as the sorrow of the poet has ended in a poem. At the end of the day (life), the darkest cloud is the pinkest. The peace of old age is compared to the peace of a beautiful sunset after a stormy day. Now the bells of the nearby church suggest to the poet that he fall asleep: that is, that he accept death. The night will be beautiful after this reconciliation with the day; death will be agreeable if the poet has accepted life for what it is. The bells sound like a lullaby, and the image of the lullaby evokes the image of the poet's mother. It is this image of love which now makes him fully accept his past life and approaching death, as in his childhood it made him accept falling asleep.

At times an inability to concretize the content fully and a retention of conceptual expressions decrease the poem's aesthetic value. Consider the following poem by Shelley, called "Love's Philosophy."

> *The fountains mingle with the river*
> *And the rivers with the ocean;*
> *The winds of heaven mix forever*
> *With a sweet emotion;*
> *Nothing in the world is single;*
> *All things by a law divine*
> *In one spirit meet and mingle.*
> *Why not I with thine?*
>
> *See the mountains kiss high heaven,*
> *And the waves clasp one another;*
> *No sister-flower would be forgiven*
> *If it disdained its brother;*
> *And the sunlight clasps the earth,*
> *And the moonbeams kiss the sea;*
> *What are all these kissings worth*
> *If thou kiss not me?*

This is a beautiful poem; however, it does not reach the level of the sublime, mainly because it is spoiled by lines 5-7. In these lines the poet attempts to give us a conceptual, not perceptualized, "philosophy" of love. His concept of love is represented better by the imagery of the rest of the poem.

Concretization of the concept through imagery is found not only in poetry, but in many other forms of art. It is frequently used in parables and in religious writings in general. We have already examined the parable of Jesus and the coin in Chapter 20. Here is a poetic gem from the Talmud: "Don't make a woman cry, for God counts her tears." The meaning is obviously that God will consider individually each one of the woman's sorrows and will not forget who is responsible for them; but the imagery of God actually counting the tears, as if they were pearls, adds strength and beauty to the expression. Proverbs often utilize the same technique. When we say, "Don't cry over spilt milk," the image of the spilt milk is employed as a symbol of something we cannot undo.

Parables and proverbs differ from poetry, however, in forms and aims. Their main purpose is to give a precept of good behavior or wisdom, whereas poetry aims to create an aesthetic experience. Although parables and proverbs concretize concepts, they do not use a metric medium, which, as discussed later in this chapter, is necessary in most poetry.

Concretization of the concept is strikingly evident in the theater. Classical tragedies, for example, reproduce some human situations (like passion, ignorance, immutable destiny, conflict between moral law and the law of the land, etc.) which bring the leading character to catastrophe. In this way the playwright "concretizes" a predicament of larger significance, at times a tragic premise about man's existence. The denouement of the play often represents the unfolding of an inevitable situation. Concepts are not expressed in philosophical, discursive ways, but concretized in action. The actions speak for themselves; the characters stand for categories of men. What happens to Macbeth, for instance, represents the final crumbling of the human being when he accepts evil. Evil leads not only to external catastrophe but also to the disintegration of the human being as a moral entity.

The concretization obtained in the theater is more realistic than in other forms of art. Living human beings, who are seen three-dimensionally and move as they do in life, stand for characters, and for the categories which the characters represent. The drama, however, is not a documentary. It represents only certain scenes which imply many others that are not seen. Accidents, irrelevancies, or any scenes which are not larger in significance than what they actually reproduce, are stripped away.

Often not only the whole denouement of a play can be seen as a great concretization, but specific scenes can be in-

terpreted as specific concretizations and paleologic rein-
forcements. For instance, *Oedipus Rex* can be said to portray
the relation between good and evil, or between truth and illusion (or knowledge and ignorance). Oedipus commits evil
because he *does not know:* he does not know that he is the
killer of his father and the husband of his own mother. The
whole drama is a denouement which leads to the discovery
of the truth. When he knows the truth, Oedipus feels he has
to pay the penalty for his horrendous actions; he gives up the
throne and blinds himself.

Freud found in this tragedy the inspiration for his concept
of the Oedipus complex, but it seems to me that the play portrays the limitation of human consciousness rather than an
incestuous desire for a mother. Oedipus' "crime" was actually
that of not knowing, or not "seeing." He had not been perceptive enough to the many clues, some subliminal, which were in
his surroundings. He certainly would not have done what he
did, had he known; but the idea of using his ignorance as an
alibi did not even occur to him. The limitation of his consciousness did not limit the severity of his conscience. Could
it be that Freud, in addition to the idea of the Oedipus complex, found in this tragedy the inspiration for his concept of
the unconscious?

Oedipus' self-inflicted punishment is also a concretization,
which becomes symbolic: he blinds himself. Since he would
not "see" in a more abstract way he feels he does not deserve
to see. This theme of not seeing is a recurring one in the play.
The only person who *saw* and *knew* was the *blind* prophet
Tiresias.

Specific concretizations also occur in *Macbeth*. The three
witches appearing at the beginning of the play are concretizations of Macbeth's emerging ambitions after his victory.
Lady Macbeth is the fourth "witch" in the play, a function
reinforced by her concrete role as Macbeth's wife.

Another reinforcing concretization of great power occurs
toward the end of the play. The witches had predicted that
Macbeth would fall only when Birnam wood itself marched
against him. Macbeth interpreted this statement as an assur-
ance that he would never fall, because woods do not move.
But in one of the last scenes it was reported to Macbeth that
the wood was indeed moving toward him. The enemy on the

march was carrying bushes as screens, thus giving the impression from a distance that the wood was moving. At one level this scene may be interpreted as a comic device of the witches and of Shakespeare, a trick to deceive the poor Macbeth (an acted-out witticism, like those described in Chapter 20). But of course the scene has a far deeper meaning. The crimes of Macbeth are so horrendous as to make even the immovable woods move in horror. The immensity of the crimes is equaled by the stupendousness of the phenomenon.

"As if" and adualism

The incident of the moving woods in *Macbeth* leads us to the study of more complicated forms of concretization, such as the phenomena of "as if" and adualism. In one of the most beautiful cantos of the *Inferno* (Canto xxxiii), for example, Dante describes his encounter with Ugolino, a count who had betrayed his fatherland, the city-state of Pisa, which was consequently defeated in war. Count Ugolino describes how the Pisans punished him for his crime: they jailed him and all his family in a tower prison and kept them there without food, until all of them died of starvation. The count describes to Dante the heart-breaking agony of his whole family. His children died one by one. He was the last to die.

After hearing Ugolino's account, Dante hurls one of his strongest invectives against the city of Pisa, for he was horrified that the city had not limited its punishment to the traitor, Ugolino, but had included his innocent children. Dante says:

Ah, Pisa, vituperio delle genti
del bel paese là dove il sì suona,
poichè i vicini a te punir son lenti

> Ah, Pisa! Shame to the people of that fair [Tuscan] land where "sì" [8] resounds, since thy neighbors are slow to punish thee,

[8] *Sì* is a symbol for the Tuscan [Italian] language, like *oui*, *oc*, and *oï'l* for other romance languages.

Movasi la Capraia e la Gorgona,
e faccian siepe ad Arno in su la foce,
si ch'egli anneghi in te ogni persona.

> The islands of Capraia and Gorgona must move and
> hedge up the Arno River at its mouth, so that every
> living soul be drowned in thee.

Chè se il conte Ugolino aveva voce
d'aver tradita te delle castella,
non dovei tu i figliuoi porre a tal croce:

> For, if Count Ugolino had the fame of having betrayed
> thee of thy castles, thou oughtest not to have put his
> sons into such torture:

innocenti facea l'età novella.

> Their youthful age made them innocent.

No translation can reproduce the terse style of Dante, the
beauty of his images, and the intensity of his emotions.
Capraia and Gorgona are two small islands in the Tyrrhenian
Sea, not too far from the mouth of the Arno River, beside
which the city of Pisa lies. Dante is perturbed by the terrible
crime that had been committed in Pisa and expresses the
wish that these two islands would move and close the mouth
of the Arno, so that every person in the city would drown.

During my adolescent years, I admired the beauty of this
passage, but I was also somewhat irritated by it. Born and
raised myself in Pisa, I resented Dante's zest for having the
whole town perish—for inflicting a punishment like that of
Sodom and Gomorrah on the city which was to become the
birthplace of Galileo. In fact, I used to go to great lengths to
demonstrate that Dante's invective here is an example of poetic incongruity and self-contradiction. He is horrified by the
murder of Ugolino's innocent children; yet he seems to propose a similar crime on a scale many times greater.

What the literalness and crusading zeal of adolescence
prevented me from seeing was that Dante in this passage did
not want to give us a piece of juridical wisdom. He knew that
no matter how intensely he wished that the islands of Capraia
and Gorgona would move, they would stay where they were.

Dante was not a Greek god, endowed with cosmic power, and he was aware of it. Had he really possessed the power to move them (the kind of power actually held by some people today, who can push a button and determine a cataclysm), he would not have contemplated using it.

What Dante did was only to resort to an artistic technique: the "as if" phenomenon. This is *artistic potentiality*, which becomes *artistic reality*. Nobody could make the islands move, but in the poetry we see them move and cause the drowning of thousands of people in an apocalyptic deluge. Dante did not want to destroy a city and its inhabitants, but to transform his intense rage into a titanic *image*. He succeeded in concretizing his feeling in an image fit for a supernatural power: that is, he was able to transform an impossibility into an image which is actual and has a real artistic effect.

The operation of adualism in schizophrenia and in dreams was discussed in Chapter 16. This mechanism causes an inability to distinguish between acts of consciousness and objects; that is, between the world of the mind and the external world. In art there is a special type of adualism. Obviously the creative person knows that what he creates is fiction. However, what is being created comes to exist in its own right—that is, as something having artistic value and effect. Thus at the same time that an artistic work is fiction, it is also reality: artistic reality. The "as if," which logically involves a possibility, becomes an artistic actuality as an expression. When Shakespeare, by resorting to a trick, makes Birnam wood move in *Macbeth*, he creates an "as if" phenomenon. The woods did not really move spontaneously, but the effect is as if they had really moved. The spectator understands that Macbeth is doomed. Here the theatrical medium permits an acted-out "as if" phenomenon.

As described in Chapter 16, the dreamer or the schizophrenic may think, "If this would happen . . . if I were king. . . ." and immediately this emerging possibility becomes transformed into a dream or a delusion in which he is a king. In a similar way a poet may think, "If islands were to move. . . ." and in the mind of the poet and of his readers, the islands move.

This phenomenon is found not only in literature, but in

other arts as well. For instance, in painting and sculpture, movement may appear as an artistically actualized potentiality. The artist is not dreaming or delusional; he knows that there is a difference and therefore dualism between art and reality, but his *artistic work*, by being both fictitious and real, becomes adualistic. Its life is a life *sui generis*, as is best exemplified in the theater. The work of art belongs to a *second reality*, which maintains a certain distance from the first reality. It differs from the delusional "reality" of the psychotic, which is fused with and therefore belongs to the first reality. During the creative act the artist sees his work as independent of him and as already having a life of its own. A playwright often feels that the characters of his play are directing him in constructing it. Jung wrote (1933) that it was not Goethe who created Faust, but Faust who created Goethe.

Positive aspect of negation

Another characteristic that primitive cognition and poetry have in common is the positive aspect of negation. Chapters 7 and 17 have already discussed this phenomenon together with the fact that Freud has described it in dreams. Susanne Langer (1953) has also described it in relation to poetry, although, if I understand her correctly, she does not connect it with primitive cognition. She quotes the last stanza of Swinburne's "The Garden of Proserpine," in which almost every line is a denial.

> *Then star nor sun shall waken,*
> *Nor any change of light;*
> *Nor sound of waters shaken,*
> *Nor any sound or sight:*
> *Nor wintry leaves nor vernal;*
> *Not days nor things diurnal;*
> *Only the sleep eternal*
> *In an eternal night.*

Langer correctly states that in a literal sense the poem is a constant rejection of the emerging ideas. But what is denied acquires artistic reality: the imagery of the sun, stars, light, waters, leaves, etc., is present.

Emphasis on verbalization

Chapter 16 provided a detailed discussion of the second principle of paleologic, or the altered balance between connotation, verbalization, and denotation. There we saw how schizophrenic thinking entails a reduction of connotation power and an emphasis on verbalization. Chapter 20 showed that the same phenomenon occurs in witticisms.

In the literary arts, especially poetry, the emphasis is also on verbalization: words acquire importance as phonetic entities or sounds. As Chapter 16 demonstrated, emphasis on verbalization rather than connotation can definitely be a regressive phenomenon. However, contrary to what happens in schizophrenia, in poetry there is no reduction in connotation. Instead of decreasing the connotation power, the emphasized verbalization increases or accentuates some aspects of it. This is another phenomenon of creativity which belongs to the tertiary, not the primary, process.

In some other fields of art, such as painting and sculpture, verbalization does not exist, and it is the denotation which acquires emphasis and significance: in other words, it is the work of art itself in its physical entity, connected, of course, with its connotative value. In poetry, denotation is not absent but assumes an unusual form. The word acquires special denotative qualities, so that in a certain way it becomes the thing that it symbolizes. The word is not just a symbol of the object; it is used to *embody* the thing which is symbolized. It becomes an actual portrait or image of the thing that it represents—a verbal icon, as it has been called by Wimsatt (1954). With the emphasis on denotation, language becomes a more vivid mirror of reality, not because it gives a sequence of meanings, but because it reproduces or elicits a series of images of aspects of reality. However, here too the phenomenon is not the primitive or regressive mechanism described in Chapters 7 and 16, but rather belongs to the tertiary process. In fact, the connotation is reinforced, not eliminated, by this special type of denotation.

The topic of verbalization in poetry has been the subject of much study and research by literary men of every age. This discussion will not necessarily deal with what is important from a literary point of view, but will stress the aspects which are relevant to our psychological study.

In ordinary language, words are predominantly carriers of meanings to be communicated to others. In poetry, words have additional qualities. We have already seen that they often stand for the things they symbolize and that they acquire the value of images. In addition, the phonetic qualities of the word are exploited to accentuate or modify the meaning, in order to make the thing which is symbolized even better embodied by the word. The word becomes a "prism" to be admired in its different facets. Following is a list of phonetic characteristics which are exploited in poetry.

1. *Onomatopoeia.* There are a certain number of words in every language whose sound suggests their meaning. In English, words like *hiss, bang, crackle, whisper* are onomatopoeic.

2. *Quantitative aspect of the syllable.* Although this characteristic was particularly emphasized in Latin and ancient Greek poetry, it has been fairly important in modern languages too. Some words convey a quick, others a slow tempo.

3. *Euphony or cacophony.* A word which has an agreeable (euphonious) sound reinforces an agreeable meaning. A disagreeable (cacophonous) sound reinforces a disagreeable content.

In sequences of words, we may have these additional characteristics:

4. *Versification.* The words are distributed in such a way as to produce a rhythm, or verbal music. They constitute a combination of sounds which is cyclical and agreeable to the ear.

5. *Rhyme.* A correspondence of the terminal sounds, rhyme is agreeable to the ear. The rhyme may be perfect or imperfect. Assonance, consonance, and alliteration are forms of partial rhyme.

6. *Archaic, obsolete, or childlike forms.* One example would be the use of the archaic "thou" and "thy" in Blake's poem "The Sick Rose." This characteristic will be discussed in Chapter 22 in reference to religious experiences.

7. *Repetition.* The repetition of the same word or combination of words is important in poetry. This device may have some distant relation to the verbal stereotypes of the schizophrenic and the perseveration of the aphasic. In a poem it provides a pleasant sound— a special type of rhyme and rhythm, we might say. If it consists of a phrase or a verse, it constitutes the refrain. Repetition may also stress the content of the words by distributing or accentuating the burden of the meaning, or by adding a special meaning. At times it leads to innumerable paths of association.

Consider Robert Frost's "Stopping by Woods on a Snowy Evening": [9]

Whose woods these are I think I know
His house is in the village though;
He will not see me stopping here
To watch his woods fill up with snow.

My little horse must think it queer
To stop without a farmhouse near
Between the wood and frozen lake
The darkest evening of the year.

He gives his harness bells a shake
To ask if there is some mistake.
The only other sound's the sweep
Of easy wind and downy flake.

The woods are lovely, dark and deep.
But I have promises to keep,
And miles to go before I sleep,
And miles to go before I sleep.

[9] From *Complete Poems of Robert Frost.* Copyright 1923 by Holt, Rinehart and Winston, Inc. Copyright 1951 by Robert Frost. Reprinted by permission of Holt, Rinehart and Winston, Inc.

This poem embodies an intensely lived drama. At first the conflict is between three categories of people: one represented by Frost himself, the unpractical poet who wants to absorb the beauty and mystery of nature, no matter how inconvenient it is to do so; the second represented by the owner of the land, who seems interested only in owning and not admiring his property; the third represented by the little horse, a realistic-unpoetic organism. The conflict then acquires momentum within Frost himself: it becomes intrapsychic. The poet soon will have to follow the suggestion of the horse. He cannot indulge in poetic contemplation; he has "promises to keep," he must face the obligations of life and the miles to go before he sleeps (perhaps a long and hurried life before he can rest with nature).

The repetition of the last line, in my opinion, concretizes or embodies a multiplicity of meanings. It portrays a sense of distance: miles and miles to go. It stresses the necessity of interrupting the poetic interlude and proceeding, with a sense of urgency. At the same time there is an almost opposite meaning: in the repetition lies a vague association with the anticipated sleep. Often verbal repetition evokes the thought of lullabies and of the act of falling asleep.

8. *Homonyms and similarities of verbalization.* These are used as springboards to unusual thought processes. We have seen in Chapters 16 and 20 how often the homonymy of words is employed in schizophrenic thinking and in witticisms to bring about paleologic identifications. We have also seen that in schizophrenic thinking, similarities of words frequently lead to unusual mental processes.

The same mechanism is found in literature, especially in poetry. We shall start with a classic example from Shakespeare. His Othello is a Negro, although in the original Italian story by Giovanni Battista Giraldi Cintio, from which Shakespeare took the plot, Othello was a white man—a Venetian patrician who served as a lieutenant in Cyprus in the year 1508. Giraldi's story gives no names, but historical documents indicate that the episodes he reported really took place and that the family name of this lieutenant was Moro. Moro in Italian means Negro or Moor; in the case of this lieutenant, however, Moro was his last name and had no connection with his race or color. It could be that Shakespeare mistook a family name for a name referring to color. But I am more inclined to believe that the coincidence stimulated his mental associations. Shakespeare may have had the inspiration that if Othello were really a Moor or Negro, the story would be given an uncommon artistic twist, and the contrast with the fair, "divine" Desdemona would be accentuated. Thus a real pun was made from the name *Moro*.

Similar puns, quasi puns, and strange plays on words are common in literature, especially in poetry. A typical one is from Petrarch, who plays on the word *Laura* (see Chapter 19 for a description of his relationship with this woman).

> *L'aura che 'l verde lauro e l'aureo crine*
> *soavemente sospirando move. . . .*

Here the name Laura is felt and heard in three different words (*l'aura*, the zephyr; *lauro*, the laurel; *l'aureo crine*, the golden hair).

Dante too utilizes plays on words, which at first impression are reminiscent of schizophrenic cognition. In *La Vita Nuova*, a book consisting of poems and poetic prose, he wrote that he saw Beatrice walking on the street *preceded* by her girl friend Giovanna, who was once the beloved of Dante's friend and fellow poet Cavalcanti. Dante wrote that Giovanna was often called *Primavera* (which in Italian means spring) because of her beauty. Dante then makes a peculiar play on words. *Primavera* signifies for him *prima verrà*, which in Italian means "She will come first, before." (That is, before or preceding Beatrice, while walking.) But his second pun is even more revealing. Dante stresses the fact that the real name of Beatrice's friend is Giovanna (the feminine of Giovanni, or John). Dante then compares her to John the Baptist, who *came before* or preceded the coming of Jesus. The underlying unconscious motivation, appearing a few times in Dante's works, resides in the wish to identify Beatrice, whom he also calls daughter of God, with Jesus Christ.

In conclusion, the phonetic characteristics which are common in schizophrenic language are also exploited by poets for artistic effect. Whereas in schizophrenic language these mechanisms contrast with the common meanings of the words and confer bizarreness, in poetry they add charm and significance and agree with the meaning, which is carried by secondary-process mechanisms. In art, these phonetic mechanisms do not represent a regression to the primary process, but the emergence of the tertiary process. To paraphrase Hughlings Jackson once again, the several meanings are stereoscopic, not dyplopic. The poetic work may show many and unexpected dimensions—some belonging to the primary and some to the secondary process; but they are concordant, not discordant, and the whole attains new and unexpected results.

Aesthetic pleasure

In examining the nature of the aesthetic pleasure elicited by the appreciation of a work of art, I shall omit some issues which are predominantly philosophical: for instance, the question whether the aesthetic value is identifiable or commensurate with the aesthetic pleasure. In the case of wit and the comic, it is relatively easy to determine the nature of the comical or witty experience. Our organism is equipped to respond to wit with laughter, smiles, or an easily expressed feeling of merriment. It is much more difficult to analyze the nature of aesthetic pleasure. Some authors define it as a pleasant emotion or state of satisfaction which occurs when one contemplates a work of art. This statement is vague and circular. Other formulations are equally tautological. For instance, if we say, "We enjoy this work of art because it is beautiful," we add nothing to our understanding, since the word *beautiful* in this context means "having the property of eliciting aesthetic pleasure." Some authors find the essence of aesthetic pleasure in the experiencing of the perceptual aspects of a work of art; others in the emotional component. In what follows we shall examine these two possibilities.

Actually the word *aesthetics*, which was coined by Baumgarten about the year 1750 from the Greek word *aestheticos*, means perceptive and sensuous. Indeed, there is an attempt

In the work of art to reduce everything to sensuous or perceptual impressions. This is obviously so in painting, sculpture, and music, where, as already mentioned, denotation acquires predominance. In poetry the attempt to perceptualize (that is, the attempt to reduce the object of contemplation to a perceptual level) is made at least in two ways: (1) by placing the emphasis on the verbalization, so that actually the phonetic aspects of the word (sound, onomatopoeia, rhyme, rhythm, assonance, etc.) acquire prominence; (2) by transforming concepts into imagery. The images cannot be reproduced as in dreams, paintings, or movies, but are represented by words and metaphors. Words become icons or images by proxy.

We must at first recognize that not all types of perceptions are apt to produce an aesthetic effect. A selection is necessary. For instance, perceptions involving taste and smell may be pleasant, but they are not conducive to aesthetic pleasure, presumably because they are not associated with abstract conceptions and cannot assume a significance which transcends the perceptual, except through other senses. In the human cerebral cortex, olfactory and gustatory stimuli receive relatively little elaboration.

It is particularly visual and auditory perceptions which have importance in aesthetics. Such perceptions, of course, can be easily divided into pleasant and unpleasant (see Chapter 2). Not all noises can become music. A chord pleases the ear only when the frequencies of its component sounds are in a simple mathematical ratio to one another. We also know that colors of certain wavelengths are more pleasing to the eye. We do not know yet why certain physical characteristics of a stimulus produce pleasure or displeasure in the human organism, but we know that they have that effect.

At times a perceptual stimulus is not pleasant per se, but its repetition or combination with others is. The repetition or the regular distribution of the same stimulus, as in architecture, poetry, dance, and music, produces a pleasant perceptual effect. Consider also the kaleidoscope—an instrument, often used by children as a toy, which contains loose bits of colored glass. These bits are reflected by mirrors many times, and even the most inartistic combination of bits of glass produces a beautiful symmetric design when it is repeated again and again.

Another sensoperceptual quality which is frequently utilized to create an aesthetic effect is art's capacity to stimulate the sexual instinct. This is particularly true in painting and sculpture; for instance, when nudes are portrayed. An artistic representation of the nude obviously transcends sexual stimulation and is not pornographic. The sexual element nevertheless plays a prominent role; the nude attracts and gratifies our sexual instinct. Other types of art resort to less obvious but equally effective sexual stimulation: for instance, literature with erotic content.

We may conclude that art requires a pleasant sensoperceptual background, generally of a visual, auditory, or sexual nature.[10] These sense perceptions are like the bricks on which the aesthetic edifice is built.

Contrary to the perceptualization that occurs in psychopathological processes, a special selection is made in art: only physiologically pleasant perceptual stimuli or spatiotemporal combinations of stimuli, directly or by proxy, are allowed to enter into the aesthetic work. Does this mean that the work of art consists only of these pleasant sensoperceptual elements? Fechner (1876) attributed the whole of aesthetic pleasure to them. With his experimental or "scientific" method, he tried to track down the elements and the "supreme formal principles" on which aesthetic pleasure is based. For a while his experiments reached a worldwide audience, but their limitations were afterward recognized. Obviously something very important was missing in his formulations. The sublime cannot be reduced to these elementary facts.

Yet it is true that perceptual elements are particularly accentuated in art. Their selection and combination often increase their perceptual quality. For instance, in reading or listening to poetry one becomes more than usually aware of

10 Some apparent exceptions, like cacophonic music, arhythmic poetry, etc., do not concern us here. These forms have departed from the original pleasant perceptual elements by complicated processes of aesthetic proxy, or for the purposes of creating a contrast.

the auditory aspect of words. In looking at paintings one becomes more aware of forms and colors, etc. It seems that in order to carry the aesthetic message, the stimulus often has to accentuate its perceptual quality, or to actualize its perceptual potentiality.

As mentioned in Chapter 2, sensations lose some of their perceptual vividness when they assume a cognitive meaning. The child, in his eidetic possibilities, primitive people, and some unusual persons who are said to be in touch with themselves, have a greater ability than the majority of people to experience the perceptual nature of things. Apparently this is a faculty that the majority of modern men have lost. Giambattista Vico was one of the first to describe this sensuous or perceptual way of experiencing which is retained by primitive people and children (1744).

Existentialists and Zen Buddhists point out how Western man, by indulging in the cognitive aspect of life, has lost touch with himself and with the intimate nature and perceptual richness of things. These philosophical schools are unfair not only to Western man but to Homo sapiens in general. As we have seen in Part I, man had no choice but to follow the expansion of his symbolic functions. Although it led him to intellectual mastery of the world, this expansion occurred to a certain extent at the expense of the "experiences of inner states" and of immediate subjectivity. It is one of the aims of art to recapture the perceptual richness which has been lost. Art can do so, but to think that perceptual richness can be reintroduced into everyday life, as the Existentialists and Zen Buddhists assume, is utopic, to say the least.

As a matter of fact, perceptual vividness is recaptured in some pathologic conditions. A few people who have undergone cerebral concussion experience vivid perceptual experiences for several minutes after they reacquire consciousness. Objects appear vague and indistinct, and yet more beautiful and "more real" than reality. At the onset of some acute schizophrenic episodes, there is also an accentuation of the perceptual characteristics of objects—everything seems to the patient to be in technicolor (Chapter 16). Such increases in perceptual qualities occur because the higher levels of cognition are impaired and decrease their inhibitory influences. However, these perceptual alterations undergo secondary or restitutional elaborations. In very primitive people and in children, the perceptual qualities of things have not yet been muffled by the enormous expansion of cognitive processes.

In my opinion it is impossible to attribute aesthetic pleasure exclusively or predominantly to mere perceptual experience or accentuation. The admirer of a work of art is not an empiricist who approaches the world by way of sensory perceptions. Perceptual enrichment is related more to decoration than to real art. Aesthetic pleasure is indeed much more than perceptual enjoyment; it occurs when the enriched perceptions are pregnant with abstract and categorical concepts. In fact, a great part of the aesthetic meaning involves the attuning of the abstract to the perceptual.

As already discussed in the section on the metaphor, the perceptual level to which we, so to say, return in art, reinforces the work of art's abstract level, just as in puns the paleologic level reinforces the logical. Art does not rely on mere perception. To be specific, we have seen how the use of metaphor, the concretization of content, the emphasis on denotation and especially on verbalization, the use of the positive aspect of negation, etc., are all archaic methods employed in the aesthetic process. Contrary to what happens in psychopathological conditions, dreams, and witticisms, there is concordance, not discordance, between these different mechanisms. Each borrows something from the others, so that the content seems to possess the beauty of the medium, and the medium the beauty of the content. In our first example, Blake's poem "The Sick Rose," the abstract concept of beauty versus evil borrows significance from the concept of the beautiful woman and a man who destroys her; the concept of the woman and of the man borrows perceptual vividness from the images of the rose and the worm; the images of the rose and the worm borrow sensuous beauty from the rhythm, rhyme, and pleasing combinations of sounds.

So far we have shown how each level borrows from a lower one. Now let us adopt a reverse process and see how each level borrows from a higher one. The medium consisting of "oral noises" is enriched by rhythm and rhyme. This phonetic pleasure is transcended because the oral sounds have not only a meaning, but a special meaning: the rose in the crimson bed. The beauty of the words fuses with the beauty of the imagery; then the image of the rose acquires further power from the fact that it may refer to a woman; but the concept of the woman acquires strength from the fact that it stands for beauty in general, or for the unfulfilled promise of a beautiful life. Similar remarks could be made about the image of the worm, who is invisible at first (in contrast to the rose's abundant crimson joy), but victorious in the end. Thus the simple words of the poem, reinforced by their sound, rhythm, and rhyme, come to carry an expanding load of meaning.

In contrast to the writers who have said that the basis of aesthetic pleasure lies in the perceptual aspects of a work of art, some important authors, such as the Russian novelist Tolstoy (1898) and the aesthetician Ducasse (1929), have propounded an emotional theory of art. According to them, the essence of art is the expression or sharing of emotion.

The relation between art and emotion was studied long ago by Aristotle, who developed the concept of catharsis (from which Freud derived his psychoanalytic theory of catharsis). Aristotle felt that during an aesthetic experience, such as seeing the theatrical performance of a tragedy, painful emotions are first aroused and then "purged" or eliminated. Turbulent emotions are transformed into serene or calm ones. Aristotle thus saw catharsis almost as a medical procedure, that of taking a purgative medicament. He failed to explain why catharsis is enjoyable. In fact, purging is useful but almost never enjoyable.

An aesthetic experience is certainly an emotional experience, but not just any emotional experience. Some emotional experiences can be very anti-aesthetic. Even psychoanalytic catharsis, which purges and may cure in a medical sense, is not an aesthetic experience.

Perhaps we can understand the problem better if we compare the ways in which emotional and cognitive elements enter into the work of art. We have seen that the cognitive content consists not only of secondary-process mechanisms, but also of lower-level mechanisms, often belonging to the primary process. Can we make the same statement for the emotions appearing in a work of art? Not at all. These emotions are not primitive experiences of inner states, not even protoemotions or naked first-order emotions; often they are on man's highest emotional level.

Strivings toward fulfillment of love, of a mission, of an ideal, or of an ethical demand—or conflicts between the aspirations and the limited power of man, between the dictates of society and those of the inner self, or between the tendency toward symbolic infinity and the finitude of man—these are the emotions which often enter into a work of art. Even if primitive emotions occur in art, like the passion which leads to sexual assault or the greediness which leads to murder, they stand for the states of imperfection of the human existence. In ordinary life, high emotions are frequently elicited by conceptual constructs, general statements, universal maxims, etc. In the work of art, they retain the majesty of universally shared emotions and concepts but acquire the vividness of a specific, generally personal, instance. This vividness is modified and made more acceptable by the pleasant perceptual medium.

The listener or observer identifies with the content of the work of art only inasmuch as he is a man and the work of art portrays a human situation. In other words, he is involved merely as an element of a larger class which includes not only the actual but also the possible. The possibility at times is merely theoretical—for instance, the possibility of finding oneself in the position of King Lear, betrayed by his daughters, or of Ulysses, who decides not to return to Ithaca, but to go "beyond the sunset." Thus the cognitive elements and the emotions, although profound, are dispersed into a class or category which has only a theoretical reality—what I have called a second reality. In the act of being attached to a hypothetical class, the emotion is experienced as not affecting the observer directly.

This is tantamount to saying that the adualism of art is transformed into *aesthetic distance*. The artist, or the admirer of the work of art, in a certain way recognizes that it has its own life, independent of the life of the artist and that of the admirer. The admirer is not detached, but he is involved only to the extent that he is a member of a hypothetical class

to which his life and the content of the work of art both belong. Thus in my opinion aesthetic distance, to which Bullough (1957) has attributed great importance, is related to
art's adualism and to the formation of hypothetical classes.
We have on one side the emotional vividness of the specific
event portrayed; on the other side the distance conferred by
adualism and the formation of a hypothetical class. And all
this is expressed through a pleasant perceptual medium. In
the theater, the aesthetic distance itself is concretized by the
physical distance between the stage and the audience. Some
people do not want seats in the first few rows of the orchestra
because from there they can see the actors as real entities
and not exclusively as the characters they impersonate.

At times, spectators who recognize in a play something
very similar to what they have experienced identify closely
with the characters and are deeply moved. In this case the
response is not so much an aesthetic one as it is a mere emotion caused by identification. Some patients suffering from
temporal lobe psychomotor epilepsy are also unable to maintain aesthetic distance and aesthetic adualism. A patient of
this author had the impression, when reading a poem or
novel or seeing a movie, that the facts and persons portrayed
were real. She would identify with them and would consequently experience intense suffering.

There are also schizophrenic patients who cannot visualize
a hypothetical category and cannot experience the sensation
of "second reality." These patients have great difficulty when
they see a theatrical performance. In the theater aesthetic
distance is as important as in poetry or novels, and yet it is
more difficult to retain. In these pathological cases aesthetic
appreciation, although diminished, is not totally absent. Thus
it would seem that aesthetic distance enriches the aesthetic
potentiality, but is not a prerequisite for a moderate appreciation of art.

At this point let us review all the elements that participate
in the formation of an aesthetic product or in the aesthetic
experience.

1. An abstract ideation or constellation of concepts is
   to a considerable extent sustained by low cognitive

forms and mechanisms: formation of primary classes, perceptualization and concretization of the concept, use of the positive aspect of negation, emphasis on verbalization, etc.

2. Contrary to what occurs in witticisms, these low cognitive forms and mechanisms are concordant with and reinforce the abstract meaning. A paleologic reinforcement often takes place.

3. The fusion of the different levels of cognition is mediated by a perceptual medium. In the process of perceptualization only those perceptions that have a pleasant physiological effect on the human organism are selected.

4. With the use of lower levels of cognition and of special types of perceptualizations there is a strong tendency to transform an act of cognition into an experience (namely, a deeply felt experience of inner status), at the same time that the cognitive meaning is retained. As a matter of fact, the cognitive meaning is generally enlarged by newly emerging classes, associative levels, marginal ideas, and, as we shall see in the next section, a return of endoceptual constructs.

5. The emotional content belongs not to the lowest but to the highest levels. Even in the cases where primitive emotions are portrayed, their expression tends to reassert the highest levels of cognition. This is true even when these levels seem to have disappeared because of the use of low cognitive forms. However, owing to the emergence of hypothetical cognitive classes, to artistic adualism, and to psychic distance, the emotional effect, no matter how intense, is not experienced as something which refers personally to the admirer of the work of art.

6. The aesthetic pleasure emerges from the fusion or concomitant occurrence of all the factors named above.[11]

---

[11] In a poem entitled "Poetry," the Italian poet and writer Niccolò Tommaseo (1802–1874) listed the different ingredients of the creative process involved in the writing of a poem:

Non la raggiante immagine,
non la riposta idea,

The sixth point is the most difficult to substantiate. In fact we cannot offer quantitative measurements of the various elements which enter into the work of art, as exact science would require, nor can we explain why the fusion of these elements causes the human organism to experience aesthetic pleasure.[12] Again we have reached that border between soma and psyche, psychology and physiology, which we are unable to cross. Remember that aesthetic pleasure is not a mere act of cognition, but predominantly a pleasant experience. Thus a poem, a melody, a painting can be read, heard, seen several times without our feeling tired of them. This attitude contrasts with the one we have toward a pure cognitive act: certainly we would not care to solve the same mathematical problem again and again.

Art work and art synthesis

The creative person seems to have special access to the primary process, just as the dreamer and the schizophrenic patient have. Dreamers generally lose their entrée to the pri-

---

non *l'armonia de' numeri,*
non e' l'amor che crea.

Idea, concento, immagine,
aura d'amor fecondo,
formansi in uno, e n' escono
il verso, il fiore, il mondo.

> Not the radiating image,
> Nor the hidden idea,
> Nor the rhythmical harmony,
> Nor love create.

> Idea, rhythm, image, air of fecund love,
> Merge into one form
> From which the verse, the flower,
> The world come out.

Incidentally, it is worth noticing in the first stanza of this poem the aesthetically positive aspect of negation, described in a preceding section. Tommaseo's use of negation is aesthetically inferior to that of Swinburne given earlier, because the negated entities are abstract concepts which do not evoke concrete images.

[12] For a scientific method in aesthetics, see the interesting book by Munro (1956).

mary process as soon as they wake up. Schizophrenics, as a rule, cannot coordinate the two processes for creative purposes. Some recovering schizophrenics, however, retain a greater accessibility to the primary process than normal persons and are nevertheless in a position to use the secondary process. The study of these patients is useful for the understanding of creative activity. Reports of such cases are rare, because the examiner has to see them during a special transitional stage which lasts a short time and is easily missed if not looked for.

Such a patient was a 13-year-old schizophrenic girl, who was admitted to the hospital following an acute psychotic episode in which she experienced hallucinations, delusions, and ideas of reference.[13] Three days after admission, during a routine mental examination, she was asked to explain the difference between character and reputation. She replied: "Character is your personality. Reputation is stamped on, and can never be erased. Your reputation is a bed, and when you get in you can't get out of it. Character is like a bedspread which can be taken off, or character is like dirt on a sheet which, if you wash it, can be removed." The patient was asked to define the word despair. She answered, "Despair is like a wall covered with thick grease, and a person is trying to climb up this wall by digging his fingers in. Down below is a deep, bottomless pit. Up at the top of the wall on the ceiling is a big, black spider. I have been in this deep pit during the past year, but now I am climbing up a rope, trying to get out of it."

When she was asked to tell the difference between idleness and laziness, she said, "Both have to be present for one to be present. You have to be idle to be lazy, but you don't have to be lazy to be idle. When you're idle you are living physically, but not really living. Laziness is when you give up." When she was asked the difference between poverty and misery, she replied, "Poverty is poor; misery is agony."

It is very unusual for a 13-year-old to express herself with such depth. She was not physically mature for her age; on

13 The author examined this patient on a consultation basis at the Institute of Living of Hartford, Connecticut. He is grateful to Dr. Francis J. Braceland, then director of the hospital, and Dr. John O'Brien, then the patient's therapist, for permitting him to report some of her productions here.

the contrary, she looked younger than 13. Although bright, she did not give the impression of being exceptionally intelligent. And yet her expressions often revealed that uncommon faculties were at her disposal. Her definitions of character, personality, and despair are not those to be found in a dictionary. She did not explain the concept or the connotation of these three words. She defined them by transforming the concept into a constellation of perceptual images. Webster defines despair, for example, as loss of hope—an accurate but also circular and prosaic definition, in comparison with that of the patient, who resorted to a sequence of vivid images: the wall covered with thick grease, the person who tries to climb up and digs his fingers in, the bottomless pit, the black spider. The girl's definition is a poetic definition; so are her definitions of character and reputation.

Was the girl's illness at least partially responsible for her ability to translate concepts into images? Most probably. She was in that rare condition where both primary and secondary processes are accessible and can be coordinated.[14] This state permitted her to change from a language of classification (or of concepts) to a language of experience when she was giving definitions such as those of character and despair. Her language was certainly not based on classifications validated by society; but could we say that it was based on experience? The girl had never climbed a wall covered with thick grease, had never dug her fingers into it while she observed a bottomless pit below and a black spider on the top. She was capable of having these experiences only by verbal proxy, as we, reading her remarks, can by proxy see and feel as she did.

This automatic translation into imagery, already described in Chapter 5, is a potentiality of the human psyche. As Giambattista Vico (1725) described, very ancient people resorted to this type of thinking more than modern people, because in ancient times abstract concepts were not yet developed to a

---

[14] Some poets and artists have tried to obtain similar states by alcoholic intoxication, smoking opium or marijuana, or use of other drugs. Mescaline or lysergic acid intoxication may also produce states vaguely related to the one experienced by the girl. The trouble with these artificially induced conditions is that either they do not regress to a primary process, or, if they do, the secondary process is lost or cannot be coordinated with the primary.

high degree. Primitive life retains a quality of freshness, genuineness, and perceptual vividness which imparts an aesthetic or artistic flavor. There is some question, however, whether it is correct to think of primitive life as "lived poetry." Although that life may be richer than ours in imagery, it does not have the concomitant abstract counterpart. In other words, it possesses the concrete and the particular, but not always the universal (at least, at a conscious and verbalized stage). When we observe the primitive life of aborigines, we automatically imprint on it our abstract concepts, so that such a life becomes artistic for us.

If primitive life is not necessarily artistic in its totality, however, primitive art is real art. Although primitives express themselves more easily in imagery, concepts are created in primitive societies too. The rarity of concepts seems more pronounced than it is because of lack of words which correspond to ours. Concepts are actually budding in primitive art, and probably reach a full conceptual level mostly because of the realizations achieved by artistic means. It is likely that the transformation of icons into ideas is more important for primitive man than for other men. Other primitive realizations are achieved through religious means, as Chapter 22 will demonstrate.

Returning to our 13-year-old girl, we find other aesthetic characteristics in addition to her visual imagery. One is the emphasis on verbalization, which appeared, for instance, when she explained the difference between idleness and laziness. As she started to define these words, she had the idea, which she later discarded, that idleness and laziness are correlational terms—that is, one cannot exist without the other (for example, the words *husband* and *wife*). Bertrand Russell in his *Introduction to Mathematical Philosophy* calls this relation a one-one relation. How much more beautiful is the girl's definition: "Both have to be present for one to be present." The contrast between the words *both* and *one* and the repetition of the words *to be present* confer aesthetic qualities on her expression.

The girl actually contradicts herself almost immediately, when she states correctly that "You have to be idle to be lazy, but you don't have to be lazy to be idle." Here again the repetition of the same words gives rhetorical emphasis. In the rest of her reply, "When you're idle you are living physically, but not really living," she achieves an aesthetic effect by repeating the word *living*, which assumes a different meaning. "Really living" means to her a full living, one not compatible with idleness, which permits living in a vegetative way. When she was asked what the difference is between poverty and misery, again she gave an artistic definition. The usual dictionary definitions are "state of being poor" for poverty and "state of great distress" for misery. The girl includes these definitions in hers, but offers much more: she succeeds in accentuating the contrast between poverty and misery. *Poverty* is a *poor* word in comparison with *misery*, which has much stronger affective associations, evoked by the word *agony*.

It is not enough to conclude that this girl had greater accessibility to the mechanisms of the primary process. We must recognize that she was also able to make good selections among the various possibilities offered by her primary process and that she could coordinate them with secondary-process mechanisms.

Another patient, a poetess, occasionally experienced quasi-schizophrenic episodes which were elusive in nature; often it was difficult to determine whether she was in a psychotic state or not. At times her poems almost resembled schizophrenic word salads; at other times they had a genuine beauty. They were nevertheless always difficult to understand, like much contemporary poetry.

At the beginning of this woman's treatment she used to speak of human beings as worms, and she wrote poems in which they were represented as worms. Her ideas could have been accepted at a metaphorical level, except that she insisted people really were worms. It was impossible to determine whether the statement was made in a metaphorical sense or not. There was a flavor of literalness in her remarks; even if she meant "worms" metaphorically, there was a resolute attachment to this metaphor, as if it literally represented reality. Her expressions seemed to me to belong to an intermediary stage, hard to delineate, between metamorphosis and metaphor. As her condition improved, she wrote poems in which the metaphorical meaning of the word *worm* could no longer be doubted.

For some reasons which cannot be fully understood, the creative person maintains a greater than average accessibility to imagery, metaphor, emphatic verbalization, and other forms related to the primary process.[14] According to Croce (1909), art is intuition, or intuitive knowledge, which produces "images" and not concepts. In this chapter I have tried to analyze Croce's assumptions psychologically. Intuition remains an obscure concept unless the underlying psychological process is clarified. "Inspiration" is the faculty that makes the creative person find a primary-process form which will hold a content from the secondary process. This accessibility to the primary process may require a state of passivity similar to that of dreaming; but the passivity cannot involve the artist's whole psyche. On the contrary, it contrasts with the increased alertness of that part of the psyche which deals with the secondary process and presides over the artistic synthesis. Thus in the act of artistic creation a complicated mental mechanism takes place which combines greater than usual passivity and greater than usual activity.

The artist must put together many elements of different origins to make syntheses of higher orders—that is, to create artistic unities. The word *poet* derives from the Greek *poietes*, the maker. And yet often the artist seems to uncover rather than to make new unities. People have the impression that they were potentially able to appreciate the poet's strange harmony and unusual meaning even before he revealed them to us. In other words, since we often respond so promptly to a work of art, we feel that the artist is simply pointing out what we already knew in an unclear or unverbalized way. The artist is seen in a role similar to that of the psychoanalyst when the analyst gives interpretations to the patient.

This point of view is valid only to a limited degree. It is

14 At times writers do not use elements coming from the primary process, but imitations of them. Then we have artifact, not art. When a poet or a playwright resorts to symbols which are purely intellectual or which come from his knowledge of previous literature or of psychoanalysis, high aesthetic levels are not reached. Even great poets like Dante resort in their weakest moments to allegories and metaphors which are the result of erudition and not of contact with the primary process.

true that on many occasions we had ready in us the elements needed to form or appreciate a work of art (see on pages 401–402 the discussion of these elements in Blake's poem). However, only the creative person could fit all the elements together in order to create the new unity. Once the unity is formed by the artist, it is easily apprehended by others. The concordance of various elements or the confluence of the various levels of cognition and affects makes it easy to grasp the unity, or at least to respond aesthetically to it. The new unity enlarges our world and our capacity for experience. Without it life seems impoverished.

In psychoanalytic terms, perhaps the aesthetic unity preexisted in us in a state of potentiality, as an unconscious endocept or as a primary aggregation (see Chapters 6 and 7). The union of disparate elements in a primitive grouping and diffuse emotional tones are found in primitive endocepts and aggregations. In the act of inspiration, the creative person is able to change the totality of the endocept or primary aggregation into a conscious conceptual experience. He becomes aware of unpremeditated interconnectedness among a relatively large number of different items of experience. The disorganized primary aggregation is organized, and an aesthetic design is discovered. This by no means implies a Platonic theory of knowledge. The new unity is actually new in the universe, but the formation of an aesthetic whole from disparate elements is facilitated by the diffuseness of endoceptual and primary-aggregation constructs. Artistic inspiration is perhaps the sudden discovery of a way to translate an endocept and a primary aggregation into an aesthetic unit.

The experience of aesthetic insight—that is, of creating an aesthetic unity—is a strong emotional experience in some ways comparable to what Maslow called "peak experiences" (1959, 1961). The artist feels that he has touched the universal. The particular, or the new unity that he has created, seems to have incorporated the universal—to have become a "concrete universal" which transcends space and time. As already mentioned, the quality of universality seems to come from two achievements: the enlargement of reality, which everybody will acknowledge, and the transformation of an endocept into a conscious and vivid experience in the inner reality of man.

At this point we can state that the formation of an aesthetic unit satisfies the three modes of operation described in Chapter 11: (1) The material necessary to form the artistic unity consists of elements which are connected in external reality or are put together by the artist in the work of art (mode of contiguity). (2) A work of art aims at imitating an aspect of life, as Aristotle thought, or consists of elements put together because of their similarity, as in metaphors, concretizations, etc. (mode of similarity). (3) A work of art stands for a class of objects, situations, events, or meanings (mode of *pars pro toto*).

A few remarks about arts, other than poetry

One important artistic field that must be completely overlooked in this study is music. How some auditory perceptions in the course of human history became aesthetic concretizations of abstract feelings and concepts is a fascinating subject, but completely beyond the author's competence. The reader interested in this topic and its related aspects is referred to the interesting books by Leonard B. Meyer (1956) and Zuckerlandl (1956).

This chapter will conclude with a few words about dance and the fine arts. Dance is generally not considered as important culturally as music and the fine arts. However, it has aspects which are very interesting from a psychological point of view. As an artistic medium it is closely associated with the theater, since dance, like drama, is acted out. Because it is enacted only through special movements, however, its form is much simpler than that of a play. Dance has accompanied the evolution of culture from antiquity to modern times. It seems that among ancient people and primitive populations of today, dance played and plays a somewhat more important role than among modern Western societies.

The unique psychological and aesthetic importance of dance comes from the fact that it is a form of creativity expressed through movements of the human body, in spite of the fact that movements and gestures, as means to communicate emotions and ideas, have decreased in importance with the cultural development of man. Chapter 7 has discussed how important the motor-gestural medium is as a precursor of language. Movements of the hand in particular acquire importance over all the other movements of the body, especially in the mechanism of denoting (by indicating with the finger). Motions of any kind eventually lose importance with the development of verbal language. In dance the movement of the leg acquires prominence over the movements of the other parts of the body, including the hand, which is relegated to an auxiliary role.

However, movement as expression has lost importance to such an extent that even dance could not be sustained as an art form without the support of other media, mainly music. The art of dance aims at achieving a harmonious fusion of sound and movement, as well as at transmitting a visual perception of movement. But the movement of the human body remains the essence of the dance; meaning or an emotional attitude finds concretization in a sequence of movements. Not all possible movements are used, of course, but only those which are pleasant to the eye. Tics and grimaces are rarely found in dance, except in some pantomimes. Often the movement is not pleasing in itself, but its repetition, sequence, rhythm, or particular distribution in time and space are. The sequence of movements becomes a design with temporal and spatial dimensions. The movements are stylized: that is, reduced to elementary pleasing forms. They are also chosen and distributed in a certain order, in a way comparable to the process by which words are chosen and distributed in poetry.

Fine arts have played a very important role in the development of civilization. Whereas in poetry the burden of representation is borne by verbalization, in the fine arts it is borne by denotation: a denotation reduced mainly to visual perception. How can visual perceptions concretize emotions and meanings? In his monumental book *Art and Visual Perception* (1954), Arnheim attempts to answer this question. He does not use the concept of the primary process, as I do. Arnheim illustrates how such basic concepts (or human motives) as rising and falling, dominance and submission, weakness and strength, harmony and discord, struggle and conformance, expansion and contraction, approach and withdrawal, which underlie all existence, are expressed by concrete visual methods. The conceptual motives are translated into a visual language, consisting of shapes, colors, light arrangements, etc. In different historical periods, different modes of stylization have been developed that have enlarged this visual language. The artist and the admirer of the work perceive the harmonious concordance between the concrete perceptual expression and the meaning.

To give some of Arnheim's examples, in Giotto's painting *Lamentation* the upsurge of the diagonal expresses the dynamic motif of resurrection, and the retreat and rise of the curve formed by the row of the mourners express awe and despair. In discussing the dome that Michelangelo designed for St. Peter's in Rome, Arnheim points out that the two contours that make up the section of the outer cupola are parts of circles and possess the firmness of circular curves. But they are not parts of the same circle; they are parts of two circles having different centers. Thus a Gothic effect is superimposed. At the same time that the symbolic image of weight is maintained, the expression of spiritual liberation dominates the construction.

It should be added, however, that the basic perceptual elements—colors, shapes, and their symmetrical arrangements and repetitions—which are used in the fine arts must be those that give a pleasant feeling. Here again we need to return to a physiological level. Ehrenzweig (1957) follows an approach to visual art which is different from Arnheim's. Ehrenzweig believes that there are two fundamentally different types of perception: depth perception and surface perception. Surface perception is gestalt-bound; depth perception is gestalt-free. He says that in art, gestalt-bound perception is superimposed on the gestalt-free. The gestalt-free perception is inarticulate, chaotic, undifferentiated, vague. The traditional artist forgets the gestalt-free vision as soon as definite formative ideas emerge. According to Ehrenzweig, the secret unconscious struggle between surface and depth perception animates the surface gestalt and adds artistic grace.

In my view, traditional art is better interpreted by Arnheim's method—that is, as an ensemble of perceptual concretizations which fit the artist's motive, at the same time that they elicit a physiological reaction of pleasantness. The concretizations which Arnheim illustrates (although he does not use the word concretization) do not include pregestalt levels.

In modern art, pregestalt perceptions are used that are similar to the ones described in Chapters 4 and 16. The somewhat undifferentiated whole acquires a meaning, just as primary aggregations eventually do (Chapter 7). At times we have either fragmentations of wholes or primary aggregations, from which forms are reconstituted and gradually emerge. In abstract art we sometimes find an almost complete disintegration of gestalts. In some other styles—for instance, in expressionistic art—forms return after they have undergone distortions of various types. The distortions fit (or concretize) the underlying emotional-conceptual theme. A fundamental difference exists, however, between modern art and the perceptual distortions or microgenetic stages described in Parts I and II. In modern art abstract ideation is retained in spite of the perceptual alteration.

22 ⊛ RELIGIOUS AND MYSTICAL EXPERIENCES

This chapter deals with the psychology of the creative process, as it finds expression in religious and mystical experiences. Any evaluation of religion as a norm for contemporary man, or any appraisal of the reality value of the objects of religion, will not be attempted.

Many religions, especially the major ones in recorded history, have cultural components which may be studied psychologically but do not strictly pertain to the realm of the religious or mystical experience: for instance, social, ethical, philosophical, legal, political, and artistic norms, tenets, and mores. Some religious leaders in particular had a multiple impact on their followers. They were not only religious innovators, but also political chiefs, legislators, philosophers, etc. These collateral aspects of religion will not be considered here.

The essence of religion as a psychological experience is to be found in the mystical aspect, that quality called *kadosh* in Hebrew and *sacer* in Latin, which includes the immediacy and the primacy of direct divinity-consciousness (Schleir-macher, 1958). Modern European languages (for instance, English, in spite of the word *holy*) do not have suitable terms to represent mystical experience in its potential intensity. To obviate this difficulty, Otto (1923) coined the word *numinous*.

From the standpoint of the creative innovator, religion consists of the following three aspects, or at least one of them: (1) an apprehension of supernatural powers which influence events affecting men; (2) a contact with these supernatural powers; (3) a visualization of norms for special ways of living which affect the totality of man and have transcendental meanings.

From the viewpoint of the religious person who is not an innovator, religion consists of the following three aspects, or at least one of them: (1) a set of beliefs in the existence of supernatural powers; (2) attempted contacts or ways of affecting the supernatural powers, by means of prayers or rituals of various sorts; (3) the adoption of special ways of living which are reputed to affect the totality of man and to have transcendental meanings.

The presentation that follows will not repeat the pattern adopted in our study of other fields of creativity. The collective participation, in a phylogenetic and historical frame of reference, will be stressed rather than individual contributions.

Insight into the supernatural

Recognition of supernatural forces is a more astonishing phenomenon in the modern world than in the ancient. What we usually call *supernatural* is not supernatural at all for the primitive. To him, nothing transcends nature; everything is immanent in it.

Actually, the appearance of the supernatural is to a large extent the result of a special application of what I have called teleological causality. According to this form of interpreting the world, which has been discussed in Chapter 7, *every event is willed*. An act of will presupposes a person or a personified entity. The primitive interprets all manifestations of nature in this way.

Cassirer, quoting Usener (1896), believes that the evolution of religious ideas started with the creation of *momentary deities*. These are fleeting mental constructs. "Every impression that man receives, every wish that stirs in him, every hope that lures him, every danger that threatens him, can affect him thus religiously. Just let spontaneous feeling invest the object before him, or his own personal condition, or some display of power that surprises him, with an air of holiness, and the momentary god has been created" (Cassirer, 1946). Everything is animated and personified, as described in Chapter 7. However, the animated or willing entity is not usually seen; it is felt or conceived as residing in the thing or in the activity in question. The brook, the tree, the rain, contain the willing elements in themselves, which become the gods.

Following Usener's concepts, Cassirer believes that the whole world of the primitive became populated with little gods, who represented functions, actions, or things. The world was seen as a pantheon. Whereas Spinoza later came to believe that the whole world is God, the primitive believes that everything has a divine essence. Spinoza's is a monotheistic version of an ancient belief. Usener and Cassirer went to the extent of declaring that the creation of gods was simultaneous with the creation of names. When the name of a thing or of a function (like hunting, plowing, or sowing) was created, the corresponding god was also conceived.

As already mentioned, the immanence of the divine in nature is consequent to a generalization of the principle of teleologic causality. It is an extension to the whole world of what the individual observes in his early and immediate interpersonal relations (Chapter 7). The human baby realizes that things and their appearance or disappearance (that is, the events) are generally willed by people, the significant adults in his life. Mother *wills* to give the baby the breast, to fondle him, to keep him on her lap, etc. Later the child attributes every event to acts of will. But some acts of will are good, some are bad. Mother is there to will good things, which will keep the child fed, warm, and alive. A feeling of hope or trust originates in the association with mother. The feeling of hope and trust is later extended to some parts of nature, which are seen as animated by good gods. The concept of physical causality (A brings about B) is not yet developed; A must be animated to bring about, or rather to will, B.

Soon, however, a primitive man becomes aware of the precariousness of his existence: scarcity of food, severe weather, epidemics, invasions, wild animals are there to endanger his survival. But if things are conceived as animated by good gods who have good intentions, the feeling of hope which originated with the contact with the good mother is experienced again in a larger context. At this level female deities predominate. Bad events are conceived as willed by bad gods, predominantly male, who have to be placated.

Thus religion can be seen from its origin as a set of cognitive constructs which prolong hope in the survival of the individual and of the small social group to which he belongs. Later, of course, hope is expanded further and embraces the survival of the tribe, state, nation, or human race; or it is focused on eternal survival (immortality) of at least a part of the individual (soul), or on general human progress, etc. Faith comes to mean two things: not only belief in the existence of the divinity, but also trust or confidence. Religion is thus not just a way of interpreting the world but of hoping. This hope is based on something which is conceived at the level of teleologic causality and which is accepted as truth. What is believed becomes truth; the unknowable becomes known. We may see in this phenomenon a form of *adualism* as described in Chapter 5 and Chapter 16. However, except for the experiences to be described in the next section, this adualism may come from others and is shared with others.

The perceptual vividness of impressions, the scarcity of logical elaborations, the elements of surprise give primitive life a picturesque and fervid atmosphere that is particularly conducive to the conception of these innumerable deities. Life, however, changes in the course of thousands and thousands of years of history. The greater the conceptual development of psychological life, the less pronounced the perceptual vividness, and the smaller the number of gods. Eventually the same god becomes responsible for many things or actions. In this way a gradual diminution in the number of gods takes place with the passage of time.

Whereas in early periods the deities are within objects or belong to the same natural world as men, a gradual abstraction of the deity takes place. The gods are no longer inside objects. They are expelled from the things in which they were incorporated and may even be relegated to a distant Olympus. From there, however, they continue to rule the things with which they were originally fused. Thus we have a change from idolatry to paganism.

In some religions, cosmogonies are created: the origin of the world is explained with teleologic causality applied to the divinity. "The world is this way because the gods willed it this way." The gods, however, are seen more and more as separate from the reality of man. They live in Olympus or heaven; they belong, so to say, to a *third reality* that is different from the reality of human life and the reality of art (Chapter 21).

Although in paganism, high processes of abstraction have permitted the separation of the gods from the things which were originally endowed with divine properties, the process of abstraction does not go beyond a certain level. The god is concretized again as he is anthropomorphized. Most of his attributes are human, although he may be endowed with some superhuman qualities (such as great power and immortality).

In the Greek pagan world the three realities (immanent, artistic, religious) are side by side, each of them having its own place in the cosmos. There is no absolute supremacy of the third reality. Moreover, in paganism entities are conceived which transcend or are even more powerful than the gods. The gods have not always existed; they originated from a primordial realm. There are two realms: that of the divine powers and that of the *metadivine* (Kaufmann, 1960). The gods are immanent in or part of these greater metadivine things. In the religion of the ancient Greeks the greater order of things, greater than the gods, the ultimate arbiter, is *ananke* (necessity) or *moira* (fate). Even Zeus, the king of the gods, is incapable of altering ananke or moira. Ananke is not seen as a physical law or an order of nature, but as an ultimate will, the personified ultimate essence of teleologic causality.

It is impossible today to account for the innovating insights which were responsible for the change from idolatry to paganism, or for the numerous variations of paganism which developed among peoples who were later considered as belonging to Western civilization. They probably occurred in prehistoric and very early historical time, and no trace of them has remained to us.

What is somewhat better known is the change from paganism to monotheism effected by Judaism. This religious revolution, later adopted by the whole Western world, consisted of further removals from concretization. Whereas primitive religions tend toward the primitive mechanisms of concretizations, paleologic transformations, and phantasmic ideation, Judaism, as a rule, emerges as a revolt against these trends.

According to the biblical account, Abraham is the first man who had the revelation that God is one and invisible. What some consider revelation, others consider insight. Of course, we have no historical proof of the existence of Abraham, the first Jew. His myth, however, represents the beginning of a very long trend in Judaism against religious concretization and other primitive mechanisms. One of the themes of the Pentateuch is this fight against the concrete gods. The gods of the surrounding polytheistic people are stigmatized as being "wood and stone" or "silver and gold." The Hebrew God loses human characteristics, becomes incorporeal and abstract. The third reality becomes by far superior to any other reality. The third reality is conceived as having preceded any other reality; as a matter of fact, as having created anything else which is existing.

The unpopularity of the Jewish religion both in ancient and modern times seems to me mainly due to this intense opposition to concretization.[1] Concretization obviously appeals to the masses, and as a rule it is necessary to give an artistic aspect to religion. The fight against concretization is

---

[1] The opposition to concretization has stimulated Jews throughout centuries to advance and contribute greatly in the fields of abstract thought. On the other hand, it has prevented them until recently from participating in the field of the fine arts. Only in modern times has a less literal observance of this attitude permitted them to contribute to the fine arts.

not absolute in the rites or in the myths of the Jewish religion, either. Paradoxically, even the revolt against concretization is "concretized" in one of the myths about Abraham, as reported in the Midrash. Abraham was the son of a man who carved and sold idols. One morning Abraham got up, went to his father's store, and broke all the idols. This episode represents a new era in religious history: fight against concrete gods.

Another important revolution occurred in the Jewish religion later—during the prophetic period. Starting with Amos, religion becomes intimately fused with moral life. The third reality becomes the moral guidance of man. Although the association between religion and morality existed in pre-prophetic Judaism, it becomes predominant in the prophetic period.

Christianity followed the general pattern of Judaism, with some fundamental variations which were made by the founders of Christianity to adapt the Jewish religion to the Greco-Roman world. Although in Christianity God transcends nature and is the creator of nature, as in Judaism, the separation of God from nature is, in one aspect, not so complete as in Judaism. For God can appear concretely as a man, as Jesus the Christ, the incarnated son of God. Furthermore, in many Christian religions the representation of the divinity in concrete artistic ways is not forbidden. Christianity, however, goes further than Judaism in abstracting "the soul" from the body and in disregarding man's physical concrete body. The mind-body problem becomes accentuated.

A third revolution, a philosophical revolution, occurred later in Judaism and Christianity, with Maimonides (1135–1204) and Thomas Aquinas (1225–1274) respectively. This development consisted mainly of an attempt to reconcile the two religions with Aristotelian philosophy.

Contact with the supernatural

The previous section dealt with religion as the apprehension of the existence of supernatural forces. This apprehension or insight was seen as based on tendencies toward concretization and abstraction competing among themselves. Over long periods of time, abstraction progressively gains the ascendancy.

Another important aspect of religion seems almost opposite to this trend toward abstraction: *the return to primitive methods of cognition to support the newly acquired abstract insights*. Religion too, like art, resorts to mechanisms of the primary process or to earlier mechanisms of the secondary process to give a structure to abstract concepts.

The religious innovator or leader does not consciously *infer* the existence of the divinity as, let us say, a philosopher or a scientist would infer a concept or make a discovery. The religious leader establishes a *direct contact* with the divinity, through the experience usually called *revelation*. But direct contact or revelation is not possible if the religious innovator relies exclusively on secondary-process mechanisms or Aristotelian logic. He must resort to the primary process or to earlier levels of cognition. Obviously, not everybody is in a position to summon the primary process in order to establish contact with supernatural powers. Special conditions are necessary, which have been described by William James in a book that marks the official entrance of the field of psychology into the study of religion (1902). For James, mystical experiences have four qualities: (1) ineffability, which he calls a negative characteristic: no words can adequately describe the mystical experience; (2) a noetic quality: new knowledge is gained as a result of the experience. The other two qualities, (3) transiency and (4) passivity, are less important.

In a recent book (1961), Marganita Laski calls ecstasy "a range of experiences characterized by being joyful, transitory, unexpected, rare, valued, and extraordinary to the point of often seeming as if derived from a praeternatural source." The ecstatic (or mystical) experience thus has many characteristics in common with the aesthetic experience. However, it has the additional quality of appearing to be derived from a "praeternatural" source which the subject interprets as supernatural.

How can an unusually enriching experience (perhaps an aesthetic experience or a peak experience, as described by

Maslow, 1959, 1961) become an ecstatic one? First of all, the mystical person experiences what Laski calls overbelief. The person believes in the supreme value of what he wishes to see realized (a principle, an accomplishment, a special answer to a challenge or question), and he assumes that the supernatural powers are in favor of the actualization of his wish. His emotions become so intense as to compel him to become a fanatic doer and to carry out his mission without delay. The evidence that the supernatural powers favor his mission is provided by unusual experiences which are based on primary-process mechanisms.

For instance, the belief that God wants the person to carry out a certain mission becomes concretized: the mystic actually sees or hears the divinity in the act of giving him that mission. He feels that a contact has been established between the divinity and himself. The insight or illumination is now projected to the divinity: it becomes a revelation. The insight must assume the form of a divine revelation in order to gain access to the person's consciousness and stimulate him to action. For a rather strong conflict or resistance existed in him before the revelation: many prophets, leaders, and saints are reported as at first repressing the inner knowledge of their mission. Realistic facts, like the hostile attitude of the authorities, or the indifference or hostility of the incredulous population, do not permit the mystic to become fully aware of his insights. At times he is only half aware of his inner impulses. The inner battle is won when a mystical experience at the level of consciousness gives him the determination to overpower his realistic inner reluctance and the anticipated opposition of the external world.

Thus we have here too what Kris would call a regression in the service of the ego and what I prefer to call a use of the primary process to sustain the secondary. The secondary process has undoubtedly formulated or worked out all the preparatory mental steps necessary for the insight. But the insight will occur only when mechanisms which are part of the primary process support what has been worked out at the secondary level. The subject realizes, obviously, that these primary-process experiences are not usual or common, but he does not interpret them as pathological. On the contrary, he believes they are the evidence that a contact with the divinity has been established. He has a feeling of absolute lucidity and absolute certainty. Now he sees, now he must move, now he must face the crowds—no matter at what price.

These mystical experiences seem to correspond to what in psychiatric terms are called hallucinations and delusions. Must we then conclude that people who have such experiences are suffering from schizophrenia, paranoia, or other psychoses? Not necessarily. It is easy to confuse religious mystics with psychotic patients, especially those psychotics who have hallucinations and delusions with religious content, but in my opinion this can and should be avoided. The following discussion of religious hallucinations and how they differ from schizophrenic ones is drawn mostly from an article published some years ago (Arieti, 1961c).

1. Religious hallucinations are predominantly visual, not auditory. Most of the time they have the aspect of apparitions. If there is an auditory component, it is as a rule secondary to the visual.
2. In their content they often involve old people, parent substitutes; but they are benevolent parents who guide the person to whom they appear.
3. Their content is gratifying in a manifest way.
4. The individual who experiences them has a marked rise in self-esteem and a sense of his being or becoming a worthwhile and very active person. He has been given a mission or a special insight, and from now on he must be on the move doing something important—more important than his own life. Although the message is experienced as an order, the subject does not feel that he is the victim of tyranny or a passive agent, but that he has been chosen to perform something of stupendous proportions.

The whole personalities and behavior of the people who experience religious hallucinations are not such as to warrant the diagnosis of psychosis. Mystics are fanatic, but not in the same way as the paranoid. They lack the bitterness and resentment or the calm resignation and disdain of the unjustly accused. They show instead a serene optimism, like that of people who have been blessed by the love of a good mother. Moreover, the hallucinatory and delusional experiences of the schizophrenic are generally accompanied by a more or less apparent disintegration of the whole person. Religious and mystical experiences seem instead to result in a strengthening and enriching of the personality.

These differential characteristics may be difficult to recognize in cases of pure paranoia or well-systematized paranoid syndromes. In such conditions the secondary process is used in the service of the regression or of the regressive forces. Some wrong premises are accepted as correct, and the secondary process is summoned to demonstrate their alleged validity. Sooner or later it will be evident that the patient's personality has not been enriched but impoverished. His motivation will be recognized as grounded in hostility, not in a desire to help others. Another important diagnostic characteristic is that whereas hallucinations are rare in paranoia and well-systematized paranoid conditions, they are common in mystical experiences.

If people who have mystical experiences are not psychotic, then what are they? There is no doubt that hallucinations and delusions of any sort, religious or not, are abnormal phenomena. Must we share Freud's point of view, expressed in *The Future of an Illusion* (1928), that religion is based on unconscious, primitive, and irrational psychic processes? Must we accept the idea that in some of its beliefs religion is a form of collective schizophrenia and in some of its practices a form of obsessive-compulsive psychoneurosis, different from the psychiatric syndromes because it is socially acceptable?

These are possibilities that we cannot easily dismiss just because we do not like them. However, another point of view, not mentioned by Freud, is suggested by our study of the aesthetic process. We have seen that one of the bases of the work of art is the use of the primary process, and yet few would deny that art has value and merit. But aesthetic methods, results, and values are certainly different from those obtained by pure secondary-process mechanisms.

In a similar way we may state that religious methods, results, and values are different from those derived from pure secondary processes. The religious value consists in giving people faith in the survival of man and man's ideals. Religion becomes an incentive to greatness of the spirit.[2] It offers new insights, such as those described in the previous section, which open up new dimensions of understandings and feeling.[3] These new dimensions, although they are abstractions constructed at higher psychological levels, need the support of lower mechanisms. We should not make the common mistake of considering the new insights and aims of religion irrational or primitive, just because they are partially founded on primary-process mechanisms.

How do the primary-process mechanisms become available to the mystical person, and how are they used? As already mentioned, the person who undergoes mystical experiences must be in a state of overbelief and must be expecting divine revelation.[4] But what are the phenomena which bring about hallucinations and delusions, in the absence of intoxication or of psychosis? They seem to me to be related to hysterical and hypnotic mechanisms. In hypnosis the subject retains the use of the secondary process but is under the influence of another person to whom he attributes great power. Gill and Brennan (1959) consider hypnosis too a regression in the service of the ego, but a regression which is time-limited and totally reversible.

In mystical experiences we have a condition of autohypnosis: the subject puts himself into a state of trance and projects power to the divinity. The state of trance permits the resurgence of primitive mechanisms. These mechanisms, however, are not used as they are in schizophrenia or dreams, since there is no abandonment of Aristotelian logic and no acceptance of the rule of the primary process. In religious experiences, as in the aesthetic process, the various levels of mentation are concordant. This concordance leads

---

[2] See also Slonimsky (1956).
[3] See also Tillich (1957).
[4] Collective phenomena consisting of religious hallucinations and delusions occurred during the Middle Ages and continue to occur in some societies (Hecker, 1832, Ferrio, 1948, Arieti and Meth, 1959). In these environments, the abnormal manifestations are acceptable to the crowd. Their acceptance, like that of a benevolent Freudian superego, enhances their occurrence.

to religious value; that is, to the establishment of faith, or to the transformation of a belief into absolute certainty. The new insights trigger the action necessary to their realization.

The subject does not believe his will is involved. He feels that he is the recipient of an experience, a passive agent: he undergoes the experience as he would undergo a dream. A strong force, which he attributes to a supernatural power, compels him to act. This strong religious force is the result first of religious preparation, then of a state of overbelief, and finally of a state of autohypnosis.

As mentioned, not only does the adopted primary process reinforce the secondary, but at times it actually makes possible an insight which is in contrast to the conventional attitudes of that historical period, and which therefore had tended to be repressed or dismissed from the person's center of consciousness. For instance, the prophets of the Old Testament had the conviction that they must convey a great message of justice and love to the people. Only a mystical experience, however, could convince them that their mission was a call from God. The mystical experience transforms uncertainty into certitude, confusion into clarity, hesitation and cautiousness into courage and determination. The mystical experience becomes a "revelation" and is accepted as "reality" by the subject. Therefore, of all creative processes it is the one that seems closest to the psychotic experience. It is a loss of "reality" but, as we have seen, it is a loss that helps open up new dimensions of reality. Furthermore, it is experienced as a "third reality," a reality distant from the first in its attributes and yet always in contact with the first.

As instances of mystical experiences I shall take two examples from my previous article (Arieti, 1961c), one concerning the Christian and the other the Jewish religions. Constantine was the first Roman emperor who was converted to Christianity, made Christianity the official religion of the Empire, and thus opened the path of Christianity to the Western world. The historian Eusebius, who was a contemporary and a friend of Constantine, wrote that the Emperor attributed his conversion to a hallucinatory experience.

According to Eusebius, Constantine was preparing for a battle against Maxentius at Saxa Rubra, a few miles from

Rome. On the afternoon before the battle, and exactly on October 27 of the year A.D. 312, Constantine saw a flaming cross in the sky with the following words: "In this sign thou shalt conquer." Constantine interpreted the vision as a divine order: he should become a Christian and he would win. He was converted, and from that time until his death his life was a series of triumphs, though the Roman Empire was already in a state of advanced decadence.

Now, Constantine was strongly predisposed to become a Christian, owing to the influence of his mother, who was a Christian. He also knew that many Christians were in Maxentius' army. If he became a convert they would rally to his support, or at least would not fight with so much will against him. The pagan majority was disorganized and divided into many creeds. The Christians were well organized and disciplined. It would be good strategy to join forces with this strong and militant minority. But Constantine, who had to carry the burden of the long Imperial pagan tradition, could not bring himself to take this momentous step. Only a mystical experience in the form of a hallucination could give him the insight at a conscious level and the impetuous determination that he required.

This hallucination shows the familiar mechanism of the concretization of the concept: the cross stands for conversion to Christianity. It also exemplifies the mechanism of projection to the external world: the message which he did not dare give to himself now comes from God. Unlike schizophrenic hallucinations, but like the world's great myths and some dreams, this hallucination carried a deep insight which also had a great practical value. The secondary process was in accord with the primary process.

The other example of religious hallucinations or possible delusions comes from the interesting and scholarly book by Gordon concerning Joseph Caro (1949). A famous figure in Judaism, Caro is the author of the book and code for religious Jews, *Shulhan Aruk*, or *The Prepared Table*. He lived 87 years, and for about 52 of them he heard a voice, the voice of the "Maggid"—an invisible messenger from heaven, a familiar spirit, and a divine mentor. "While Caro was bent over his sacred tomes in search of deeper meanings, grave fears and daring ambitions would rise in his soul. The spirit would then enter Caro's mouth, articulate his tongue, and reveal his destiny, unveil the coming events of his life" (Gordon, 1949). Caro described these experiences in a book called *Maggid Mesharim*. It is uncertain from a technical point of view whether they should be called hallucinations or delusions. Caro states that the Maggid was using his (Caro's) mouth in order to speak. Thus, if Caro was hearing his own voice, used by the Maggid, the phenomenon would be more delusional than hallucinatory. In some passages, however, Caro refers to the voice of the Maggid as the "Voice of My Beloved" which "began to resound again in my mouth." At any rate, whether these experiences are predominantly delusional and only occasionally hallucinatory or not, it does not matter very much. The important point is that no matter how we classify them, they are usually found in psychotics.

In his book Gordon, who is both a rabbi and a psychiatrist, asks whether Caro was mentally ill, and if so, what psychiatric syndrome did he have? We know many things about the life and work of Caro. Gordon, reviewing them, rightly concludes that he was not psychotic. It is obvious that Caro's abnormal experiences of 52 years' duration occurred while he was in religious ecstasies or in states of autohypnosis. They did not have a harmful effect, but on the contrary a constructive one, inasmuch as it was during these experiences that Caro could conceive and write the *Shulhan Aruk*, a book honored for centuries.

One difficulty which Gordon has not fully considered arises from the fact that, as we have seen, religious hallucinations are predominantly visual. Caro's experiences were auditory and therefore were more like those experienced by schizophrenics than is usual with mystic phenomena. It is true that the voice seemed to come from a parental symbol, but it was the voice of a disembodied entity using Caro's mouth. Perhaps this predominantly auditory character can be explained by the fact that in the Jewish religion the divinity is represented as an abstract entity which must not be represented by a visual image.[5]

The whole idea that the mystic experience is a source of

[5] Bowers and Glasner (1958) and Werblowsky (1961) have reported in other Jewish religious leaders phenomena similar to those experienced by Caro.

potential enrichment for humanity could be objected to on grounds that religious "illuminations and revelations" have often led to wars, persecutions, hate, prejudices. Results such as these are obviously not to be valued. It must be said that when religion leads to these results it fails, just as bad poetry fails—except that in the failure of religion the consequences are much more harmful. On the other hand, good religious insights become norms for generations to come. By promoting the survival of man or of his ideals, they are recognized as valid by the high levels of the psyche.

To give an example, the precept of the Sabbath, that is, of the observance of rest one day every seven, was once considered a wasteful practice not only by the masses but also by the intellectuals. For instance, Seneca, probably the best thinker of his generation, considered this custom of the Jews absurd. He felt that it was unpractical to arrest all activities; it was a waste of a seventh of one's life, and furthermore it was against nature, because the sun, the stars, the rivers, do not arrest their course one day every seven. Although in a certain way, to rest is to regress, it is a physiological regression like sleep, needed by the organism. In the precept of observing the Sabbath all levels of the psyche concord, as they do in aesthetic work.

This chapter has repeatedly mentioned the similarities between the aesthetic and the religious processes. These similarities often confer to religion a poetic or artistic aspect. Moreover, religious ceremonies often add some artistic features (music, poetry, pageantry, etc.) to increase the intensity of the experience.

A characteristic common to religion and to poetry is the tendency to resort to or at least retain archaic modes. In many religious services it has become the tradition to use languages no longer spoken. For many centuries services in synagogues have been held in Hebrew, a language which, until its recent revival in Israel, was known only to an elite and almost ignored by the masses. Services in Catholic churches were held in Latin until recently; services in Greek Orthodox churches are held in Hellenistic-Byzantine Greek; the extinct Pali language is used in Buddhist ceremonies. The congregations have accepted these linguistic practices, perhaps because the obscurity of the ritual gives concrete representation to the religious mystery, adding the flavor of the arcanum.

Rite and magic

Religious practices or cults consist of many rites which cannot be included in our study. Although they must have originated as acts of creativity, their individual origin is difficult to trace, and no attempt to do so will be made here. Many of these rituals have already been the object of psychoanalytic studies, among which is the important work of Reik (1946). Our discussion will also omit the practices of occultism, spiritism, mediumship, metaphysics, extrasensory perception, and related subjects.

This section will examine magic, which can be considered a primitive form of rite. Magic is a method of influencing the course of events (1) by procedures aimed at permitting the deity to intervene, or (2) by use of some principles of nature even more powerful than the deity itself.

Frazer devotes some of the most important chapters of *The Golden Bough* to the study of magic (1922). He finds two laws ruling magic: the first, that like produces like, or that an effect resembles its cause; the second, that things which have once been in contact with each other will continue to act on each other after the physical contiguity has been severed. As an example of the first law, Frazer mentions the "imitating of rain," a procedure which primitive peoples believe will make rain fall. As an example of the second law, he refers to the common belief that a piece of clothing or a fingernail belonging to a person has all the properties of that person.

Frazer calls the first law the law of similarity, which rules imitative magic, and the second law the law of contact, which rules contagious magic. He rightly sees a connection between these two forms of magic and the laws of association of ideas (the laws of similarity and contiguity). There is also a connection between magic and the three modes of psychological operation described in Chapter 11. The law of contiguity corresponds to Chapter 11's mode of contiguity and the law of similarity to its mode of similarity. We can add the mode of *pars pro toto;* in fact, the performed magical act also stands for what is supposed to happen as a result of it.

According to Frazer, magic is based on a fundamental conception which is similar to that of modern science: an implicit faith in the order and uniformity of nature. But for Frazer, who follows Tylor (1874), magic is not science but a pseudoscience, because it is based on two types of erroneous association of ideas.

Religion does not assume the immutability of nature; on the contrary, it offers a method (cult) by which an attempt is made to induce the divinities to change the course of nature. Frazer thus distinguishes magic from religion, and upholds the superiority of the latter. He feels that the use of magic implies the operation of elementary mental associations which occur also in subhuman animals. Frazer states:

> The very beasts associate the idea of things that are like each other or that have been found together in their experience; and they could hardly survive for a day if they ceased to do so. But who attributes to the animals a belief that the phenomena of nature are worked by a multitude of invisible animals or by one enormous and prodigiously strong animal behind the scenes?

Frazer thus concludes that belief in superior beings (religion) appears in evolution after magic. These ideas of Frazer reflect a series of errors. The fact that subhuman animals are capable of learning does not imply that they "believe" in the uniformity of nature, a concept which is highly complicated and has occurred only to civilized man. It is true that by following the three modes of operation of the nervous system, subhuman animals parallel the uniformities of nature. But no animals, and not all men, are aware of such uniformities (see Chapters 11 and 12). Psychopathological observations, although they cannot be taken as absolute proof, suggest that magic develops later than the belief in the existence of gods, or at least of gods incorporated in things. Magic practices could be compared to the compulsions of neurotics, symptoms of less primitive character than the paranoid ideations (projections) found in psychoses.

In magic there is a form of depersonalization that occurs in less primitive forms of mentation. In some respects magic is the opposite of animism. It could even be that magic represents an attempt by primitive man to decrease the animistic forces of the world. If everything in nature has a will, the life of the primitive is always at the mercy of these wills residing in the things. Magic may help to transform animistic objects into things, and nature into a nonanimistic, less primitive "reality." A world dominated by what Buber calls I-Thou relations becomes transformed into a world where I-It relations also exist. I-Thou relations, however, continue to exist, especially in religious practices. Too, magic becomes mixed with earlier religious customs. It becomes a way of controlling the world by propitiating the gods and also a way of influencing forces stronger than the gods.

Although magic in the life of the primitive has the role that science takes in the world of modern man, this role does not qualify it as a scientific procedure. Magic solves a need of primitive man, when he finds himself threatened by overwhelming forces. As De Martino (1948) and Tullio-Altan (1960) point out, magic has a historical role, and must be considered not as something necessarily absurd, even if founded on primitive mechanisms, but an important part of a stage in man's development. Furthermore, magic "works" at times, in spite of its inherent error, because of suggestion, or the faith it elicits. A sword reputed to be magic is likely to improve the fighting ability of its owner and lead him more easily to victory.

Magic may become organized in a system of rites. Every religion has a combination of beliefs in the supernatural and adherence to rites. In modern ethical culture, the supernatural is eliminated and the rite tends to be replaced by ethical behavior. Faith in survival thus is based only on the ethical behavior of man and on secondary-process mechanisms. Whether the religious needs of man can be fulfilled without also resorting to the primary process is a debatable question.

23 ° *CREATIVITY IN SCIENCE*

At the present time the creative process is being studied more intensively in relation to science than to any other field. There are several reasons for this focus on science. The first is the twentieth century's bias in favor of scientific knowledge. A second reason is found in the belief held by many investigators that it is easier to study the creative process in scientists than in artists. Scientists seem to be more methodical in their observations, and therefore should be more capable of reporting their inner experiences. A third reason is the assumption by many investigators that the process of scientific creativity consists of logical or mathematical steps which can be easily traced back.

As to the first reason, we must accept its historical validity. The second and third reasons, however, contain only grains of truth. The scientist's methodology is of little help in the attempt to recapture the inner experiences which led to a scientific innovation. Moreover, although the tracing back of the logical steps in scientific creativity is indeed important, it does not lead to insights into the unconscious mechanisms or the overall modes of operation which are followed even in the conscious steps.

Before examining the process of creativity in scientific discovery, we must clarify one point: Discoveries are not always the result of scientific creativity. An explorer who discovers an unknown land is not necessarily endowed with creative ability. Inventions that require only rearrangements or practical application of principles discovered by others are more properly considered as pertaining to technology than creativity, no matter how important their practical effects are. On the other hand, some scientific principles which are among the highest products of creativity may not have practical applications for long periods of time.

Poincaré's and other contributions

One of the aims of students of scientific creativity has been to recapture the different phases of thinking which have led to the creative act. Personal accounts given by great scientists are particularly valuable, but unfortunately only a small percentage of them have provided this information. One who did is the physiologist Helmholtz (1896). He recognized three stages in his creative work: (1) an initial investigation carried on until it is impossible to go further; (2) a period of rest and recovery; (3) the occurrence of a sudden and unexpected solution.

One of the best accounts of the creative process in science was given by the mathematician Poincaré (1913). In a report which has become a classic in the literature on creativity, Poincaré described the discovery of the theory of Fuchsian groups and Fuchsian functions which made him famous.

Poincaré studied the problem for 15 days, trying to conclude what later proved to be a false idea: that no such functions existed. A sleepless night spent on this problem brought no apparent results. He had drunk black coffee and could not sleep, and he later wrote about that memorable night: "Ideas rose in crowds; I felt them collide *until pairs interlocked,* so to speak, making a stable construction." The following day, on the way to a geological excursion, he got on a bus. At the moment when he put his foot on the step, the idea came to him, apparently without any conscious effort and without his even thinking about this problem, that the transformations he "had used to define the Fuchsian functions were identical with those of non-Euclidian geometry." This was the creative moment. Poincaré went on with the business of the day, but later he verified this sudden illumination. A few days later, in another sudden flash, he realized that the "arithmetic transformations of indefinite ternary quadratic forms were identical with those of non-Euclidian geometry." These breakthroughs led to great expansions of the field of mathematics.

Poincaré added another stage to those described by Helmholtz: a second period of conscious effort, after the illumination, to validate the insight obtained. In a subsequent study, Wallas (1926) gave these stages of creative thinking the names by which they are generally known today: (1) preparation, (2) incubation, (3) illumination, (4) verification. Hadamard (1945), in his interesting book on the psychology of invention in the field of mathematics, mostly follows Poincaré's ideas.

Wallas' four stages are recognizable not only in the creative process but in the solution of every problem. However, whereas the subject applies known procedures in an ordinary problem-solving situation, in the creative process he devises a new way. This new way is often found in an experience of *sudden illumination,* or "Eureka!"

Of the four stages, the first (preparation—requiring study of the subject, collection of data, etc.) and the last (verification through other examples, models, mathematical proofs, etc.) are in the realm of consciousness and easy to understand. It is in reference to the stages of incubation and especially illumination that our knowledge and understanding leave much to be desired.

As far as incubation is concerned, a well-known fact, even in simple learning, is that a process of consolidation is necessary. For instance, students know that they cannot retain well what they have studied and learned just before taking a test, for instance, in the early morning hours immediately preceding the examination. They must "sleep on" the material.

It could be that the material which is to be committed to memory must reverberate in the neuronal circuits, completely outside of our consciousness, in order to make lasting connections. In creativity the process is more complicated: connections occur which were never made before—and they are not just random connections or combinations, for some of them will lead to acquisition of new knowledge.

Poincaré has carefully considered this important topic. Combinations which will lead to new knowledge are a small minority; useless combinations are a potentially endless number. How is it that during the incubation period "good combinations" are made and reach consciousness in the subsequent stage of illumination? To my way of thinking, it seems impossible to attribute the good combination to mere chance, as some authors do. For how can chance explain the fact that many creative people make more than one discovery?

Poincaré believed that these combinations occur in the unconscious, or subliminal self, and he also offered the hypothesis that the subliminal self is in no way inferior to the conscious self. He wrote: "Does it follow that the subliminal self, having divined by a delicate intuition that these combinations would be useful, has formed only these, or has it rather formed many others which were taking an interest and have remained unconscious?"

In trying to understand how the selection which leads to the useful combination is made, Poincaré advanced two hypotheses. (1) The first concerns the aesthetic quality of the combination. Perhaps the mind, like a delicate sieve, lets pass through the threshold of consciousness only those combinations which are striking for their beauty and elegance. (2) The second assumes that during the preparatory work the mind has put into motion not all possible ideas, but only those which have something to do with the object of the study. Poincaré says that if we compare these ideas to atoms which are hooked on the walls, we can imagine the mind unhooking only the possible ingredients for the new ideas. The "mobilized atoms" are those from which we might reasonably expect the desired solution. Some of these "atoms" collide and enter into new combinations. The good combination is one in which at least one atom was freely chosen by the will.

The first hypothesis does not seem convincing. It is true that several useful mathematical formulas have the characteristics of beauty and elegance that Poincaré has mentioned. But their being aesthetically attractive does not make them valid. Poincaré himself has stated that some false ideas can still gratify "a natural feeling for mathematical elegance."

The second hypothesis seems acceptable at first examination. Certainly in the preparatory stage the creative person consciously mobilizes only those ideas which have something to do with the object of his research. In many instances, however, the new combinations that emerge in the flash of illumination have been suggested by something which was completely unrelated to the object of inquiry. Often it is by the unpredictable application to one field of what is valid in another field that the valuable new combinations have occurred. Now, in the case of Poincaré, obviously he put only mathematical ideas into motion in his preparatory work; not, let us say, historical, geographical, and literary notions. This restriction, however, does not seem very important, because the field of mathematics was vast enough even in his time to permit infinite combinations.

The process of discovery

Let us reconsider the first important illumination that Poincaré experienced. "At the moment when I put my foot on the step the idea came to me . . . that the transformation I had used to define the Fuchsian functions were identical with those of non-Euclidian geometry." The act of illumination consisted of seeing an *identity* between two transformations previously reputed to be *dissimilar:* those that Poincaré had used to define the Fuchsian functions and those of non-Euclidian geometry.

Another illumination came later, when Poincaré had the idea "with just the same characteristics of brevity, suddenness and immediate certainty, that the arithmetic transformations of indeterminate ternary quadratic forms were identical with those of non-Euclidian geometry." Again the moment of illumination is the moment when Poincaré sees an identity between two subjects reputed to be dissimilar.

Instances could be multiplied endlessly in which great discoveries were made by the act of perceiving an identity among two or more things which had been thought dissimilar or unrelated. In the classic example, Newton observed an apple falling from a tree and saw a common quality in the apple attracted by the earth and the heavenly bodies. He perceived the similarity between two forces—that which causes an apple to fall to the earth and that which holds the moon in its orbit. He validated this insight by comparing the rate of falling bodies on the earth with the rate at which the moon deviates from the straight line which it would follow if the earth did not exist.

We could say that many scientific discoveries are the result of individualizing a common characteristic or connection between things which were deemed dissimilar or unrelated before. But of course the observation of similarity is not enough. Transformations used by Poincaré and those of non-Euclidian geometry are not identical in every respect. An apple is very dissimilar in size, origin, and chemical structure from the moon; yet Newton saw a similarity. In what way are the moon and the apple similar? What does their partial identity consist of? Of being members of a class of bodies subject to gravitation. Thus, at the same time that Newton saw the similarity between the apple and the moon, *a new class was formed*, to which an indefinite number of members could be added. The new object for which he was searching and which he found was a class.

Is this new class a primary class, as described in Chapter 7? Is the identical quality of being subjected to gravitation a releasing element, as illustrated in Chapter 4? Obviously not. When Newton perceived the identical element, he did not respond to the stimulus but to the class. Had he been a regressed schizophrenic who saw a similarity between the moon and the apple, he could have paleologically identified the moon with the apple. He could have thought that the moon could be eaten like an apple, or sucked like the maternal breast, as Renée, a by now famous schizophrenic patient reported by Sechehaye, did during a stage of her illness (1951). Newton was not interested in the apple, or even much in the moon; he was looking for a universal principle. The discovery of the common element—in this case the quality of being subject to gravitational force—did not have the result of affecting the discoverer psychodynamically. It was immediately conceived as something pertaining to the external reality, not to the inner one.

Newton also responded differently from, let us say, the neurotic patient described in Chapter 17, who reacted the same to every elderly red-haired woman. There the common element elicited a psychological reaction in the patient. With Newton, the falling apple elicited the formation of a conscious secondary class whose importance was centrifugal; that is, it referred to the world (or rather, the mesocosm), not to Newton as an individual. In the moment of discovery Newton was not affected directly by the gravitational quality, but by the concept of gravitation. The new concept or class revealed a new piece of the order of the universe, because each member of the class was recognized as having similar properties.

The individualized essential property should not be considered a neutral stimulus which, after Newton, acquired a meaning. For instance, it is not like a previously neutral ringing of a bell, which becomes connected in a dog's conditioned reflex. In some situations a neutral stimulus may be attached artificially to a new whole. The fundamental element of a secondary class cannot be attached artificially; it is an inherent and necessary component.

Is this new class discovered by Newton exclusively the result of secondary-process mechanisms—that is, of what Reichenbach called induction by enumeration (1951)? Obviously not. As discussed in Chapter 8, induction by enumeration is the procedure by which a man, having observed that some sequences (say, the daily alternation of light and darkness) recur again and again, feels entitled to draw a general principle ("night follows day"). Induction by enumeration is a simple procedure, even for the average man. Obviously this is not what Newton did. His is a case of what some authors have called "induction by intuition" and other authors "induction by imagination" or "induction by guessing" (Frank, 1957).

I shall call this type of induction "induction by creativity." The creativity consists of (1) individualizing a common property—for instance, in the moon and the apple; (2) *not* identifying the objects having the common property (e.g., moon and apple) by putting them into a primary class; (3) recognizing that they belong to an unsuspected secondary class (such as gravitational bodies). In this type of induction an increased ability to recognize similarities, which is a characteristic of the primary process, is connected with a concept, and the tertiary process emerges. The concept of the new class is much more important than the recognition of the similarity; but the mental grasping of the similarity is necessary to evoke the concept of class at the level of consciousness.

Once the concept of the new class is created, it will be easy to use in induction by enumeration; for instance, in recognizing that all bodies are subjected to a gravitational force. It will also be easy to apply the concept in deductive procedures: since A is a body, it is subjected to a gravitational force.

From this description it can be seen that the tertiary process in scientific creativity uses mechanisms which are different from those found in aesthetic creativity. Blake's poem "The Sick Rose" (analyzed in Chapter 21) compares the sick woman to the sick rose and makes us aware of a class "beautiful life destroyed by illness." However, the rose and the woman, although not identical as they would be in schizophrenic thinking, are not clearly distinct either, the way the apple and the moon are. The members of a secondary class which emerges through the aesthetic process retain the tendency to fuse together, or to exchange nonessential predicates. Consequently, even the class "beautiful life destroyed by illness" is not so definite as the class of gravitational bodies is. The poet leaves things somewhat indistinct. It is part of our aesthetic appreciation first to experience the ambiguity of the unfinished statement, and then to attempt a clarification of that statement by finding psychological resonances in our feelings and ideas.

The scientist instead tries to make the statement as clear as possible, leaving no room for doubts or exceptions. His new secondary class loses all its original connections with the primary process. Here too, however, the search is not ended even though the new class is very well defined. The understanding of the Newtonian system is a prerequisite to the eventual discovery of the Einsteinian world of classes.

In many instances the process of creativity consists of discovering a similarity between one system or field of knowledge and another. One of the most important examples of this type is that of Darwin. In 1838 Darwin happened to read the book written by Malthus 40 years before, *Essay on the Principle of Population."* Malthus had advanced the idea that Rousseau's optimistic views about humanity are unsound because (1) the natural tendency of population is to increase faster than the means of subsistence; and (2) this fast increase results in a struggle for existence. Darwin extended these views to the whole field of biology, so that principles formulated in relation to human society were applied by him to organic life in general.

The transcendence of the discovery

When a scientific innovation results in the formation of a new class or the organization of a system, its importance transcends that of the immediate discovery. It eventually leads to the discovery of additional properties hidden in the members of the class or in the system.

Let us take as an example the fictitious discovery represented in Figures 23–1, 23–2, and 23–3. In Figure 23–1 we see four black bodies, apparently located at random. They may

Figure 23–1

represent atoms, planets, islands, or whatever we would like to imagine. At first no order whatsoever is detected. But one day a hypothetical discoverer recognizes a common property in the four black bodies: they are equally distant from a point C (Figure 23–2). They belong to a category of bodies

Figure 23–2

which are equally distant from C. But points which are equally distant from a given point are part of a circumference. Thus he has discovered a circumference, which always existed in potentiality. Moreover, he can assume that if other bodies exist which have the same properties of the four he knows, they must be placed along the same circumference. The light dots in Figure 23–3 are the hypothetical bodies that the discoverer will find when he travels along the potential circumference.

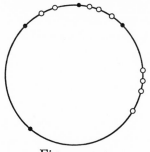

Figure 23–3

Even more remote wholes are gradually revealed in other discoveries. For instance, Galileo[1] discovered that the ac-

[1] To a large extent this interpretation of Galileo's thinking is based on Wertheimer (1945).

celeration of falling bodies decreases consistently with their angle of inclination. From the angle it is possible to deduce the acceleration (see the lower part of Figure 23-4). Galileo found out that each falling body had the common quality of accelerating in an order that corresponded to the order of inclination. But Galileo felt this was only half the picture. When a body is thrown upward, the retardation decreases as the angle of inclination diminishes from 90° (see the upper part of Figure 23-4). Then what if the body remains at point O; that is, what if the angle is zero? Obviously the body is neither retarded nor accelerated; its velocity remains constant.

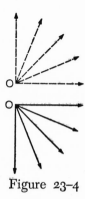

Figure 23-4

Rest thus becomes a special case of constant velocity, a case of the absence of positive or negative acceleration. Rest assumes a new meaning: it is no longer the absence of movement, but the absence of change in velocity, be the velocity zero or that of a fast-moving object. Also, a body can now be seen not as something pushed from outside *a tergo*, or by an imposed force, but as a mass which is propelled by an inner force until it is affected by external forces such as friction. Galileo did not generalize the principle to include all directions. Newton did so and thereby extended Galileo's findings in his own concept of inertia. As a consequence of his experiments and deductions, however, Galileo could assume the presence of a completely isolated body—a body which is not under the influence of any external force. Such a body cannot exist in nature (Cassirer, 1953); it is only a theoretical possibility.

This is an example of an *as if* phenomenon; but of a type different from that described in Chapter 21. The uninfluenced body would exist *if* no external forces operated on it. But every body is under the influence of some external force. Such a body would seem not to exist; but as a theoretical construct, it does exist. In fact, its properties, logically deduced, explain the empirical findings of physical dynamics. Is such a theoretical construct a fiction, like a work of art or a human device to explain complex phenomena? The temptation to consider it as such is great, since we know that the possibility of the uninfluenced body cannot be materialized.

However, scientists (and in this they differ from some philosophers) do not at all consider such a construct fictitious; on the contrary, they find it much more realistic than the data and opinions that are derived from perceptions or from commonsense reasoning. We almost get the impression from them that reality is not realistic enough to live up to the theoretical construct. Is the reality of a theoretical construct (like the construct of Galileo) a *fourth* reality? "Not at all," would be the scientist's answer. "It is the first reality." Reality *does* live up to the construct, in spite of appearances to the contrary. It cannot escape doing so. An invariable association exists between all the bodies of nature: all bodies are subject to natural laws. The scientist thinks that this alleged "fourth reality" is actually the first reality in its purest form. As a matter of fact, he may think that there is only one reality, and that all the other constructs are fictions. Some thinkers believe instead that the "fourth reality" is a creation of man. If so, we would have to explain why the first and the "fourth" realities coincide.[2]

This example from Galileo also shows that in science as well as in art the negative emerges as an important factor. What before Galileo was defined as a state of rest became a state of *absence* of acceleration of any kind (positive or negative).

So far we have studied examples of scientific creativity in which a similarity is perceived and leads to the formation of a

[2] The paranoid patient too "discovers an underlying arrangement" in his environment, at times in everything which surrounds him. Actually he does not discover any arrangements; he creates the mental representation of an arrangement which is not in agreement with the first reality.

new secondary class and to the subsequent discoveries. In this type of innovation the mode of similarity, described in Chapter 11, is fully in effect.

The *pars pro toto* mode of operation is also applied when what is recognized as valid for a few elements is extended to the whole class. The first mode of operation occurs too in these great discoveries; namely, in the period of preparation or of collection of data. This collection of data is at first disorganized, or poorly organized. It consists of bits of information which are loosely associated, although not disparate or completely unrelated. It probably corresponds to a primary-aggregation stage, as described in Chapter 7, except that it occurs at a much higher level.

When the act of discovery is completed, what was a loose contiguity reminiscent of a primary aggregation becomes an *invariable association*. Newton's discovery may be reformulated in the following way: "Every body is associated with the force of gravity." We must, however, be aware of an important fact: in great discoveries or theories, the invariable association, or the higher unity, is reached by passing through the stage of the mode of similarity.

Many discoveries which are not of the highest creative order reach the stage of invariable association without going through the stage of similarity. And of course, it can happen that their individual practical results are more consequential than those of discoveries of the highest type. For instance, an observer is struck by an unusual sequence, never noticed before: an unusual event B occurs after an unusual occurrence of A and he jumps to the conclusion (which later he has to confirm with other experiments) that there is an invariable association between A and B. At other times the association is a negative one. B cannot be associated with A. A great deal of medical research is based on negative association (for instance, if penicillin [A] is present, a certain microorganism [B] will not multiply).

Many inventions and discoveries have occurred by this method of seeing an invariable association or by filling some gap between invariable associations.[3] When the invariable

[3] For a more detailed discussion of the type of creativity connected with inventions, see Rossman (1931).

association is discovered without going through the stage of the mode of similarity, we have only a practical invention, or at most an *empirical law*. The law is explained only by the empirical proof, but is not sustained by a new class or by a greater understanding of the world. It is doubtful that the tertiary process is used in discoveries made by empirical relation.

Some inventions seem to have occurred purely by accident. If Roentgen had not chanced to observe a glowing barium platinocyanide screen, X rays would not have been discovered. The creativity, if we can use this term, here consists of not accepting the chance, or the accident, or what seems an anomaly, but of trying to understand the event as part of the order of the universe. What appeared fortuitous or anomalous is recognized as an inevitable occurrence.

A curious fact about scientific discoveries is the frequent importance in them of these little fortuitous incidents, like that of Newton and the apple, that of Galileo and the lamp in the cathedral of Pisa. Many people doubt the historical validity of these episodes, which seem almost like myths which have grown up around the memory of great men. The stories have the flavor of parables, "artistic concretizations" which popular cult has created out of the ideas of these men.

At the risk of appearing gullible, I must say that I believe in many of these little episodes which led to great illuminations. That small chance episodes are responsible for some inventions and discoveries is beyond doubt, since we have plenty of reports on this subject. There is no reason why incidents like those reported about Newton and Galileo could not have occurred to offer a genius the opportunity to grasp a regularity he was searching for. The episode becomes a concretization of the idea, just as a work of art stands for an abstract concept. The falling apple concretizes the force of gravity. Here it is nature that does the concretizing, not man. Man's genius consists of recognizing the concretization and unraveling it by finding the universal in the particular. The particular is not just a symbol of the universal, as in art; instead it belongs to the class of the universal. Both are parts of the same reality.

24° *BIOLOGICAL AND HUMAN CREATIVITY*

Biological creativity

The concept of the tertiary process as an integration of processes at the primary and secondary levels may appear to some people a denial of the innovating power of creativity. The answer to this criticism can only be that whatever is new in the universe known to man is merely a new combination of what already existed. New combinations may engender the emergence of unforeseeable characteristics, just as a special combination of two gases, hydrogen and oxygen, brings about that apparently unrelated liquid which is water.

Only *creation*, not creativity, can be considered as emerging *ex nihilo* (from nothingness). But creation is a theological, not a scientific concept. Human creativity has no other resort but the use of what is available. However, the range of what is available is enlarged by the resumed use of primary and archaic secondary-process mechanisms.

Biological evolution, as it is understood at our stage of knowledge, follows similar courses. The phylogeny of the central nervous system provides many examples. When new nervous structures emerge as a result of series of mutations and take over some functions from more caudal (or lower) structures, these caudal structures (which, at a psychological level, correspond to our obsolete, archaic, or primary-process mechanisms) are not eliminated, but readjusted and reintegrated to form a functional subsystem with the more encephalic structure. For instance, the evolution of movement culminates with the appearance of the motor cortex in mammals. When the motor cortex takes over the government of voluntary movements, the basal ganglia do not fall into disuse. In their new integration with the cortex, they modify and increase the flexibility of the postural movements and add automatic movements. They also organize synergies between the flexors and extensors of the limbs.

To take another example, the archipallium, which is very important in the lower mammals for the elaboration of olfactory perceptions, to a large extent loses this specific function in higher mammals, which depend less on the sense of smell. But as Papez's studies have indicated, the archipallium does not discontinue functioning. In a process of biological creativity, it becomes reintegrated with neopallial areas and comes to play an important role in the experiencing of higher emotions.

Neurology could provide many similar examples. However, we do not need to confine our examples to this science which is closely related to psychology. The appearance of new species in biological evolution can be explained in similar ways, provided we take into account also the environmental changes.

Mutations are inaccuracies in the hereditary constitution and may be considered as caused by failures in some circumstances to maintain full and mature structures. Most of these mutations, which can be compared to our psychopathological or primary-process forms, are harmful from the point of view of survival. A minimal percentage of mutations are favorable, if they happen to occur when improbable environmental situations have also developed which enhance their survival and enable them to compete successfully with other nonmutant forms. For example, the common tapeworm belongs to the family of cestodes, organisms which appeared on earth long before man. At one point in the history of the species, it happened that some cestodes underwent some mutations by which they could survive only in such an improbable environment as the intestine of man. Had man not existed then, that particular strain of mutant cestodes would have perished. But man happened to exist and the mutant cestode, the tapeworm, emerged in an act of biological creativity— much to our discomfort.

Mutations provide the raw material of evolution. The special environmental situations (for the tapeworm, the existence of man) act like secondary-process mechanisms and transform pathological forms into something new, more complicated, and capable of survival. What was at first an accident or a random occurrence becomes integrated into a more organized pattern.

Phylogenetic creativity has at its disposal two assets: one is infinite time, so that even the most improbable mutations, and the most improbable combinations with favorable environmental conditions, eventually do occur. The second lies in the survival and genetic reproduction of the favorable combinations.

Man does not have infinite time at his disposal; but with his cognitive mechanisms, his cumulative experience transmitted from previous generations, and most of all his conscious purpose and goal-directedness, he is able to immeasurably reduce the time required for creativity. For example, some instruments devised by men, like optic and photographic equipment, computers of various types, etc., are the equivalents of organs of the body which took evolution billions of years to create merely through chance mutations and favorable environmental situations.

Human creativity: search and similarity

The main difference between human and biological creativity is to be found in the subjective state of search and attainment that man experiences. Actually this subjective state occurs, in the most varied forms, not only in creativity but in all the psychological processes described in this book, from the teleologic regression of the psychotic to the creative realization of the gifted man. It finds its culminating points in the adjustment or achievement of the average person (Chapter 9), in the psychotic insight of the schizophrenic (Chapter 16), in the psychopathic insight of the psychopath (Chapter 15), in the inspiration of the artist (Chapter 21), in the revelation of the religious person (Chapter 22), in the eureka experience of the scientist (Chapter 23). It is the tendency to build, enlarge, or modify various types of object relations or of inner reality.

If this subjective state of search and attainment is the most important subjective characteristic of the psyche, the most important objective one, common to the primary, secondary, and tertiary processes, seems to reside in what I have called the second mode of operation, or ability to differentiate similarities from manifold experience (Chapter 11). Similarity indicates that there is some kind of recurrence and, therefore, regularity in the universe. It is from these segments of regularity that the human mind plunges into the understanding of the cosmos and into the making of its own inner reality. In psychopathology, normality, and creativity, the ability to register similarity is the common guiding principle—a tremulous little light with which to search and attain, with which to break the secret of the universal night and make a piece of understanding a piece of ourselves.

It is on the varying responses to similarity that the ultimate rise or fall of man depends. We can represent these variations by resorting to the imagery of an expression: For the primary process, all that glitters is gold. It will be the labor of the secondary process to discover that all that glitters is not gold. The tertiary process will do at least one of two things: Either it will create a new class of glittering objects, or, by bestowing the glittering on other substances, will beautify them artistically, as gold can do.

BIBLIOGRAPHY

Abel, K. 1884. *Über den Gegensinn der Urworte.* Quoted by Freud (1910).

Abse, D. W. 1959. "Hysteria." In Arieti, S. (ed.), *American Handbook of Psychiatry,* I, 272–292. New York: Basic Books.

Ach, A. 1905. *Über die Willenstätigkeit und das Denken.* Göttingen: Vandenhoeck und Rupprecht.

Ach, N. 1935. "Analyse des Willens." *Handbuch der Biologischen Arbeitsmiethoden,* Abt. VI. Berlin: Urban und Schwartzenberg.

Adler, Alexandra. 1944. "Disintegration and Restoration of Optic Recognition in Visual Agnosia." *Archives of Neurology and Psychiatry,* LI, 243–259.

Adler, Alexandra. 1950. "Course and Outcome of Visual Agnosia." *Journal of Nervous and Mental Diseases,* CXI, 41–51.

Adler, Alexandra. 1959. "The Concept of Compensation and Overcompensation in Alfred Adler's and Kurt Goldstein's Theories." *Journal of Individual Psychology,* XV, 79–82.

Adler, Alfred. 1927. *Understanding Human Nature.* Garden City, N.Y.: Garden City Publishing Co.

Alexander, F. 1950. *Psychosomatic Medicine: Its Principles and Applications.* New York: Norton.

Allport, G. W. 1955. *Becoming: Basic Considerations for a Psychology of Personality.* New Haven: Yale University Press.

Anderson, H. H. (ed.). 1959. *Creativity and Its Cultivation.* New York: Harper & Row.

Archer, W. 1889. *Masks or Faces.* New York: Longmans, Green.

Arieti, S. 1944. "The 'Placing-into-Mouth' and Coprophagic Habits." *Journal of Nervous and Mental Diseases,* XCIX, 959.

Arieti, S. 1945a. "Primitive Habits and Perceptual Alterations in the Terminal Stage of Schizophrenia." *Archives of Neurology and Psychiatry*, LIII, 378–384.

Arieti, S. 1945b. "Primitive Habits in the Preterminal Stage of Schizophrenia." *Journal of Nervous and Mental Diseases*, CII, 267.

Arieti, S. 1947. "The Processes of Expectation and Anticipation." *Journal of Nervous and Mental Diseases*, CVI, 471–481.

Arieti, S. 1948. "Special Logic of Schizophrenic and Other Types of Autistic Thought." *Psychiatry*, XI, 325.

Arieti, S. 1950. "New Views on the Psychology and Psychopathology of Wit and of the Comic." *Psychiatry*, XIII, 43.

Arieti, S. 1955. *Interpretation of Schizophrenia*. New York: Brunner.

Arieti, S. 1956a. "Some Basic Problems Common to Anthropology and Modern Psychiatry." *American Anthropologist*, LVIII, 26–39.

Arieti, S. 1956b. "The Possibility of Psychosomatic Involvement of the Central Nervous System in Schizophrenia." *Journal of Nervous and Mental Diseases*, CXXIII, 324–333.

Arieti, S. 1957a. "The Two Aspects of Schizophrenia." *Psychiatric Quarterly*, XXXI, 403–416.

Arieti, S. 1957b. "What Is Effective in the Therapeutic Process." *American Journal of Psychoanalysis*, XVII, 30.

Arieti, S. (ed.). 1959a. *American Handbook of Psychiatry*. New York: Basic Books.

Arieti, S. 1959b. "Manic-Depressive Psychosis." In Arieti, S. (ed.), *American Handbook of Psychiatry*, II, 444–446. New York: Basic Books.

Arieti, S. 1959c. "Schizophrenia: The Manifest Symptomatology, the Psychodynamic and Formal Mechanisms." In Arieti, S. (ed.), *American Handbook of Psychiatry*, I, chap. 23. New York: Basic Books.

Arieti, S. 1959d. "Some Socio-Cultural Aspects of Manic-Depressive Psychosis and Schizophrenia." In *Progress in Psychotherapy*, IV, 140–152. New York: Grune & Stratton, 1959.

Arieti, S. 1960. "The Experiences of Inner Status." In Kaplan B., and Wapner, L. (eds.), *Perspectives in Psychological Theory*. New York: International Universities Press.

Arieti, S. 1961a. "Volition and Value: A Study Based on Catatonic Schizophrenia." *Comprehensive Psychiatry*, II, 74.

Arieti, S. 1961b. "A Re-examination of the Phobic Symptom and of Symbolism in Psychopathology." *American Journal of Psychiatry*, CXVIII, 106–110.

Arieti, S. 1961c. "The Loss of Reality." *Psychoanalysis and the Psychoanalytic Review*, XLVIII, 3–24.

Arieti, S. 1962a. "The Microgeny of Thought and Perception." *Archives of General Psychiatry*, VI, 454.

Arieti, S. 1962b. "Hallucinations, Delusions and Ideas of Reference Treated with Psychotherapy." *American Journal of Psychotherapy*, XVI, 52.

Arieti, S. 1963. "The Psychotherapy of Schizophrenia in Theory and Practice." In *Psychiatric Research Report 17*, American Psychiatric Association, November.

Arieti, S. 1964. "The Rise of Creativity: From Primary to Tertiary Process." *Contemporary Psychoanalysis*, I, 51.

Arieti, S. 1965. "Contributions to Cognition from Psychoanalytic Theory." In Masserman, G. (ed.), *Science and Psychoanalysis*, VIII. New York: Grune & Stratton.

Arieti, S. 1966. "Creativity and Its Cultivation: Relation to Psychopathology and Mental Health." In Arieti, S. (ed.), *American Handbook of Psychiatry*, III. New York: Basic Books.

Arieti, S., and Meth, J. 1959. "Rare, Unclassifiable, Collective and Exotic

Psychotic Syndromes." In Arieti, S. (ed.), *American Handbook of Psychiatry*, I. New York: Basic Books.

Aristotle. *Poetics.* Quoted by Kaplan (1960).

Arnheim, R. 1954. *Art and Visual Perception: A Psychology of the Creative Eye.* Berkeley: University of California Press.

Arnold, M. B. 1960. *Emotion and Personality.* New York: Columbia University Press.

Asch, S. E. 1952. *Social Psychology.* Englewood Cliffs, N.J.: Prentice-Hall.

Ascher, E. 1948. "Psychodynamic Considerations in Gilles de la Tourette's Disease (*Maladie des Tics*). *American Journal of Psychiatry,* CV, 267.

Ascher, E. 1966. "Tics, Spasms, Gilles de la Tourette's Disease, and Other Motor Syndromes of Functional or Undetermined Origin." In Arieti, S. (ed.), *American Handbook of Psychiatry,* III. New York: Basic Books.

Baldwin, J. M. 1929. Quoted by Piaget (1929).

Barber, T. X. 1959. "Toward a Theory of Pain: Relief of Chronic Pain by Prefontal Leucotomy, Placebos, and Hypnosis." *Psychological Bulletin,* LVI, 430–460.

Baumann, 1868. *Die Lehren von Zeit, Raum und Mathematik.* Berlin. Quoted by Frege (1953).

Becker, E. 1962. "Toward a Theory of Schizophrenia." *Archives of General Psychiatry,* VII, 170–181.

Bell, C. 1913. *Art.* New York: Capricorn Books, Putnam's Sons.

Bellak, L. 1952. *Manic-Depressive Psychosis and Allied Conditions.* New York: Grune & Stratton.

Bellak, L. (ed.). 1958. *Schizophrenia: A Review of the Syndrome.* New York: Logos Press.

Bender, M. B. 1952. *Disorders in Perception with Particular Reference to Extinction and Displacement.* Springfield, Ill.: Thomas.

Bergson, H. 1912. *An Introduction to Metaphysics.* New York and London: Putnam's Sons.

Best, C. H., and Taylor, N. B. 1939. *The Physiological Basis of Medical Practice.* Baltimore: Williams & Wilkins.

Bexton, W. H., Hero, W., and Scott, T. H. 1954. "Effects of Decreased Variation in the Sensory Environment." *Canadian Journal of Psychology,* VIII, 70.

Bieber, I. 1958. "A Critique of the Libido Theory." *American Journal of Psychoanalysis,* XVIII, 52–65.

Binet, A. 1903. *Étude Experimentale de l'Intelligence.* Paris: Schleicher.

Binet, A. 1911. "Qu'est-ce qu'une emotion, qu'est-ce qu'un acte intellectuel?" *Anneé Psychologique,* 1–47.

Bishop, M. 1963. *Petrarch and His World.* Bloomington: Indiana University Press.

Black, M. 1933. *The Nature of Mathematics.* London: Routledge & Kegan Paul.

Bleuler, E. 1913. "Autistic Thinking." *American Journal of Insanity,* LXIX, 873.

Bleuler, E. 1950. *Dementia Praecox, or the Group of Schizophrenias.* New York: International Universities Press.

Blum, H. F. 1955. *Time's Arrow and Evolution,* 2d ed. Princeton: Princeton University Press.

Bosanquet, B. 1892. *A History of Aesthetic.* London: Allen & Unwin, 1949.

Bostroem, A. 1928. "Storungen der Wollens." In Bumke, O. (ed.), *Handbuch des Geisteskrankheiten.* Band 11, Teil 11, 1–90. Berlin: Springer.

Bouman, L., and Grunbaum, A. A. 1925. "Experimentell-psychologische Untersuchungen zur Aphasie und Paraphasie." *Zentralblatt für die*

Gesamte Neurologie und Psychiatrie, XCVI, 481–538. Quoted by Werner (1956).

Bowers, M. K., and Glasner, S. 1958. "Auto-hypnotic Aspects of the Jewish Cabbalistic Concept of Kavanah." *Journal of Clinical and Experimental Hypnosis*, VI, 3.

Bruner, J. S., Goodnow, J. J., and Austin, G. A. 1956. *A Study of Thinking*. New York: Wiley.

Buber, M. 1953. *I and Thou*. Edinburgh: Clark.

Bugelski, R. 1956. *The Psychology of Learning*. New York: Holt, Rinehart and Winston.

Bullough, E. 1957. *Aesthetics: Lectures and Essays*. Stanford, Calif.: Stanford University Press.

Bychowski, G. 1943. "Physiology of Schizophrenic Thinking." *Journal of Nervous and Mental Diseases*, XCVIII, 368–386.

Cameron, N. 1938. "Reasoning, Regression and Communication in Schizophrenics." *Psychological Monographs*, L, 1.

Cannon, W. B., 1929. *Bodily Changes in Pain, Hunger, Fear and Rage*. New York: Appleton-Century-Crofts.

Cannon, W. B., 1939. *The Wisdom of the Body*. New York: Norton.

Capek, M. 1957. "The Development of Reichenbach's Epistemology." *Review of Metaphysics*, IX, 42–67.

Caponigri, A. R. 1953. *Time and Idea: The Theory of History in Giambattista Vico*. Chicago: Regnery.

Carrara, E. 1948. "Sintomatologia psichica del Buerger cerebrale." *Rivista Patologia Nervosa e Mentale*, LXIX, 475–480.

Carrara, E. 1948. "Sul Buerger cerebrale." *Rivista Patologia Nervosa e Mentale*, LXIX, 13–43.

Cassirer, E. 1923. *Substance and Function and Einstein's Theory of Relativity*. New York: Dover, 1953.

Cassirer, E. 1946. *Language and Myth*. New York: Harper & Row.

Cassirer, E. 1953. *An Essay on Man*. Garden City, N.Y.: Doubleday.

Cassirer, E. 1953, 1955, 1957. *The Philosophy of Symbolic Forms* (3 vols.). New Haven: Yale University Press.

Ciardi, J. 1959. *How Does a Poem Mean?* Boston: Houghton Mifflin.

Cleckley, H. M. 1955. *The Mask of Sanity*. St. Louis: Mosby.

Cobb, S. 1950. *Emotions and Clinical Medicine*. New York: Norton.

Coghill, C. E. 1930. "The Structured Basis of the Integration of Behavior." *Proceedings, National Academy of Science, Washington*, XVI, 637–643.

Cohen, A. K. 1955. *Delinquent Boys: The Culture of the Gang*. New York: Free Press.

Cohen, R. 1953. "Role of 'Body Image Concept' in Pattern of Ipsilateral Clinical Extinction." *A.M.A. Archives of Neurology and Psychiatry*, LXX, 503–510.

Committee on Nomenclature and Statistics. 1952. *Diagnostic and Statistical Manual of Mental Disorders*. Washington, D.C.: American Psychiatric Association.

Conrad, K. 1947. "Über den Begriff der Vorgestalt und seine Bedeutung für die Hirnpathologie." *Nervenarzt*, XVIII, 289–293.

Critchley, M. 1953. *The Parietal Lobes*. London: Arnold.

Critchley, M. D. 1956. "Congenital Indifference to Pain." *American Internal Medicine*, XLV, 737.

Croce, B. 1909. *Aesthetic*. New York: Noonday, 1953.

Croce, B. 1947. *La Filosofia d' Giambattista Vico*. Bari: Laterza.

Dantzig, T. 1954. *Number: The Language of Science*. Garden City, N.Y.: Doubleday.

Darwin, C. 1873. *The Expression of Emotions in Man and Animals*. New York: Philosophical Library, 1955.

De Martino, E. 1948. *Il Mondo Magico*. Turin: Quoted by Tullio-Altan (1960).

Dement, W. 1961. "Experimental Studies of Sleep and Dreaming." Lecture delivered at the Association for the Advancement of Psychotherapy, New York, May 19.

Denny-Brown, D. 1950. "Disintegration of Motor Function Resulting from Cerebral Lesions." *Journal of Nervous and Mental Diseases*, CXII, 1–45.

Denny-Brown, D. 1958. "The Nature of Apraxia." *Journal of Nervous and Mental Diseases*, CXXVI, 9–32.

Denny-Brown, D., and Chambers, R. A. 1958. "The Parietal Lobe and Behavior." In *Research Publications of the Association for Research in Nervous and Mental Disease, No. 1. The Brain and Human Behavior.* Baltimore: Williams & Wilkins.

Diamond, A. S. 1959. *The History and Origin of Language*. London: Methuen.

Diamond, S., Balvin, R. S., and Diamond, F. R. 1963. *Inhibition and Choice: Neurobehavioral Approach to Problems of Plasticity in Behavior.* New York: Harper & Row.

Ditchburn, R. W. 1961. "Report to the Experimental Psychology Group, University of Reading, Reading, England, 1957." Quoted by Brunner, J. S., in *Sensory Deprivation-Symposium*. Cambridge: Harvard University Press.

Ducasse, C. J. 1929. *The Philosophy of Art*. New York: Dial.

Dunbar, F. 1946. *Emotions and Bodily Changes*. New York: Columbia University Press.

Du Noüy, Lecomte P. 1947. *Human Destiny*. New York: Longmans, Green.

Durkheim, E. 1950. *The Rules of Sociological Method*. New York: Free Press.

Eccles, J. C. 1953. *The Neurophysiological Basis of Mind*. Oxford: Oxford University Press.

Eccles, J. C. 1957. *The Physiology of Nerve Cells*. Baltimore: Johns Hopkins Press.

Ehrenzweig, A. 1957. *The Psychoanalysis of Artistic Vision and Hearing*. New York: Julian Press.

Ehrlich, S. K. and Keogh, R. P. 1956. "The Psychopath in a Mental Institution." *A.M.A. Archives of Neurology and Psychiatry*, LXXVI, 286–295.

Eiduson, B. T. 1962. *Scientists: Their Psychological World*. New York: Basic Books.

Eisenberg, L., Ascher, E., Kanner, C. 1959. "A Clinical Study of Gilles De La Tourette's Disease (*Maladie des Tics*) in Children." *American Journal of Psychiatry*, CXV, 715.

English, H. B., and English, A. C. 1958. *A Comprehensive Dictionary of Psychological and Psychoanalytical Terms.* New York: Longmans, Green.

English, O. S., and Pearson, G. H. J. 1937. *Common Neuroses of Children and Adults.* New York: Norton.

Erikson, E. H. 1953. "Growth and Crises of the Healthy Personality." In Kluckhohn, C., Murray, H. A., and Schneider, D. M. (eds.), *Personality in Nature, Society and Culture.* New York: Knopf.

Fairbairn, W. R. D. 1952. *Psychoanalytic Studies of the Personality*. New York: Basic Books.

Fechner, G. T. 1876. *Vorschule der Aesthetik*, Leipzig: Breitkopf & Härtel.

Federn, P. 1952. *Ego Psychology and the Psychoses*. New York: Basic Books.

Fenichel, O. 1945. *The Psychoanalytic Theory of Neurosis*. New York: Norton.

Ferenczi, S. 1913. "Stages in the Development of the Sense of Reality." In

Ferenczi, S. (ed.), *Sex in Psychoanalysis*. New York: Basic Books, 1950.

Ferrio, C. 1948. *La Psiche e i Nervi*. Turin: Utet.

Festinger, L. 1957. *A Theory of Cognitive Dissonance*. Stanford, Calif.: Stanford University Press.

Field, J. (ed.). 1960. *Handbook of Physiology*. Section 1: *Neurophysiology* (Magoun, H. W., ed.), vols. I, II, III. Washington: American Physiological Society.

Fisher, C. 1954. "Dream and Perception. The Role of Preconscious and Primary Modes of Perception in Dream Formation." *Journal of the American Psychoanalytic Association*, II, 380–445.

Fisher, C. 1960. "Subliminal and Supraliminal Influences on Dreams." *American Journal of Psychiatry*, CXVI, 1009–1017.

Fisher, C., and Paul, J. H. 1959. "The Effect of Subliminal Visual Stimulation on Images and Dreams: A. Validation Study." *Journal of the American Psychoanalytic Association*, VII, 35–83.

Flavell, J. H. 1963. *The Developmental Psychology of Jean Piaget*. Princeton: Van Nostrand.

Flavell, J. H., and Draguns, J. 1957. "A Microgenetic Approach to Perception and Thought." *Psychological Bulletin*, LIV, 197–217.

Fletcher, R. 1957. *Instinct in Man*. New York: International Universities Press.

Ford, C. S., and Beach, F. A. 1951. *Patterns of Sexual Behavior*. New York: Harper & Row.

Forrest, D. V. 1965. "Poiesis and the Language of Schizophrenia" *Psychiatry*, XXVIII, 1.

Foss, M. 1949. *Symbol and Metaphor in Human Experience*. Princeton: Princeton University Press.

Frank, P. 1957. *Philosophy of Science*. Englewood Cliffs, N.J.: Prentice-Hall.

Frazer, J. G. 1922. *The Golden Bough*. New York: Macmillan.

Frege, G. 1953. *The Foundations of Arithmetic*. London: Blackwell & Mott, Ltd., reprinted in Harper Torchbook, New York: Harper & Row, 1960.

Freud, S. 1893. "On the Psychical Mechanism of Hysterical Phenomena." *Collected Papers*, I, 24. New York: Basic Books, 1959.

Freud, S. 1894. "The Justification for Detaching from Neurasthenia a Particular Syndrome: The Anxiety Neurosis." *Collected Papers*, I, 76. New York: Basic Books, 1959.

Freud, S. 1901. *The Interpretation of Dreams*. New York: Basic Books, 1960.

Freud, S. 1908. "Character and Anal Eroticism." *Collected Papers*, II, 48. New York: Basic Books, 1959.

Freud, S. 1909. "Analysis of a Phobia in a Five-year-old Boy." *Collected Papers*, III, 149. New York: Basic Books, 1959.

Freud, S. 1910. "The Anthithetical Sense of Primal Words." *Collected Papers*, IV, 184–191. New York: Basic Books, 1959.

Freud, S. 1911. "Formulations Regarding the Two Principles in Mental Functioning." *Collected Papers*, IV, 13–21. New York: Basic Books, 1959.

Freud, S. 1914. "The Moses of Michelangelo." *Collected Papers*, IV, 257–287. New York: Basic Books, 1959.

Freud, S. 1915a. "Repression." *Collected Papers*, IV. New York: Basic Books, 1959.

Freud, S. 1915b. "The Unconscious." *Collected Papers*, IV, 84. New York: Basic Books, 1959.

Freud, S. 1916. *Wit and Its Relation to the Unconscious*. New York: Moffat, Yard. Also in, Brill, A. A. (ed.), *The Basic Writings of Sigmund Freud*. New York: Modern Library, 1938.

Freud, S. 1920. *A General Introduction to Psychoanalysis.* Garden City, N.Y.: Garden City Publishing Co., 1938.

Freud, S. 1925. "Negation." *Collected Papers,* V, 181. New York: Basic Books, 1959.

Freud, S. 1927. *The Ego and the Id.* London: Hogarth Press, 1947.

Freud, S. 1928. *The Future of an Illusion.* New York: Liveright, 1949.

Freud, S. 1938. "Psychopathology of Everyday Life." In Brill, A. A. (ed.), *The Basic Writings of Sigmund Freud.* New York: Modern Library, 1938.

Friedman, M. 1964. *The Worlds of Existentialism.* New York: Random House.

Froeschels, E. 1948. *Philosophy in Wit.* New York: Philosophical Library.

Gabel, J. 1948. "Symbolisme et Schizophrenie." *Revue Suisse de Psychologie et de Psychologie Appliquée,* VII, 268.

Gantt, W. H. 1936. "An Experimental Approach to Psychiatry." *American Journal of Psychiatry,* XCII, 1007–1021.

Gerard, R. W. 1956. "Brain Physiology: A Basic Science." In Rado, S., and Daniels, G. E. (eds.), *Changing Concepts of Psychoanalytic Medicine.* New York: Grune & Stratton.

Gerstmann, J. 1958. "Psychological and Phenomenological Aspects of Disorders of the Body Image." *Journal of Nervous and Mental Diseases,* CXXVI, 499.

Gesell, A. 1945. *The Embriology of Behavior.* New York: Harper & Row.

Getzels, J. W., and Jackson, P. W. 1962. *Creativity and Intelligence: Explorations with Gifted Children.* New York: Wiley.

Ghiselin, B. 1952. *The Creative Process.* Berkeley: University of California Press.

Gilbert, K., and Kuhn, H. 1953. *A History of Esthetics.* Bloomington: Indiana University Press.

Gill, M. M., and Brennan, M. 1959. *Hypnosis and Related States.* New York: International Universities Press.

Gilles de la Tourette. 1885. "Étude sur une affection nerveuse caracterisée par de l'incoordination motrice, accompagnée d'echolalie et de coprolalie." *Archives de Neurologie,* IX, 19:159.

Glueck, S., and Glueck, E. T. 1956. *Physique and Delinquency.* New York: Harper & Row.

Goldman, A. E. 1960. "Symbolic Representation in Schizophrenia." *Journal of Personality,* XXVIII, 293–316.

Goldman, A. E. 1961. "The Classification of Sign Phenomena." *Psychiatry,* XXIV, 299–306.

Goldstein, K. 1939. *The Organism.* New York: American Book Co.

Goldstein, K. 1940. *Human Nature in the Light of Psychopathology.* Cambridge: Harvard University Press.

Goldstein, K. 1943. "Some Remarks on Russel Brain's Article Concerning Visual Object Agnosia." *Journal of Nervous and Mental Disorders,* XCVIII, 148–153.

Goldstein, K., and Gelb, A. 1920. "Psychologische Analyse hirnpathologischer Falle." Leipzig: Barth, I, 1–143.

Gordon, H. L. 1949. *The Maggid of Caro.* New York: Pardes.

Gregory, J. C. 1924. *The Nature of Laughter.* London: Kegan Paul.

Grinker, R. R. 1961. "The Physiology of Emotions." In Simon, A., Herbert, C. C., and Straus, R. (eds.), *The Physiology of Emotions.* Springfield, Ill.: Thomas.

Gruber, H. E., Terrell, G., and Wertheimer, M. 1962. *Contemporary Approaches to Creative Thinking.* New York: Atherton Press.

Hadamard, J. 1945. *The Psychology of Invention in the Mathematical Field.* Princeton: Princeton University Press.

Hammer, E. F. 1961. *Creativity.* New York: Random House.

Harlow, J. M. 1848. "Passage of an Iron Rod through the Head." *Boston Medical and Surgical Journal*, 389–393.

Harlow, J. M. 1868. "Recovery from the Passage of an Iron Bar through the Head." *Massachusetts Medical Society Publications*, II, 327–346.

Hartmann, H. 1950a. "Psychoanalysis and Development Psychology." In *The Psychoanalytic Study of the Child*, V. New York: International Universities Press.

Hartmann, H. 1950b. "Comments on the Psychoanalytic Theory of the Ego." In *Psychoanalytic Study of the Child*, V. New York: International Universities Press.

Hartmann, H. 1964. *Essays on Ego Psychology: Selected Problems in Psychoanalytic Theory*. New York: International Universities Press.

Hartmann, H., and Kris, L. 1945. "The Genetic Approach in Psychoanalysis." In *The Psychoanalytic Study of the Child*. I, 11–29. New York: International Universities Press.

Hartmann, H., Kris, E., and Lowenstein, R. M. 1946. "Comments on the Formation of Psychic Structures." *The Psychoanalytic Study of the Child*. II, 11–38. New York: International Universities Press.

Hayes, K. J., and Hayes, C. 1951. The Intellectual Development of a Home-raised Chimpanzee. *Proceedings of the American Philosophical Society*, XCV, 105–109.

Hebb, D. O. 1949. *The Organization of Behavior*. New York: Wiley.

Hecker, J. F. C. 1832. *Die Tanzwuth: eine Volkskrankheit im Mittelalter*. Berlin.

Helmholtz, H. von. 1896. *Vortrage und Reden, 5th aufl*. Brammschweig: Vieweg und John.

Heron, W.; Doane, B. K., and Scott, T. H. 1956. "Visual Disturbances after Prolonged Isolation." *Canadian Journal of Psychology*, X, 13.

Herrick, C. J. 1948. *The Brain of the Tiger Salamander, Ambystoma Ligrirum*. Chicago: University of Chicago Press.

Hilgard, E. R. 1956. *Theories of Learning*, 2d ed. New York: Appleton-Century-Crofts.

Hilgard, E. R., and Marquis, D. C. 1940. *Conditioning and Learning*. New York: Appleton-Century-Crofts.

Hill, D. 1952. "EEG in Episodic Psychotic and Psychopathic Behavior." *Electroencephalography and Clinical Neurophysiology*, IV, 439.

Hill, D. 1955. "Electroencephalography." In Brain, W. R., and Strauss, E. B. (eds.), *Recent Advances in Neurology and Neuropsychiatry*. London: G. A. Churchill.

Hillman, J. 1960. *Emotion*. London: Routledge & Kegan Paul.

Horney, K. 1950. *Neurosis and Human Growth*. New York: Norton.

Huguet, E. 1904. *Les Metaphores et les Comparaisons dans l'Ouevre de Victor Hugo*. Paris. Quoted by Konrad (1958).

Huizinga, J. 1924. *The Waning of the Middle Ages*. Reprinted in Anchor Books, Garden City, N.Y.: Doubleday, 1956.

Hull, C. L. 1920. "Quantitative Aspects of the Evolution of Concepts." *Psychological Monographs*, 123.

Humphrey, G. 1951. *Thinking: An Introduction to Its Experimental Psychology*. London and New York: Methuen and Wiley, 1951.

Huxley, J. S. 1953. *Evolution in Action*. New York: Harper & Row.

Jackson, J. H. 1932. "On Affections of Speech from Disease of the Brain." In Taylor, J. (ed.), *Selected Writings of John Hughlings Jackson*, II, 184–204. London: Hodder and Stoughton.

Jackson, J. H. 1932b. "An Address on the Psychology of Joking." *British Medical Journal*, Oct. 22, 1887; reprinted in *Selected Writings of John Hughlings Jackson*, II, 359. London: Hodder and Stoughton.

James, W. 1902. *The Varieties of Religious Experience*. New York: Modern Library, 1929.

Janis, I. L., and Frick, F. 1943. "The Relationship between Attitudes toward Conclusions and Errors in Judging Logical Validity of Syllogisms." *Journal of Experimental Psychology*, XXXIII, 73–77.

Jenkins, R. L. 1960. "The Psychopathic or Antisocial Personality." *Journal of Nervous and Mental Disorders*, CXXXI, 318–334.

Jespersen, O. 1922. *Language: Its Nature, Development and Origin*. London: Allen & Unwin.

Johnson, A. 1959. "Juvenile Delinquency." In Arieti, S. (ed.), *American Handbook of Psychiatry*, I, 840–856. New York: Basic Books.

Jones, E. 1953. *The Life and Work of Sigmund Freud*, I. New York: Basic Books.

Jossman, P. 1929. "Zur Psychopathologie der Optisch-agnostischen Störungen." *Monatschrift für Psychiatrie und Neurologie*. LXXII, 81–149.

Jung, C. G. 1903. *The Psychology of Dementia Praecox*. Nervous and Mental Disease Monograph, Series No. 3. New York, 1936.

Jung, C. G. 1933. *Modern Man in Search of a Soul*. London: Routledge & Kegan Paul.

Jung, C. G. 1959. "The Archetypes and the Collective Unconscious." *Collected Works*. New York: Pantheon.

Kanner, L. 1942. *Child Psychiatry*. Springfield, Ill.: Thomas.

Kaplan, B. 1955. "Some Psychological Methods for the Investigation of Expressive Language." In Werner, H. (ed.), *On Expressive Language*. Worcester, Mass.: Clark University Press.

Kaplan, B. 1957. "On the Phenomena of Opposite Speech." *Journal of Abnormal and Social Psychology*, CV, 389–393.

Kaplan, B. 1960. "Radical Metaphor, Aesthetic and the Origin of Language." *Review of Existential Psychology and Psychiatry*. II, 75–84.

Karpman, B. 1941. "On the Need for Separating Psychopathy into Two Disinct Clinical Types: Symptomatic and Idiopathic." *Journal of Criminal Psychopath*. III, 112–137.

Kaufmann, Y. 1960. *The Religion of Israel*. Chicago: University of Chicago Press.

Kellogg, W. N., and Kellogg, L. A. 1933. *The Ape and the Child*. New York: McGraw-Hill.

Kelsen, H. 1943. *Society and Nature*. Chicago: University of Chicago Press.

Klein, M. 1948a. *Contributions to Psycho-Analysis*. London: Hogarth Press.

Klein, M. 1948b. "A Contribution to the Psychogenesis of Manic-Depressive States." In Klein, M. (ed.), *Contributions to Psycho-Analysis, 1945*. London: Hogarth Press.

Klein, M., Heimann, P., and Money-Kyrle, R. 1955. *New Directions in Psychoanalysis*. New York: Basic Books.

Klüver, H. 1933. *Behavior Mechanisms in Monkeys*. Chicago: University of Chicago Press.

Klüver, H. 1936. "The Study of Personality and the Method of Equivalent and Non-equivalent Stimuli." *Character and Personality*, V, 91–112.

Klüver, H. 1951. "Functional Differences between the Occipital and Temporal Lobes." In Jeffress, L. A. (ed.), *Cerebral Mechanisms of Behavior*. New York: Wiley.

Koestler, A. 1949. *Insight and Outlook*. New York: Macmillan.

Koestler, A. 1964. *The Act of Creation*. New York: Macmillan.

Konrad, H. 1958. *Etude sur la Metaphore*. Paris: Vrin.

Kraepelin, E. 1919. *Dementia Praecox and Paraphrenia*. Edinburgh: Livingstone.

Kraepelin, E., 1921. *Manic-Depressive Insanity and Paranoia*. Edinburgh: Livingstone.

Kretschmer, E. 1934. *A Text-Book of Medical Psychology* (trans. E. B. Strauss). Oxford: Oxford University Press.

Kris, E. 1950. "On Preconscious Mental Processes." *Psychoanalytic Quarterly.* XIX, 542. Reprinted in Kris (1952).

Kris, E. 1952. *Psychoanalytic Explorations in Art.* New York: International Universities Press.

Kroeber, A. L. 1948. *Anthropology.* New York: Harcourt, Brace & World, 1948.

Kubie, L. S. 1958. *Neurotic Distortion of the Creative Process.* Lawrence: University of Kansas Press.

Lacey, J. I., Bateman, D. E., and Van Lehn, R. 1953. "Automatic Response Specificity: An Experimental Study." *Psychosomatic Medicine,* XV, 8.

Lacey, J. I., and Lacey, B. C. 1958. "Verification and Extension of the Principle of Autonomic Response-Stereotopy." *American Journal of Psychology,* LXXI, 50.

Laffal, J., Lenkoski, L., and Arneen, L. 1956. " 'Opposite Speech' in a Schizophrenic Patient." *Journal of Abnormal and Social Psychology,* LII, 409–413.

Langer, S. K. 1942. *Philosophy in a New Key.* Cambridge: Harvard University Press.

Langer, S. K. 1953. *Feeling and Form.* New York: Scribner.

Langer, S. K. 1962. "Speculations on the Origins of Speech and Its Communicative Function," in *Philosophical Sketches.* Baltimore: Johns Hopkins.

Lapassade, G. 1963. *L'Entrée dans la Vie.* Paris: De Minuit.

Lashley, K. S. 1949. "Persistent Problems in the Evolution of Mind." *Quarterly Review of Biology,* XXVI, 28. Reprinted in Beach, F. A., Hebb, D. O., Morgan, C. T., and Nissen, H. W. (eds.), *The Neuropsychology of Lashley.* New York: McGraw-Hill, 1960.

Lashley, K. S., and Colby, K. M. 1957. "An Exchange of Views on Psychic Energy and Psychoanalysis." *Behavioral Science,* II, 230–240.

Laski, M. 1961. *Ecstasy: A Study of Some Secular and Religious Experiences.* London: Cresset Press.

Laurendeu, M., and Pinard, A. 1962. *Causal Thinking in the Child: A Genetic and Experimental Approach.* New York: International Universities Press.

Lelut, 1846. *L'Amulette de Pascal; pour Servir à l'Histoire des Hallucinations.* Quoted by Morgue, R., in *Neurobiologic de l'Hallucination.* Brussels: Lamertin, 1932.

Leonhard, K. 1960. *Die Aufteilung der Endogenen Psychosen.* Berlin: Academic Verlag.

Leonard, K. 1961. "Cycloid Psychoses—Endogenous Psychoses Which Are Neither Schizophrenic nor Manic-Depressive." *Journal of Mental Science,* CVII, 633.

Levin, M. 1936. "On the Causation of Mental Symptoms." *Journal of Mental Science,* LXXXII, 1–27.

Levy, D. 1939. "Maternal Overprotection." *Psychiatry,* II, 99.

Lévy-Bruhl, L. 1910. *Les Fonctions Mentales dans les Sociétés Inférieures.* Paris: Alcan.

Liddell, H. S. 1938. "The Experimental Neurosis and the Problem of Mental Disorder." *American Journal of Psychiatry,* XCIV, 1035–1043.

Lilly, J. C. 1959. "Mental Effects of Reduction of Ordinary Levels of Physical Stimuli on Intact, Healthy Persons." *Psychiatric Research Report* No. 5, American Psychiatric Association.

Lindesmith, A. R. 1947. *Opiate Addiction.* Bloomington: Principia Press.

Lindsley, D. B. 1964. "The Ontogeny of Pleasure: Neural and Behavioral Development." In Heath, R. G. (ed.), *The Role of Pleasure in Behavior.* New York: Hoeber.

Linn, L. 1954. "The Discriminating Function of the Ego." *Psychoanalytic Quarterly,* XXIII, 38–47.

Lombroso, C. 1864. *Genio e follia*. Milan.
Lombroso, C. 1876. *L'uomo delinquente in rapporto alla antropologia, alla giurisprudenza ed alle discipline carcerarie*. Milan.
Lombroso, C. 1898. *Genio e degenerazione*. Palermo.
Lorenz, K. 1937. "The Nature of Instinct: The Conception of Instinctual Behavior." In Schiller, Claire H. (ed.), *Instinctual Behavior: The Development of a Modern Concept*. New York: International Universities Press, 1957.
Lorenz, K. Z. 1953. "Comparative Behaviourology." In *Discussions on Child Development*, I. World Health Organization on the Psychobiological Development of the Child, Geneva. New York: International Universities Press.
Lotmar, F. 1919. "Zur Kenntnis der erschwerten Wortfindung und ihrer Bedeutung fur das Denken des Aphasischen." *Schweizer Archiv für Neurologie und Psychologie*, V, 206–239.
Mach, E. 1883. *Mechanick*.
MacIntyre, A. C. 1958. *The Unconscious: A Conceptual Study*. London: Routledge & Kegan Paul. New York: Humanities Press.
MacLean, P. D. 1949. "Psychosomatic Disease and the 'Visceral Brain': Recent Developments Bearing on the Papez Theory of Emotion." *Psychosomatic Medicine*, XI, 338–353.
MacLean, P. D. 1955. "The Limbic System ('Visceral Brain') and Emotional Behavior." *A.M.A. Archives of Neurology and Psychiatry*, LXXIII, 130–134.
MacLean, P. D. 1957a. "Chemical and Electrical Stimulation of Hippocampus in Unrestrained Animals: 1. Methods and Electroencephalographic Findings." *A.M.A. Archives of Neurology and Psychiatry*, LXXVIII, 113.
MacLean, P. D. 1957b. "Chemical and Electrical Stimulation of Hippocampus in Unrestrained Animals: 2. Behavioral Findings." *A.M.A. Archives of Neurology and Psychiatry*, LXXVIII, 128.
MacLean, P. D. 1959. "The Limbic System with Respect to Two Basic Life Principles." In Brazier, M. A. B. (ed.), *The Central Nervous System and Behavior*. New York: Macy.
MacLean, P. D. 1960. "Psychosomatics." In Field, J. (ed.), *Handbook of Physiology, Section One: Neurophysiology*. III, 1723–1744. Washington: American Physiological Society.
Magee, K. R., Schneider, S. F., and Rosenzweig, N. 1961. "Congenital Indifference to Pain." *Journal of Nervous and Mental Disorders*, CXXXII, 249–259.
Malmo, R. B. 1942. "Interference Factors in Delayed Response in Monkeys after Removal of Frontal Lobes." *Journal of Neurophysiology*, V, 295.
Marbe, K. 1901. *Experimentell-psychologische Untersuchungen über das Urteil*. Leipzig. Quoted by Humphrey, G., in *Thinking: An Introduction to Experimental Psychology*. London and New York: Methuen and Wiley, 1951.
Maslow, A. H. 1948. Cognition of the Individual and of the Generic. *Psychological Review*, LV, 22–40. Reprinted in Maslow (1954).
Maslow, A. H. 1954. *Motivation and Personality*. New York: Harper & Row.
Maslow, A. H. 1959. "Cognition of Being in the Peak Experiences." *Journal of Genetic Psychology*, XCIV, 43–66.
Maslow, A. H. 1961. "Peak Experiences as Acute Identity Experiences." *American Journal of Psychoanalysis*, XXI, 254–260.
Matte-Blanco, I. 1959. "Expression in Symbolic Logic of the Characteristics of the System UCS or the Logic of the System UCS." *International Journal of Psychoanalysis*, XI, 1.
Matte-Blanco, I. 1965. "A Study of Schizophrenic Thinking: Its Expression in Terms of Symbolic Logic and Its Representation in Terms of

Multi-Dimensional Space." *International Journal of Psychiatry*, I, 91.

May, R. 1950. *The Meaning of Anxiety*. New York: Ronald Press.

McDougall, W. 1926. *An Introduction to Social Psychology*. Boston: John W. Luce.

Mead, G. H. 1934. *Mind, Self and Society*. Chicago: University of Chicago Press.

Meares, A. 1960. *A System of Medical Hypnosis*. Philadelphia: Saunders.

Messer, A. 1906. "Experimentelle psychologische Untersuchungen über das Denken." *Archiv für die Gesamte Psychologie*, VIII, 1–224.

Meyer, L. B. 1956. *Emotion and Meaning in Music*. Chicago: University of Chicago Press.

Miller, J. G. 1942. *Unconsciousness*. New York: Wiley.

Milner, B. 1958. "Psychological Defects Produced by Temporal Lobe Excision." *Research Publications of the Association for Research in Nervous and Mental Diseases*, 36. Baltimore: Williams and Wilkins.

Milner, B. 1959. "The Memory Defect in Bilateral Hippocampal Lesions." In Cameron, D. E., and Greenblatt, M. (eds.), *Recent Advances in Neuro-Physiological Research*. Psychiatric Research Reports of the American Psychiatric Association, No. 11, 33.

Morris, C. 1946. *Signs, Language and Behavior*. Englewood Cliffs, N.J.: Prentice-Hall.

Mowrer, O. H. 1960a. *Learning Theory and Behavior*. New York: Wiley.

Mowrer, O. H. 1960b. *Learning Theory and the Symbolic Process*. New York: Wiley.

Munro, T. 1956. *Toward Science in Aesthetics: Selected Essays*. New York: Liberal Art Press.

Muratori, L. A. 1774. *Della forza della fantasia umana*. Naples: Langiacomo.

Nielsen, J. M. 1946. *Agnosia, Apraxia, Aphasia: Their Value in Cerebral Localization*. New York: Hoeber.

Nunberg, H. 1955. *Principles of Psychoanalysis*. New York: International Universities Press.

Nyswander, M. 1956. *The Drug Addict as a Patient*. New York: Grune & Stratton.

Ogden, C. K., and Richards, J. A. 1947. *The Meaning of Meaning*. New York: Harcourt, Brace & World.

Ogden, T. E., Robert, F., and Carmichael, T. E. 1959. "Some Sensory Syndromes in Children: Indifference to Pain and Sensory Neuropathy." *Journal of Neurological and Neurosurgical Psychiatry*, XXII, 267–276.

Oparin, A. I. 1938. *Origin of Life*. New York: Macmillan.

Ostow, M. 1955. "A Psychoanalytic Contribution to the Study of Brain Function: II. The Temporal Lobes. III. Synthesis." *Psychoanalytic Quarterly*, XXIV, 383–423.

Otto, Rudolf. 1923. *The Idea of the Holy*. Oxford: Oxford University Press, 1957.

Papez, J. W. 1937. "A Proposed Mechanism of Emotion." *Archives of Neurology and Psychiatry*, XXXVIII, 725–743.

Penfield, W. 1958. "Functional Localization in Temporal and Deep Sylvian Areas." *Research Publications of the Association for Research in Nervous and Mental Diseases*, 36, 210. Baltimore: Williams and Wilkins.

Penfield, W., and Milner, B. 1958. "The Memory Defect Produced by Bilateral Lesions of the Hippocampal Zone." *A.M.A. Archives of Neurology and Psychiatry*, LVIII, 477.

Penfield, W., and Rasmussen, T. 1952. *The Cerebral Cortex of Man*. New York: Macmillan.

Peters, R. S. 1958. *The Concept of Motivation*. London: Routledge & Kegan Paul. New York: Humanities Press.

Philipson, M. 1963. *Outline of a Jungian Aesthetics*. Evanston, Ill.: Northwestern University Press.

Piaget, J. 1929. *The Child's Conception of the World.* New York: Harcourt, Brace & World.

Piaget, J. 1930. *The Child's Conception of Physical Causality.* New York: Harcourt, Brace & World.

Piaget, J. 1952. *The Origins of Intelligence in Children.* New York: International Universities Press.

Piaget, J. 1957. *Logic and Psychology.* New York: Basic Books.

Poincaré, H. 1913. "Mathematical Creation." In *The Foundations of Science.* Lancaster: The Science Press, 1946.

Pötzl, O. 1917. "Experimentell erregte Traumbilder in ihren Beziehungen zum indirekten Sehen." *Zeitschrift für Neurologie und Psychiatrie,* XXXVII, 278–349.

Pötzl, O., Allers, R., and Teler, J. 1960. *Preconscious Stimulation in Dreams, Associations, and Images.* New York: International Universities Press.

Pritchard, R. M., Heron, W., and Hebb, D. O. 1960. "Visual Perception Approached by the Method of Stabilized Images." *Canadian Journal of Psychology,* XIV, 67–77.

Purnes-Stewart, J., and Worster-Drought, C. 1952. *The Diagnosis of Nervous Diseases,* 10th ed. London: Arnold & Co.

Rapaport, D. 1951. "Toward a Theory of Thinking." In Rapaport, D. (ed.), *Organization and Pathology of Thought.* New York: Columbia University Press. Reprinted in Gill, M. (ed.), *The Collected Papers of David Rapaport.* New York: Basic Books, 1967.

Rapaport, D. 1953. Appendix in Schilder, P., *Medical Psychology.* New York: International Universities Press. Reprinted in Gill, M. (ed.), *The Collected Papers of David Rapaport.* New York: Basic Books, 1967.

Rapaport, D. 1954. "On the Psychoanalytic Theory of Affects." In Knight, R. P. (ed.), *Psychoanalytic Psychiatry and Psychology.* New York: International Universities Press. Reprinted in Gill, M. (ed.), *The Collected Papers of David Rapaport.* New York: Basic Books, 1967.

Rapaport, D. 1960. *The Structure of Psychoanalytic Theory.* New York: International Universities Press.

Razzan, G. 1961. "The Observable Unconscious and the Inferable Conscious in Current Soviet Psychophysiology: Interecoceptive Conditioning, Semantic Conditioning, and the Orienting Reflex." *Psychological Review,* LXVIII, 81.

Reichenbach, H. 1951. *The Rise of Scientific Philosophy.* Berkeley: University of California Press.

Reik, T. 1946. *Ritual: Psychoanalytic Studies.* New York: Farrar, Straus & Giroux.

Riesen, A. H. 1947. "The Development of Visual Perception in Man and Chimpanzee." *Science,* CVI, 107–108.

Riggs, L. A., and Tulunay, S. U. 1959. "Visual Effects of Varying the Extent of Compensation for Eye Movements." *Journal of the Optic Society of America,* IX, 741–745.

Robbins, B. S. 1955. "The Myth of Latent Emotion: A Critique of the Concept of Repression." *Psychotherapy: Journal of the Robbins Institute,* I, 3.

Rossman, J. 1931 *The Psychology of the Inventor: A Study of the Patentee.* Washington, D.C.: The Inventor Publishing Co.

Ruesch, J. 1955. "Nonverbal Language and Therapy." *Psychiatry,* XVIII, 323.

Ruesch, J. 1957. *Disturbed Communication.* New York: Norton.

Ruesch, J. 1961. *Therapeutic Communication.* New York: Norton.

Ruesch, J., and Kees, W. 1956. *Nonverbal Communication.* Berkeley: University of California Press.

Rush, J. H. 1957. *The Dawn of Life.* Garden City, N.Y.: Hanover House.

Russell, B. 1912. *The Problems of Philosophy*. London: Oxford University Press (reprinted in 1951).

Russell, B. 1919. *Introduction to Mathematical Philosophy*.

Russell, E. S. 1945. *The Directiveness of Organic Activities*. Cambridge: Harvard University Press.

Sapir, E. 1949. "The Unconscious Patterning of Behavior in Society." In Mandelbaum, S. C. (ed.), *Selected Writings of Edward Sapir in Language, Culture and Personality*. Berkeley: University of California Press.

Schachtel, E. G. 1954. "The Development of Focal Attention and the Emergence of Reality." *Psychiatry*, XVII, 309.

Schachtel, E. G. 1959. *Metamorphosis*. New York: Basic Books.

Scheler, M. 1928. *Man's Place in Nature*. Boston: Beacon Press, 1961.

Schilder, P. 1953. *Medical Psychology*. New York: International Universities Press.

Schleirmacher, F. 1958. *On Religion*. London: Routledge & Kegan Paul. Reprinted by Harper & Row, New York.

Schlesinger, B. 1962. "Higher Cerebral Functions and Their Clinical Disorders." New York: Grune & Stratton.

Schneck, J. M. 1960. "Gilles de la Tourette's Disease." *American Journal of Psychiatry*, CXVII, 78.

Schneirla, T. C. 1939. "A Theoretical Consideration of the Basis for Approach-Withdrawal Adjustments in Behavior." *Psychological Bulletin*, XXXVII, 501–502.

Schneirla, T. C. 1949. "Levels in the Psychological Capacities of Animals." In Sellars, R. W. (ed.), *Philosophy for the Future*. New York: Macmillan.

Schneirla, T. C. 1959. "An Evolutionary and Developmental Theory of Biphasic Processes Underlying Approach and Withdrawal." In *Nebraska Symposium on Motivation*, 1–42. Lincoln: University of Nebraska Press.

Sechehaye, M. A. 1951. *Symbolic Realization*. New York: International Universities Press.

Sells, S. B. 1936. "The Atmosphere Effect: An Experimental Study of Reasoning." *Archives of Psychology*, 200.

Shatan, C. 1963. "Unconscious Motor Behavior, Kinesthetic Awareness and Psychotherapy." *American Journal of Psychotherapy*, XVII, 17.

Shaw, C. R., and McKay, H. O. 1931. *Social Factors in Juvenile Delinquency*. National Commission on Law Observance and Enforcement; Report on the Causes of Crimes. Washington, D.C.: GPO.

Sherrington, C. S. 1948. *The Integrative Action of the Nervous System*. (Revision of 1906 ed.) New Haven: Yale University Press.

Silberer, H. 1909. "Report on a Method of Eliciting and Observing Certain Symbolic Hallucination Phenomena." Republished in Rapaport (1951).

Silberer, H. 1912. "On Symbol Formation." Republished in Rapaport (1951).

Silverberg, W. V. 1952. *Childhood Experience and Personal Destiny*. New York: Springer.

Simon, A., Herbert, C. C., and Strauss, R. 1961. *The Physiology of Emotions*. Springfield, Ill.: Thomas.

Simons, D. J., and Diethelm 1946. "Electroencephalographic Studies of Psychopathic Personalities." *Archives of Neurology and Psychiatry*, LV, 619–626.

Singleton, C. S. 1954. *Commedia: Elements of Structure*. Cambridge: Harvard University Press.

Sinnott, E. W. 1955. *The Biology of the Spirit*. New York: Viking Press.

Sinnott, E. W. 1959. "The Creativeness of Life." In Anderson, H. H. (ed.), *Creativity and Its Cultivation*. New York: Harper & Row.

Slonimsky, H. 1956. "The Philosophy Implicit in the Midrash." *Hebrew Union College Annual*, XXVI, 235–290.

Smith, P. 1959. *Creativity: An Examination of the Creative Process*. New York: Hastings House.

Spencer, H. 1899. *The Principles of Psychology*. London: Williams and Norgate.

Spiegel, H. 1959. "Hypnosis and Transference: A Theoretical Formulation." *A.M.A. Archives of General Psychiatry*, I, 634.

Spitz, R. A. 1957. *No and Yes: On the Genesis of Human Communication*. New York: International Universities Press.

Stein, M. I., and Heinze, S. J. 1960. *Creativity and the Individual: Summary of Selected Literature in Psychology and Psychiatry*. New York: Free Press.

Stolnitz, J. 1961. "On the Origins of 'Aesthetic Disinterestedness.'" *Journal of Aesthetics and Art Criticism*, XX, 131.

Sullivan, H. S. 1953. *Conceptions of Modern Psychiatry*. New York: Norton.

Szasz, T. S. 1961. *The Myth of Mental Illness*. New York: Hoeber-Harper.

Szurek, S. A. 1942. "Notes on the Genesis of Psychopathic Personality Trends." *Psychiatry*, V, 1.

Taylor, G. W., and Barron, F. 1963. *Scientific Creativity: Its Recognition and Development*. New York: Wiley.

Terzuolo, C. A., and Adey, W. R. 1960. "Sensorimotor Cortical Activities." In Field, J. (ed.), *Handbook of Physiology: Section 1, Neurophysiology*, II, 797–835. Washington, D.C.: American Physiological Society.

Thompson, C. 1950. *Psychoanalysis: Evolution and Development*. New York: Hermitage House.

Thorndike, E. L. 1903. *Educational Psychology*. New York: Lemeke and Buechner.

Thorpe, W. H. 1956. *Learning and Instinct in Animals*. Cambridge: Harvard University Press.

Tillich, P. 1957. *Dynamics of Faith*. New York: Harper & Row.

Tinbergen, N. 1951. *The Study of Instinct*. Oxford: Oxford University Press.

Tolstoy, L. N. 1898. *What Is Art?* Oxford: Oxford University Press, 1955.

Truman, H. S. 1948. Speech delivered in Cleveland Oct. 26, 1948, during Presidential campaign.

Tullio-Altan, C. 1960. *Lo spirito religioso del mondo primitivo*. Milan: Saggiatore.

Tylor, E. B. 1874. *Primitive Culture*. London.

Usener, H. 1896. *Gotternamen. Versuch einer Lehre von der Religiösen Begriffsbildung*. Born. Quoted by Cassirer (1946).

Vico, G. 1744. *The New Science*. Garden City, N.Y.: Anchor Books, Doubleday, 1961.

Von Bertalanffy, L. 1956. "General System Theory." In Von Bertalanffy, L., and Rapaport, A. (eds.), *General Systems Yearbook of the Society for the Advancement of General Systems Theory*. Ann Arbor: University of Michigan Press.

Von Bertalanffy, L. 1964. "The Mind-Body Problem: A New View." *Psychosomatic Medicine*, XXIV, 29.

Von Domarus, E. 1944. "The Specific Laws of Logic in Schizophrenia." In Kasanin, J. S. (ed.), *Language and Thought in Schizophrenia: Collected Papers*. Berkeley: University of California Press.

Von Neumann, John. 1958. *The Computer and the Brain*. New Haven: Yale University Press.

Von Senden, M. 1960. *Space and Sight: The Perception of Space and Shape in Congenitally Blind Patients before and after Operation.* London: Methuen.

Von Uexküll, J. 1957. "A Stroll through the World of Animals and Men." In Schiller, C. H. (ed.), *Instinctive Behavior: The Development of a Modern Concept.* New York: International Universities Press.

Wallas, G. 1926. *The Art of Thought.* New York: Harcourt, Brace & World.

Walsh, E. G. 1957. *Physiology of the Nervous System.* New York: Longmans, Green.

Weinstein, E. A., and Kahn, R. L. 1955. *Denial of Illness: Symbolic and Physiological Aspects.* Springfield, Ill.: Thomas.

Weinstein, E. A., and Kahn, R. L. 1959. "Symbolic Reorganization in Brain Injuries." In Arieti, S. (ed.), *American Handbook of Psychiatry,* 964–981. New York: Basic Books.

Weiss, E. 1960. *The Structure and Dynamics of the Human Mind.* New York: Grune & Stratton.

Wenger, M. A., Clemens, T. L., Coleman, D. R., Cullen, T. D., and Engel, B. T. 1961. "Autonomic Response Specificity." *Psychosomatic Medicine,* XXIII, 185–193.

Wenger, M. A., Engel, B. T., and Clemens, T. L. 1957. "Studies of Autonomic Responses. Patterns: Rationale and Methods." *Behavioral Science,* II, 216.

Werblowsky, R. J. Z. 1961. "Mystical and Magical Contemplation: The Kabbalists in Sixteenth Century Safed." *History of Religions,* I, 1:9–39.

Werner, H. 1956. "Microgenesis and Aphasia." *Journal of Abnormal and Social Psychology,* LII, 347–353.

Werner, H. 1957a. *Comparative Psychology of Mental Development.* New York: International Universities Press.

Werner, H. 1957b. "The Concept of Development from a Comparative and Organismic Point of View." In Harris, D. B. (ed.), *The Concept of Development.* Minneapolis: University of Minnesota Press.

Werner, H., and Kaplan, B. 1963. *Symbol Formation: An Organismic-Developmental Approach to Language and the Expression of Thought.* New York: Wiley.

Wertheimer, M. 1945. *Productive Thinking.* New York: Harper & Row.

Wheelwright, P. 1954. *The Burning Fountain: A Study in the Language of Symbolism.* Bloomington: Indiana University Press.

Wheelwright, P. 1962. *Metaphor and Reality.* Bloomington: Indiana University Press.

White, L. A. 1949. "Cultural Determinants of Mind." In White, L. A. (ed.), *The Science of Culture.* New York: Farrar, Straus & Giroux.

Whorf, B. L. 1956. *Language, Thought and Reality.* New York: Wiley.

Wikler, A. 1953. "Drug Addiction." In *Tice's Practice of Medicine.* Hagerstown, Md.: Prior.

Wilbrand, H., and Sanger, A. 1917. *Die Neurologie des Auges,* VII, 393–446. Wiesbaden: Bergmann.

Wimsatt, W. K., Jr. 1954. *The Verbal Icon: Studies in the Meaning of Poetry.* New York: Noonday Press.

Wolpert, L. 1924. "Die Simultanagnosie-Störung der Gesamtauffassung." *Zeitschrift für die Gesamte Neurologie und Psychiatrie,* XCIII, 397–415.

Yerkes, R. M. 1943. *Chimpanzees: A Laboratory Colony.* New Haven: Yale University Press.

Zangwill, O. L. 1960. *Cerebral Dominance and Its Relation to Psychological Function.* Edinburgh: Oliver and Boyd.

Zuckerkandl, V. 1956. *Sound and Symbol: Music and the External World.* New York: Pantheon Books.

INDEX